LOGIC OF CHANCE

THE

LOGIC OF CHANCE

BY

JOHN VENN

FOURTH EDITION

"So careful of the type she seems
So careless of the single life."

CHELSEA PUBLISHING COMPANY
NEW YORK, N.Y.

First Edition 1866
Second Edition 1876
Third Edition 1888
Fourth Edition 1962

The Present, Fourth, Edition is an Unaltered
Reprint of the Third Edition.

Library of Congress Catalogue Card No. 62-11698
Printed in the United States of America

PREFACE TO FIRST EDITION.

ANY work on Probability by a Cambridge man will be so likely to have its scope and its general treatment of the subject prejudged, that it may be well to state at the outset that the following Essay is in no sense mathematical. Not only, to quote a common but often delusive assurance, will 'no knowledge of mathematics beyond the simple rules of Arithmetic' be required to understand these pages, but it is not intended that any such knowledge should be acquired by the process of reading them. Of the two or three occasions on which algebraical formulæ occur they will not be found to form any essential part of the text.

The science of Probability occupies at present a somewhat anomalous position. It is impossible, I think, not to observe in it some of the marks and consequent disadvantages of a *sectional* study. By a small body of ardent students it has been cultivated with great assiduity, and the results they have obtained will always be reckoned among the most extraordinary products of mathematical genius. But by the general body of thinking men its principles seem to be regarded with indifference or suspicion. Such persons may admire the ingenuity displayed, and be struck with the profundity of many of the calculations, but there seems to them, if I may so express it, an *unreality* about the whole treatment of the subject. To many persons the mention of Probability suggests little else than the notion of a set of rules, very ingenious and profound rules no doubt, with which mathematicians amuse themselves by setting and solving puzzles.

It must be admitted that some ground has been given for such an opinion. The examples commonly selected by writers on the subject, though very well adapted to illustrate its rules, are for the most part of a special and peculiar character, such as those relating to dice and cards. When they have searched for illustrations drawn from the practical business of life, they have very generally, but unfortunately, hit upon just the sort of instances which, as I shall endeavour to show hereafter, are among the very worst that could be chosen for the purpose. It is scarcely possible for any unprejudiced person to read what has been written about the credibility of witnesses by eminent writers, without his experiencing an invincible distrust of the principles which they adopt. To say that the rules of evidence sometimes given by such writers are broken in practice, would scarcely be correct; for the rules are of such a kind as generally to defy any attempt to appeal to them in practice.

This supposed want of harmony between Probability and other branches of Philosophy is perfectly erroneous. It arises from the belief that Probability is a branch of mathematics trying to intrude itself on to ground which does not altogether belong to it. I shall endeavour to show that this belief is unfounded. To answer correctly the sort of questions to which the science introduces us does generally demand some knowledge of mathematics, often a great knowledge, but the discussion of the fundamental principles on which the rules are based does not necessarily require any such qualification. Questions might arise in other sciences, in Geology, for example, which could only be answered by the aid of arithmetical calculations. In such a case any one would admit that the arithmetic was extraneous and acci- dental. However many questions of this kind there might be here, those persons who do not care to work out special results for themselves might still have an accurate know- ledge of the principles of the science, and even considerable acquaintance with the details of it. The same holds true in Probability; its connection with mathematics, though cer- tainly far closer than that of most other sciences, is still of much the same kind. It is principally when we wish to work out results for ourselves that mathematical knowledge is required; without such knowledge the student may still have a firm grasp of the principles and even see his way to many of the derivative results.

The opinion that Probability, instead of being a branch of the general science of evidence which happens to make much use of mathematics, *is* a portion of mathematics, erroneous as it is, has yet been very disadvantageous to the science in several ways. Students of Philosophy in general have thence conceived a prejudice against Probability, which has for the most part deterred them from examining it. As soon as a subject comes to be considered 'mathematical' its claims seem generally, by the mass of readers, to be either on the one hand scouted or at least courteously rejected, or on the other to be blindly accepted with all their assumed conse- quences. Of impartial and liberal criticism it obtains little or nothing.

The consequences of this state of things have been, I think, disastrous to the students themselves of Probability. No science can safely be abandoned entirely to its own devo- tees. Its details of course can only be studied by those who

make it their special occupation, but its general principles
are sure to be cramped if it is not exposed occasionally to
the free criticism of those whose main culture has been of
a more general character. Probability has been very much
abandoned to mathematicians, who as mathematicians have
generally been unwilling to treat it thoroughly. They have
worked out its results, it is true, with wonderful acuteness,
and the greatest ingenuity has been shown in solving various
problems that arose, and deducing subordinate rules. And
this was all that they could in fairness be expected to do.
Any subject which has been discussed by such men as
Laplace and Poisson, and on which they have exhausted all
their powers of analysis, could not fail to be profoundly
treated, so far as it fell within their province. But from this
province the real principles of the science have generally
been excluded, or so meagrely discussed that they had better
have been omitted altogether. Treating the subject as mathematicians such writers have naturally taken it up at the
point where their mathematics would best come into play,
and that of course has not been at the foundations. In the
works of most writers upon the subject we should search in
vain for anything like a critical discussion of the fundamental principles upon which its rules rest, the class of
enquiries to which it is most properly applicable, or the
relation it bears to Logic and the general rules of inductive
evidence.

This want of precision as to ultimate principles is perfectly compatible here, as it is in the departments of Morals
and Politics, with a general agreement on processes and
results. But it is, to say the least, unphilosophical, and
denotes a state of things in which positive error is always
liable to arise whenever the process of controversy forces us
to appeal to the foundations of the science.

With regard to the remarks in the last few paragraphs, prominent exceptions must be made in the case of two recent works at least[1]. The first of these is Professor de Morgan's *Formal Logic*. He has there given an investigation into the foundations of Probability as conceived by him, and nothing can be more complete and precise than his statement of principles, and his deductions from them. If I could at all agree with these principles there would have been no necessity for the following essay, as I could not hope to add anything to their foundation, and should be far indeed from rivalling his lucid statement of them. But in his scheme Probability is regarded very much from the Conceptualist point of view; as stated in the preface, he considers that Probability is concerned with formal inferences in which the premises are entertained with a conviction short of absolute certainty. With this view I cannot agree. As I have entered into criticism of some points of his scheme in one of the following chapters, and shall have occasion frequently to refer to his work, I need say no more about it here. The other work to which I refer is the profound *Laws of Thought* of the late Professor Boole, to which somewhat similar remarks may in part be applied. Owing however to his peculiar treatment of the subject, I have scarcely anywhere come into contact with any of his expressed opinions.

The view of the province of Probability adopted in this Essay differs so radically from that of most other writers on the subject, and especially from that of those just referred to, that I have thought it better, as regards details, to avoid all criticism of the opinions of others, except where conflict was

[1] I am here speaking, of course, of those only who have expressly treated of the foundations of the science. Mr Todhunter's admirable work on the *History of the Theory of Probability* being, as the name denotes, mainly historical, such enquiries have not directly fallen within his province.

unavoidable. With regard to that radical difference itself Bacon's remark applies, behind which I must shelter myself from any change of presumption.—"Quod ad universalem istam reprehensionem attinet, certissimum vere est rem reputanti, eam et magis probabilem esse et magis modestam, quam si facta fuisset ex parte."

Almost the only writer who seems to me to have expressed a just view of the nature and foundation of the rules of Probability is Mr Mill, in his *System of Logic*[1]. His treatment of the subject is however very brief, and a considerable portion of the space which he has devoted to it is occupied by the discussion of one or two special examples. There are moreover some errors, as it seems to me, in what he has written, which will be referred to in some of the following chapters.

The reference to the work just mentioned will serve to convey a general idea of the view of Probability adopted in this Essay. With what may be called the Material view of Logic as opposed to the Formal or Conceptualist,—with that which regards it as taking cognisance of laws of things and not of the laws of our own minds in thinking about things,— I am in entire accordance. Of the province of Logic, regarded from this point of view, and under its widest aspect, Probability may, in my opinion, be considered to be a portion. The principal objects of this Essay are to ascertain how great a portion it comprises, where we are to draw the boundary between it and the contiguous branches of the general science

---

[1] This remark, and that at the commencement of the last paragraph, having been misunderstood, I ought to say that the only sense in which originality is claimed for this Essay is in the thorough working out of the Material view of Logic as applied to Probability. I have given a pretty full discussion of the general principles of this view in the tenth chapter, and have there pointed out some of the peculiarities to which it leads.

of evidence, what are the ultimate foundations upon which its rules rest, what the nature of the evidence they are capable of affording, and to what class of subjects they may most fitly be applied. That the science of Probability, on this view of it, contains something more important than the results of a system of mathematical assumptions, is obvious. I am convinced moreover that it can and ought to be rendered both interesting and intelligible to ordinary readers who have any taste for philosophy. In other words, if the large and growing body of readers who can find pleasure in the study of books like Mill's *Logic* and Whewell's *Inductive Sciences*, turn with aversion from a work on Probability, the cause in the latter case must lie either in the view of the subject or in the manner and style of the book.

I take this opportunity of thanking several friends, amongst whom I must especially mention Mr Todhunter, of St John's College, and Mr H. Sidgwick, of Trinity College, for the trouble they have kindly taken in looking over the proof-sheets, whilst this work was passing through the Press. To the former in particular my thanks are due for thus adding to the obligations which I, as an old pupil, already owed him, by taking an amount of trouble, in making suggestions and corrections for the benefit of another, which few would care to take for anything but a work of their own. His extensive knowledge of the subject, and his extremely accurate judgment, render the service he has thus afforded me of the greatest possible value.

GONVILLE AND CAIUS COLLEGE,
September, 1866.

PREFACE TO SECOND EDITION.

THE principal reason for designating this volume a second edition consists in the fact that the greater portion of what may be termed the first edition is incorporated into it. Besides various omissions (principally where the former treatment has since seemed to me needlessly prolix), I have added new matter, not much inferior in amount to the whole of the original work. In addition, moreover, to these alterations in the matter, the general arrangement of the subject as regards the successive chapters has been completely changed; the former arrangement having been (as it now seems to me) justly objected to as deficient and awkward in method.

After saying this, it ought to be explained whether any change of general view or results will be found in the present treatment.

The general view of Probability adopted is quite unchanged, further reading and reflection having only confirmed me in the conviction that this is the soundest and most fruitful way of regarding the subject. It is the more necessary to say this, as to a cursory reader it might seem otherwise; owing to my having endeavoured to avoid the needlessly polemical tone which, as is often the case with those who are making their first essay in writing upon any subject, was doubtless too prominent in the former edition. I have not thought it necessary, of course, except in one or two cases, to indicate points of detail which it has seemed necessary to correct.

A number of new discussions have been introduced upon topics which were but little or not at all treated before. The principal of these refer to the nature and physical origin of Laws of Error (Ch. II.); the general view of Logic, and consequently of Probability, termed the Material view, adopted here (Ch. X.); a brief history and criticism of the various opinions held on the subject of Modality (Ch. XII.); the logical principles underlying the method of Least Squares (Ch. XIII.); and the practices of Insurance and Gambling, so far as the principles involved in them are concerned (Ch. XV.). The Chapter on the Credibility of Extraordinary Stories is also mainly new; this was the portion of the former work which has since seemed to me the least satisfactory, but owing to the extreme intricacy of the subject I am far from feeling thoroughly satisfied with it even now.

I have again to thank several friends for the assistance they have so kindly afforded. Amongst these I must prominently mention Mr C. J. Monro, late fellow of Trinity. It is only the truth to say that I have derived more assistance from his suggestions and criticisms than has been consciously obtained from all other external sources together. Much of this criticism has been given privately in letters, and notes on the proof-sheets; but one of the most elaborate of his discussions of the subject was communicated to the Cambridge Philosophical Society some years ago; as it was not published, however, I am unfortunately unable to refer the reader to it. I ought to add that he is not in any way committed to any of my opinions upon the subject, from some of which in fact he more or less dissents. I am also much indebted to Mr J. W. L. Glaisher, also of Trinity College, for many hints and references to various publications upon the subject of Least Squares, and for careful criticism (given in the midst of much other labour) of the chapter in which that subject is treated.

I need not add that, like every one else who has had to discuss the subject of Probability during the last ten years, I have made constant use of Mr Todhunter's History.

I may take this opportunity of adding that a considerable portion of the tenth chapter has recently appeared in the January number of *Mind*, and that the substance of several chapters, especially in the more logical parts, has formed part of my ordinary lectures in Cambridge; the foundation and logical treatment of Probability being now expressly included in the Schedule of Subjects for the Moral Sciences Tripos.

March, 1876.

PREFACE TO THIRD EDITION

THE present edition has been revised throughout, and in fact rewritten. Three chapters are new, viz. the fifth (On the conception of Randomness) and the eighteenth and nineteenth (On the nature, and on the employment, of Averages). The eighth, tenth, eleventh, and fifteenth chapters have been recast, and much new matter added, and numerous alterations made in the remaining portions[1]. On the other hand three chapters of the last edition have been nearly or entirely omitted.

These alterations do not imply any appreciable change of view on my part as to the foundations and province of Probability. Some of them are of course due to the necessary changes involved in the attempt to write up to date upon a subject which has not been stationary during the last eleven years. For instance the greatly increased interest now taken in what may be called the Theory of Statistics has rendered it desirable to go much more fully into the Nature and treatment of Laws of Error. The omissions are mainly

[1] I have indicated the new chapters and sections by printing them in italics in the Table of Contents.

due to a wish to avoid increasing the bulk of this volume more than is actually necessary, and to a feeling that the portions treating specially of Inductive Logic (which occupied some space in the last edition) would be more suitable to a regular work on that subject. I am at present engaged on such a work.

The publications which I have had occasion to notice have mostly appeared in various scientific journals. The principal authors of these have been Mr F. Galton and Mr F. Y. Edgeworth: to the latter of whom I am also personally much obliged for many discussions, oral and written, and for his kindness in looking through the proof-sheets. His published articles are too numerous for separate mention here, but I may say generally, in addition to the obligations specially noticed, that I have been considerably indebted to them in writing the last two chapters. Two authors of works of a somewhat more substantial character, viz. Prof. Lexis and Von Kries, only came under my notice unfortunately after this work was already in the printer's hands. With the latter of these authors I find myself in closer agreement than with most others, in respect of his general conception and treatment of Probability.

December, 1887.

TABLE OF CONTENTS[1].

PART I.

PHYSICAL FOUNDATIONS OF THE SCIENCE OF PROBABILITY.
Chh. I—V.

CHAPTER I.

THE SERIES OF PROBABILITY.

CHAPTER II.

ARRANGEMENT AND FORMATION OF THE SERIES. LAWS OF ERROR.

---

[1] Chapters and sections which are nearly or entirely new are printed in *italics*.

CHAPTER III.

ORIGIN OR PROCESS OF CAUSATION OF THE SERIES.

CHAPTER IV.

HOW TO DISCOVER AND PROVE THE SERIES.

CHAPTER V.

THE CONCEPTION OF RANDOMNESS.

PART II.

LOGICAL SUPERSTRUCTURE ON THE ABOVE PHYSICAL FOUNDATIONS. Chh. VI—XIV.

CHAPTER VI.

MEASUREMENT OF BELIEF.

CHAPTER VII.

THE RULES OF INFERENCE IN PROBABILITY.

CHAPTER VIII.

THE RULE OF SUCCESSION.

CHAPTER IX.

INDUCTION.

CHAPTER X.

CHANCE, CAUSATION AND DESIGN.

CHAPTER XI.

MATERIAL AND FORMAL LOGIC.

CHAPTER XII.

CONSEQUENCES OF THE DISTINCTIONS OF THE PREVIOUS CHAPTER.

CHAPTER XIII.

ON MODALITY.

CHAPTER XIV.

FALLACIES.

PART III.

VARIOUS APPLICATIONS OF THE THEORY OF PROBABILITY.
Chh. XV—XIX.

CHAPTER XV.

INSURANCE AND GAMBLING.

CHAPTER XVI.

APPLICATION OF PROBABILITY TO TESTIMONY.

CHAPTER XVII.

CREDIBILITY OF EXTRAORDINARY STORIES.

CHAPTER XVIII.

ON THE NATURE AND USE OF AN AVERAGE, AND ON THE DIFFERENT KINDS OF AVERAGE.

CHAPTER XIX.

THE THEORY OF THE AVERAGE AS A MEANS OF APPROXIMATION TO THE TRUTH.

THE LOGIC OF CHANCE.

CHAPTER I.

ON CERTAIN KINDS OF GROUPS OR SERIES AS THE FOUNDATION OF PROBABILITY.

§ 1. It is sometimes not easy to give a clear definition of a science at the outset, so as to set its scope and province before the reader in a few words. In the case of those sciences which are more immediately and directly concerned with what are termed objects, rather than with what are termed processes, this difficulty is not indeed so serious. If the reader is already familiar with the objects, a simple reference to them will give him a tolerably accurate idea of the direction and nature of his studies. Even if he be not familiar with them, they will still be often to some extent connected and associated in his mind by a name, and the mere utterance of the name may thus convey a fair amount of preliminary information. This is more or less the case with many of the natural sciences; we can often tell the reader beforehand exactly what he is going to study. But when a science is concerned, not so much with objects directly, as with processes and laws, or when it takes for the subject of its enquiry some comparatively obscure feature drawn from phenomena which have little or nothing else in common, the difficulty of giving preliminary information becomes greater. Recognized classes of objects have then to be disregarded and even broken up, and an entirely novel arrangement of the objects to be made.   In such cases it is the study of the science that first gives the science its unity, for till it is studied the objects with which it is concerned were probably never thought of together.   Here a definition cannot be given at the outset, and the process of obtaining it may become by comparison somewhat laborious.

The science of Probability, at least on the view taken of it in the following pages, is of this latter description.   The reader who is at present unacquainted with the science cannot be at once informed of its scope by a reference to objects with which he is already familiar.   He will have to be taken in hand, as it were, and some little time and trouble will have to be expended in directing his attention to our subject-matter before he can be expected to know it.   To do this will be our first task.

§ 2.   In studying Nature, in any form, we are continually coming into possession of information which we sum up in general propositions.   Now in very many cases these general propositions are neither more nor less certain and accurate than the details which they embrace and of which they are composed.   We are assuming at present that the truth of these generalizations is not disputed; as a matter of fact they may rest on weak evidence, or they may be uncertain from their being widely extended by induction; what is meant is, that when we resolve them into their component parts we have precisely the same assurance of the truth of the details as we have of that of the whole.   When I know, for instance, that all cows ruminate, I feel just as certain that any particular cow or cows ruminate as that the whole class does.   I may be right or wrong in my original statement, and I may have obtained it by any conceivable mode in which truths can be obtained; but whatever the value of the general proposition may be, that of the particulars is neither greater nor less. The process of inferring the particular from the general is not accompanied by the slightest diminution of certainty. If one of these 'immediate inferences' is justified at all, it will be equally right in every case.

But it is by no means necessary that this characteristic should exist in all cases. There is a class of immediate inferences, almost unrecognized indeed in logic, but constantly drawn in practice, of which the characteristic is, that as they increase in particularity they diminish in certainty. Let me assume that I am told that *some* cows ruminate; I cannot infer logically from this that any particular cow does so, though I should feel some way removed from absolute disbelief, or even indifference to assent, upon the subject; but if I saw a herd of cows I should feel more sure that some of them were ruminant than I did of the single cow, and my assurance would increase with the numbers of the herd about which I had to form an opinion. Here then we have a class of things as to the individuals of which we feel quite in uncertainty, whilst as we embrace larger numbers in our assertions we attach greater weight to our inferences. It is with such classes of things and such inferences that the science of Probability is concerned.

§ 3. In the foregoing remarks, which are intended to be purely preliminary, we have not been able altogether to avoid some reference to a subjective element, viz. the degree of our certainty or belief about the things which we are supposed to contemplate. The reader may be aware that by some writers this element is regarded as the subject-matter of the science. Hence it will have to be discussed in a future chapter. As however I do not agree with the opinion of the writers just mentioned, at least as regards treating this element as one of primary importance, no further allusion will be made to it here, but we will pass on at once to a more minute investigation of that distinctive characteristic of certain classes of things which was introduced to notice in the last section.

In these classes of things, which are those with which Probability is concerned, the fundamental conception which the reader has to fix in his mind as clearly as possible, is, I take it, that of a series. But it is a series of a peculiar kind, one of which no better compendious description can be given than that which is contained in the statement that it combines individual irregularity with aggregate regularity. This is a statement which will probably need some explanation. Let us recur to an example of the kind already alluded to, selecting one which shall be in accordance with experience. Some children will not live to thirty. Now if this proposition is to be regarded as a purely indefinite or, as it would be termed in logic, 'particular' proposition, no doubt the notion of a series does not obviously present itself in connection with it. It contains a statement about a certain unknown proportion of the whole, and that is all. But it is not with these purely indefinite propositions that we shall be concerned. Let us suppose the statement, on the contrary, to be of a numerical character, and to refer to a given proportion of the whole, and we shall then find it difficult to exclude the notion of a series. We shall find it, I think, impossible to do so as soon as we set before us the aim of obtaining accurate, or even moderately correct inferences. What, for instance, is the meaning of the statement that two new-born children in three fail to attain the age of sixty-three ? It certainly does not declare that in any given batch of, say, thirty, we shall find just twenty that fail: whatever might be the strict meaning of the words, this is not the import of the statement. It rather contemplates our examination of a large number, of a long succession of instances, and states that in such a succession we shall find a numerical proportion, not indeed fixed and accurate at first, but which tends in the long run to become so. In every kind of example with which we shall be concerned we shall find this reference to a large number or succession of objects, or, as we shall term it, *series* of them.

A few additional examples may serve to make this plain.

Let us suppose that we toss up a penny a great many times; the results of the successive throws may be conceived to form a series. The separate throws of this series seem to occur in utter disorder; it is this disorder which causes our uncertainty about them. Sometimes head comes, sometimes tail comes; sometimes there is a repetition of the same face, sometimes not. So long as we confine our observation to a few throws at a time, the series seems to be simply chaotic. But when we consider the result of a long succession we find a marked distinction; a kind of order begins gradually to emerge, and at last assumes a distinct and striking aspect. We find in this case that the heads and tails occur in about equal numbers, that similar repetitions of different faces do so also, and so on. In a word, notwithstanding the individual disorder, an aggregate order begins to prevail. So again if we are examining the length of human life, the different lives which fall under our notice compose a series presenting the same features. The length of a single life is familiarly uncertain, but the average duration of a batch of lives is becoming in an almost equal degree familiarly certain. The larger the number we take out of any mixed crowd, the clearer become the symptoms of order, the more nearly will the average length of each selected class be the same. These few cases will serve as simple examples of a property of things which can be traced almost everywhere, to a greater or less extent, throughout the whole field of our experience. Fires, shipwrecks, yields of harvest, births, marriages, suicides; it scarcely seems to matter what feature we single out for observation[1]. The irregularity of the single instances diminishes when we take a large number, and at last seems for all practical purposes to disappear.

In speaking of the effect of the average in thus diminishing the irregularities which present themselves in the details, the attention of the student must be prominently directed to the point, that it is not the *absolute* but the *relative* irregularities which thus tend to diminish without limit. This idea will be familiar enough to the mathematician, but to others it may require some reflection in order to grasp it clearly. The absolute divergences and irregularities, so far from diminishing, show a disposition to increase, and this (it may be) without limit, though their relative importance shows a corresponding disposition to diminish without limit. Thus in the case of tossing a penny, if we take a few throws, say ten, it is decidedly unlikely that there should be a difference of six between the numbers of heads and tails; that is, that

---

[1] The following statistics will give a fair idea of the wide range of experience over which such regularity is found to exist: "As illustrations of equal amounts of fluctuation from totally dissimilar causes, take the deaths in the West district of London in seven years (fluctuation 13·66), and offences against the person (fluctuation 13·61); or deaths from apoplexy (fluctuation 5·54), and offences against property, without violence (fluctuation 5·48); or students registered at the College of Surgeons (fluctuation 1·85), and the number of pounds of manufactured tobacco taken for home consumption (fluctuation 1·89); or out-door paupers (fluctuation 3·45) and tonnage of British vessels entered in ballast (fluctuation 3·43), &c." [Extracted from a paper in the Journal of the Statistical Society, by Mr Guy, March, 1858; the 'fluctuation' here given is a measure of the amount of irregularity, that is of departure from the average, estimated in a way which will be described hereafter.]

there should be as many as eight heads and therefore as few
as two tails, or *vice versâ*. But take a thousand throws, and
it becomes in turn exceedingly likely that there should be
as much as, or more than, a difference of six between the
respective numbers. On the other hand the *proportion* of
heads to tails in the case of the thousand throws will be very
much nearer to unity, in most cases, than when we only took
ten. In other words, the longer a game of chance continues
the larger are the spells and runs of luck in themselves, but
the less their relative proportions to the whole amounts
involved.

§ 4. In speaking as above of events or things as to the
details of which we know little or nothing, it is not of course
implied that our ignorance about them is complete and universal, or, what comes to the same thing, that irregularity
may be observed in all their qualities. All that is meant is
that there are *some* qualities or marks in them, the existence
of which we are not able to predicate with certainty in the
individuals. With regard to all their other qualities there
may be the utmost uniformity, and consequently the most
complete certainty. The irregularity in the length of human
life is notorious, but no one doubts the existence of such
organs as a heart and brains in any person whom he happens
to meet. And even in the qualities in which the irregularity
is observed, there are often, indeed generally, positive limits
within which it will be found to be confined. No person,
for instance, can calculate what may be the length of any
particular life, but we feel perfectly certain that it will not
stretch out to 150 years. The irregularity of the individual
instances is only shown in certain respects, as e.g. the length
of the life, and even in these respects it has its limits. The
same remark will apply to most of the other examples with
which we shall be concerned. The disorder in fact is not

universal and unlimited, it only prevails in certain directions
and up to certain points.

§ 5.   In speaking as above of a series, it will hardly be
necessary to point out that we do not imply that the objects
themselves which compose the series must occur successively
in time; the series may be formed simply by their coming
in succession under our notice, which as a matter of fact
they may do in any order whatever.   A register of mortality,
for instance, may be made up of deaths which took place
simultaneously or successively; or, we might if we pleased
arrange the deaths in an order quite distinct from either of
these.   This is entirely a matter of indifference; in all these
cases the series, for any purposes which we need take into
account, may be regarded as being of precisely the same description.   The objects, be it remembered, are given to us in
nature; the order under which we view them is our own private arrangement.   This is mentioned here simply by way of
caution, the meaning of this assertion will become more plain
in the sequel.

I am aware that the word 'series' in the application with
which it is used here is liable to some misconstruction, but I
cannot find any better word, or indeed any as suitable in all
respects.   As remarked above, the events need not necessarily have occurred in a regular sequence of time, though
they often will have done so.   In many cases (for instance,
the throws of a penny or a die) they really do occur in succession; in other cases (for instance, the heights of men, or
the duration of their lives), whatever may have been the
order of their actual occurrence, they are commonly brought
under our notice in succession by being arranged in statistical
tables.   In all cases alike our processes of inference involve
the necessity of examining one after another of the members
which compose the group, or at least of being prepared to do

this, if we are to be in a position to justify our inferences. The force of these considerations will come out in the course of the investigation in Chapter VI.

The late Leslie Ellis[1] has expressed what seems to me a substantially similar view in terms of genus and species, instead of speaking of a series. He says, " When individual cases are considered, we have no conviction that the ratios of frequency of occurrence depend on the circumstances common to all the trials. On the contrary, we recognize in the determining circumstances of their occurrence an extraneous element, an element, that is, extraneous to the idea of the genus and species. Contingency and limitation come in (so to speak) together; and both alike disappear when we consider the genus in its entirety, or (which is the same thing) in what may be called an ideal and practically impossible realization of all which it potentially contains. If this be granted, it seems to follow that the fundamental principle of the Theory of Probabilities may be regarded as included in the following statement,—The conception of a genus implies that of numerical relations among the species subordinated to it." As remarked above, this appears a substantially similar doctrine to that explained in this chapter, but I do not think that the terms genus and species are by any means so well fitted to bring out the conception of a tendency or limit as when we speak of a series, and I therefore much prefer the latter expression.

§ 6. The reader will now have in his mind the conception of a series or group of things or events, about the individuals of which we know but little, at least in certain respects, whilst we find a continually increasing uniformity as we take larger numbers under our notice. This is definite

---

[1] Transactions of the Cambridge Philosophical Society, Vol. IX. p. 605. Reprinted in the collected edition of his writings, p. 50.

enough to point out tolerably clearly the kind of things
with which we have to deal, but it is not sufficiently definite
for purposes of accurate thought. We must therefore attempt a somewhat closer analysis.

There are certain phrases so commonly adopted as to
have become part of the technical vocabulary of the subject, such as an 'event' and the 'way in which it can
happen.' Thus the act of throwing a penny would be called
an event, and the fact of its giving head or tail would be
called the way in which the event happened. If we were
discussing tables of mortality, the former term would denote the mere fact of death, the latter the age at which
it occurred, or the way in which it was brought about,
or whatever else in it might be the particular circumstance
under discussion. This phraseology is very convenient, and
will often be made use of in this work, but without explanation it may lead to confusion. For in many cases the
way in which the event happens is of such great relative
importance, that according as it happens in one way or
another the event would have a different name; in other
words, it would not in the two cases be nominally the same
event. The phrase therefore will have to be considerably
stretched before it will conveniently cover all the cases to
which we may have to apply it. If for instance we were
contemplating a series of human beings, male and female,
it would sound odd to call their humanity an event, and
their sex the way in which the event happened.

If we recur however to any of the classes of objects
already referred to, we may see our path towards obtaining
a more accurate conception of what we want. It will easily
be seen that in every one of them there is a mixture of
similarity and dissimilarity; there is a series of events
which have a certain number of features or attributes in

common,—without this they would not be classed together. But there is also a distinction existing amongst them; a certain number of other attributes are to be found in some and are not to be found in others. In other words, the individuals which form the series are compound, each being made up of a collection of things or attributes; some of these things exist in all the members of the series, others are found in some only. So far there is nothing peculiar to the science of Probability; that in which the distinctive characteristic consists is this;—that the occasional attributes, as distinguished from the permanent, are found on an extended examination to tend to exist *in a certain definite proportion of the whole number of cases.* We cannot tell in any given instance whether they will be found or not, but as we go on examining more cases we find a growing uniformity. We find that the proportion of instances in which they are found to instances in which they are wanting, is gradually subject to less and less comparative variation, and approaches continually towards some apparently fixed value.

The above is the most comprehensive form of description; as a matter of fact the groups will in many cases take a far simpler form; they may appear, e.g. simply as a succession of things of the same kind, say human beings, with or without an occasional attribute, say that of being left-handed. We are using the word attribute, of course, in its widest sense, intending it to include every distinctive feature that can be observed in a thing, from essential qualities down to the merest accidents of time and place.

§ 7. On examining our series, therefore, we shall find that it may best be conceived, not necessarily as a succession of events happening in different ways, but as a succession of groups of things. These groups, on being analysed, are found in every case to be resolvable into collections of sub-

stances and attributes. That which gives its unity to the
succession of groups is the fact of some of these substances or
attributes being common to the whole succession; that which
gives their distinction to the groups in the succession is the
fact of some of them containing only a portion of these substances and attributes, the other portion or portions being
occasionally absent. So understood, our phraseology may
be made to embrace every class of things of which Probability can take account.

§ 8. It will be easily seen that the ordinary expression
(viz. the 'event,' and the 'way in which it happens') may be
included in the above. When the occasional attributes are
unimportant the permanent ones are sufficient to fix and
appropriate the name, the presence or absence of the others
being simply denoted by some modification of the name or
the addition of some predicate. We may therefore in all such
cases speak of the collection of attributes as 'the event,'—
the same event essentially, that is—only saying that *it* (so as
to preserve its nominal identity) happens in different ways
in the different cases. When the occasional attributes however are important, or compose the majority, this way of
speaking becomes less appropriate; language is somewhat
strained by our implying that two extremely different assem-
blages are in reality the same event, with a difference only
in its mode of happening. The phrase is however a very
convenient one, and with this caution against its being misunderstood, it will frequently be made use of here.

§ 9. A series of the above-mentioned kind is, I apprehend, the ultimate basis upon which all the rules of
Probability must be based. It is essential to a clear comprehension of the subject to have carried our analysis up
to this point, but any attempt at further analysis into the
intimate nature of the events composing the series, is not

required. It is altogether unnecessary, for instance, to form any opinion upon the questions discussed in metaphysics as to the independent existence of substances. We have discovered, on examination, a series composed of groups of substances and attributes, or of attributes alone. At such a series we stop, and thence investigate our rules of inference; into what these substances or attributes would themselves be ultimately analysed, if taken in hand by the psychologist or metaphysician, it is no business of ours to enquire here.

§ 10. The stage then which we have now reached is that of having discovered a quantity of things (they prove on analysis to be groups of things) which are capable of being classified together, and are best regarded as constituting a series. The distinctive peculiarity of this series is our finding in it an order, gradually emerging out of disorder, and showing in time a marked and unmistakeable uniformity.

The impression which may possibly be derived from the description of such a series, and which the reader will probably already entertain if he have studied Probability before, is that the gradual evolution of this order is indefinite, and its approach therefore to perfection unlimited. And many of the examples commonly selected certainly tend to confirm such an impression. But in reference to the theory of the subject it is, I am convinced, an error, and one liable to lead to much confusion.

The lines which have been prefixed as a motto to this work, " So careful of the type she seems, so careless of the single life," are soon after corrected by the assertion that the type itself, if we regard it for a long time, changes, and then vanishes and is succeeded by others. So in Probability; that uniformity which is found in the long run, and which presents so great a contrast to the individual disorder, though durable is not everlasting. Keep on watching it long enough, and it will be found almost invariably to fluctuate, and in time may prove as utterly irreducible to rule, and therefore as incapable of prediction, as the individual cases themselves. The full bearing of this fact upon the theory of the subject, and upon certain common modes of calculation connected with it, will appear more fully in some of the following chapters ; at present we will confine ourselves to very briefly establishing and illustrating it.

Let us take, for example, the average duration of life. This, provided our data are sufficiently extensive, is known to be tolerably regular and uniform. This fact has been already indicated in the preceding sections, and is a truth indeed of which the popular mind has a tolerably clear grasp at the present day. But a very little consideration will show that there may be a superior as well as an inferior limit to the extent within which this uniformity can be observed; in other words whilst we may fall into error by taking too few instances we may also fail in our aim, though in a very different way and from quite different reasons, by taking too many. At the present time the average duration of life in England may be, say, forty years; but a century ago it was decidedly less ; several centuries ago it was presumably very much less; whilst if we possessed statistics referring to a still earlier population of the country we should probably find that there has been since that time a still more marked improvement. What may be the future tendency no man can say for certain. It may be, and we hope that it will be the case, that owing to sanitary and other improvements, the duration of life will go on increasing steadily ; it is at least conceivable, though doubtless incredible, that it should do so without limit. On the other hand, and with much more likelihood, this duration might gradually tend towards some fixed length. Or, again, it is perfectly possible that future generations might prefer a short and a merry life, and therefore reduce their average longevity. The duration of life cannot but depend to some extent upon the general tastes, habits and employments of the people, that is upon the ideal which they consciously or unconsciously set before them, and he would be a rash man who should undertake to predict what this ideal will be some centuries hence. All that it is here necessary however to indicate is, that this particular uniformity (as we have hitherto called it, in order to mark its relative character) has varied, and, under the influence of future eddies in opinion and practice, may vary still; and this to any extent, and with any degree of irregularity. To borrow a term from Astronomy, we find our uniformity subject to what might be called an irregular *secular* variation.

§ 11. The above is a fair typical instance. If we had taken a less simple feature than the length of life, or one less closely connected with what may be called by comparison the great permanent uniformities of nature, we should have found the peculiarity under notice exhibited in a far more striking degree. The deaths from small-pox, for example, or the instances of duelling or accusations of witchcraft, if examined during a few successive decades, might have shown a very tolerable degree of uniformity. But these uniformities have risen possibly from zero; after various and very great fluctuations seem tending towards zero again, at least in this century; and may, for anything we know, undergo still more rapid fluctuations in future. Now these examples must be regarded as being only extreme ones, and not such very extreme ones, of what is the almost universal rule in nature. I shall endeavour to show that even the few apparent exceptions, such as the proportions between male and female births, &c., may not be, and probably in reality are not, strictly speaking, exceptions. A type, that is, which shall be in the fullest sense of the words, persistent and invariable is scarcely to be found in nature. The full import of this conclusion will be seen in future chapters. Attention is only directed here to the important inference that, although statistics are notoriously of no value unless they are in suffi-cient numbers, yet it does not follow but that in certain cases we may have too many of them. If they are made too ex-tensive, they may again fall short, at least for any particular time or place, of their greatest attainable accuracy.

§ 12. These natural uniformities then are found at length to be subject to fluctuation. Now contrast with them any of the uniformities afforded by games of chance; these latter seem to show no trace of secular fluctuation, however long we may continue our examination of them. Criticisms will be offered, in the course of the following chapters, upon some of the common attempts to prove *à priori* that there must be this fixity in the uniformity in question, but of its existence there can scarcely be much doubt. Pence give heads and tails about equally often now, as they did when they were first tossed, and as we believe they will continue to do, so long as the present order of things continues. The fixity of these uniformities may not be as absolute as is commonly supposed, but no amount of experience which we need take into account is likely in any appreciable degree to interfere with them. Hence the obvious contrast, that, whereas natural uniformities at length fluctuate, those af-forded by games of chance seem fixed for ever.

§ 13. Here then are series apparently of two different kinds. They are alike in their initial irregularity, alike in their subsequent regularity; it is in what we may term their ultimate form that they begin to diverge from each other. The one tends without any irregular variation towards a fixed numerical proportion in its uniformity; in the other the uniformity is found at last to fluctuate, and to fluctuate, it may be, in a manner utterly irreducible to rule.

As this chapter is intended to be little more than explanatory and illustrative of the foundations of the science, the remark may be made here (for which subsequent justification will be offered) that it is in the case of series of the former kind only that we are able to make anything which can be interpreted into strict scientific inferences. We shall be able however in a general way to see the kind and extent of error that would be committed if, in any example, we were to substitute an imaginary series of the former kind for any actual series of the latter kind which experience may present to us. The two series are of course to be as alike as possible in all respects, except that the variable uniformity has been replaced by a fixed one. The difference then between them would not appear in the initial stage, for in that stage the distinctive characteristics of the series of Probability are not apparent; all is there irregularity, and it would be as impossible to show that they were alike as that they were different; we can only say generally that each shows the same kind of irregularity. Nor would it appear in the next subsequent stage, for the real variability of the uniformity has not for some time scope to make itself perceived. It would only be in what we have called the ultimate stage, when we suppose the series to extend for a very long time, that the difference would begin to make itself felt[1]. The proportion of persons, for example, who die each year at the age of six months is, when the numbers examined are on a

---

[1] We might express it thus:—a few instances are not sufficient to display a law at all; a considerable number will suffice to display it; but it takes a very great number to establish that a *change* is taking place in the law.

small scale, utterly irregular; it becomes however regular when the numbers examined are on a larger scale; but if we continued our observation for a very great length of time, or over a very great extent of country, we should find this regularity itself changing in an irregular way. The substitution just mentioned is really equivalent to saying, Let us assume that the regularity is fixed and permanent. It is making a hypothesis which may not be altogether consistent with fact, but which is forced upon us for the purpose of securing precision of statement and definition.

§ 14. The full meaning and bearing of such a substitution will only become apparent in some of the subsequent chapters, but it may be pointed out at once that it is in this way only that we can with perfect strictness introduce the notion of a 'limit' into our account of the matter, at any rate in reference to many of the applications of the subject to purely statistical enquiries. We say that a certain proportion begins to prevail among the events in the long run; but then on looking closer at the facts we find that we have to express ourselves hypothetically, and to say that if present circumstances remain as they are, the long run will show its characteristics without disturbance. When, as is often the case, we know nothing accurately of the circumstances by which the succession of events is brought about, but have strong reasons to suspect that these circumstances are likely to undergo some change, there is really nothing else to be done. We can only introduce the conception of a limit, towards which the numbers are tending, by assuming that these circumstances do not change; in other words, by substituting a series with a fixed uniformity for the actual one with the varying uniformity[1].

[1] The mathematician may illustrate the nature of this substitution by the analogies of the 'circle of curvature' in geometry, and the 'instantaneous

§ 15. If the reader will study the following example, one well known to mathematicians under the name of the Petersburg[1] problem, he will find that it serves to illustrate several of the considerations mentioned in this chapter. It serves especially to bring out the facts that the series with which we are concerned must be regarded as indefinitely extensive in point of number or duration; and that when so regarded certain series, but certain series only (the one in question being a case in point), take advantage of the indefinite range to keep on producing individuals in it whose deviation from the previous average has no finite limit whatever. When rightly viewed it is a very simple problem, but it has given rise at one time or another, to a good deal of confusion and perplexity.

The problem may be stated thus:—a penny is tossed up; if it gives head I receive one pound; if heads twice running two pounds; if heads three times running four pounds, and so on; the amount to be received doubling every time that a fresh head succeeds. That is, I am to go on as long as it continues to give a succession of heads, to regard this succession as a 'turn' or set, and then take another turn, and so on; and for each such turn I am to receive a payment; the occurrence of tail being understood to yield nothing, in fact being omitted from our consideration. However many times head may be given in succession, the number of pounds I may claim is found by raising two to a power one less

ellipse' in astronomy. In the cases in which these conceptions are made use of we have a phenomenon which is continuously varying and also changing its rate of variation. We take it at some given moment, suppose its rate at that moment to be fixed, and then complete its career on that supposition.

[1] So called from its first mathematical treatment appearing in the *Commentarii* of the Petersburg Academy; a variety of notices upon it will be found in Mr Todhunter's History of the Theory of Probability.

than that number of times.   Here then is a series formed by
a succession of throws.   We will assume,—what many persons will consider to admit of demonstration, and what
certainly experience confirms within considerable limits,—
that the rarity of these 'runs' of the same face is in direct
proportion to the amount I receive for them when they do
occur.   In other words, if we regard only the occasions on
which I receive payments, we shall find that every other
time I get one pound, once in four times I get two pounds,
once in eight times four pounds, and so on without any end.
The question is then asked, what ought I to pay for this
privilege ?   At the risk of a slight anticipation of the results
of a subsequent chapter, we may assume that this is equivalent to asking, what amount paid each time would on the
average leave me neither winner nor loser ?   In other words,
what is the average amount I should receive on the above
terms ?   Theory pronounces that I ought to give an *infinite*
sum: that is, no finite sum, however great, would be an
adequate equivalent.   And this is really quite intelligible.
There is a series of indefinite length before me, and the
longer I continue to work it the richer are my returns, and
this without any limit whatever.   It is true that the very
rich hauls are extremely rare, but still they do come, and
when they come they make it up by their greater richness.
On every occasion on which people have devoted themselves
to the pursuit in question, they made acquaintance, of course,
with but a limited portion of this series; but the series on
which we base our calculation is unlimited; and the inferences usually drawn as to the sum which ought in the long
run to be paid for the privilege in question are in perfect
accordance with this supposition.

The common form of objection is given in the reply, that
so far from paying an infinite sum, no sensible man would

give anything approaching to £50 for such a chance. Probably not, because no man would see enough of the series to make it worth his while. What most persons form their practical opinion upon, is such small portions of the series as they have actually seen or can reasonably expect. Now in any such portion, say one which embraces 100 turns, the longest succession of heads would not amount on the average to more than seven or eight. This is observed, but it is forgotten that the formula which produced these, would, if it had greater scope, keep on producing better and better ones without any limit. Hence it arises that some persons are perplexed, because the conduct they would adopt, in reference to the curtailed portion of the series which they are practically likely to meet with, does not find its justification in inferences which are necessarily based upon the series in the completeness of its infinitude.

§ 16. This will be more clearly seen by considering the various possibilities, and the scope required in order to exhaust them, when we confine ourselves to a *limited* number of throws. Begin with three. This yields eight equally likely possibilities. In four of these cases the thrower starts with tail and therefore loses: in two he gains a single point (i.e. £1); in one he gains two points, and in one he gains four points. Hence his total gain being eight pounds achieved in four different contingencies, his average gain would be two pounds.

Now suppose he be allowed to go as far as n throws, so that we have to contemplate 2^n possibilities. All of these have to be taken into account if we wish to consider what happens on the average. It will readily be seen that, when all the possible cases have been reckoned once, his total gain will be (reckoned in pounds),

$$2^{n-2} + 2^{n-3} \cdot 2 + 2^{n-4} \cdot 2^2 + \ldots\ldots + 2 \cdot 2^{n-3} + 2^{n-2} + 2^{n-1},$$

viz. $(n + 1)\ 2^{n-2}$.

This being spread over 2^{n-1} different occasions of gain his average gain will be $\frac{1}{2}(n + 1)$.

Now when we are referring to averages it must be remembered that the minimum number of different occurrences necessary in order to justify the average is that which enables each of them to present itself once.   A man proposes to stop short at a succession of ten heads.   Well and good.   We tell him that his average gain will be £5. 10s. 0d.: but we also impress upon him that in order to justify this statement he must commence to toss at least 1024 times, for in no less number can all the contingencies of gain and loss be exhibited and balanced.   If he proposes to reach an average gain of £20, he will require to be prepared to go up to 39 throws. To *justify* this payment he must commence to throw 2^{39} times, i.e. about a million million times.   Not before he has accomplished this will he be in a position to prove to any sceptic that this is the true average value of a 'turn' extending to 39 successive tosses.

Of course if he elects to toss to all eternity we must adopt the line of explanation which alone is possible where questions of infinity in respect of number and magnitude are involved.   We cannot tell him to pay down 'an infinite sum,' for this has no strict meaning.   But we tell him that, however much he may consent to pay each time runs of heads occur, he will attain at last a stage in which he will have won back his total payments by his total receipts.   However large n may be, if he perseveres in trying 2^n times he *may* have a true average receipt of $\frac{1}{2}(n + 1)$ pounds, and if he continues long enough onwards he *will* have it.

The problem will recur for consideration in a future chapter.

CHAPTER II.

§ 1. IN the course of the last chapter the nature of a particular kind of series, that namely, which must be considered
to constitute the basis of the science of Probability, has received a sufficiently general explanation for the preliminary
purpose of introduction. One might indeed say more than
this; for the characteristics which were there pointed out are
really sufficient in themselves to give a fair general idea of
the nature of Probability, and of the sort of problems with
which it deals. But in the concluding paragraphs an indication was given that the series of this kind, as they actually occur in nature or as the results of more or less artificial
production, are seldom or never found to occur in such a
simple form as might possibly be expected from what had
previously been said; but that they are almost always seen
to be associated together in groups after a somewhat complicated fashion. A fuller discussion of this topic must now
be undertaken.

We will take for examination an instance of a kind with
which the investigations of Quetelet will have served to
familiarize some readers. Suppose that we measure the
heights of a great many adult men in any town or country.
These heights will of course lie between certain extremes in

each direction, and if we continue to accumulate our measures it will be found that they tend to lie continuously
between these extremes; that is to say, that under those
circumstances no intermediate height will be found to be
permanently unrepresented in such a collection of measurements. Now suppose these heights to be marshalled in the
order of their magnitude. What we always find is something of the following kind;—about the middle point between the extremes, a large number of the results will be
found crowded together: a little on each side of this point
there will still be an excess, but not to so great an extent;
and so on, in some diminishing scale of proportion, until as
we get towards the extreme results the numbers thin off and
become relatively exceedingly small.

The point to which attention is here directed is not the
mere fact that the numbers thus tend to diminish from the
middle in each direction, but, as will be more fully explained
directly, the *law* according to which this progressive diminution takes place. The word 'law' is here used in its mathematical sense, to express the formula connecting together the
two elements in question, namely, the height itself, and the
relative number that are found of that height. We shall
have to enquire whether one of these elements is a function
of the other, and, if so, what function.

§ 2. After what was said in the last chapter, it need
hardly be insisted upon that the interest and significance of
such investigations as these are almost entirely dependent
upon the statistics being very extensive. In one or other of
Quetelet's works on Social Physics[1] will be found a selection
of measurements of almost every element which the physical
frame of man can furnish:—his height, his weight, the mus-
cular power of various limbs, the dimensions of almost every

[1] *Essai de Physique Sociale*, 1869. *Anthropométrie*, 1870.

part and organ, and so on. Some of the most extensive of
these express the heights of 25,000 Federal soldiers from the
Army of the Potomac, and the circumferences of the chests
of 5738 Scotch militia men taken many years ago. Those
who wish to consult a large repertory of such statistics cannot be referred to any better sources than to these and other
works by the same author[1].

Interesting and valuable, however, as are Quetelet's statistical investigations (and much of the importance now
deservedly attached to such enquiries is, perhaps, owing
more to his efforts than to those of any other person), I cannot but feel convinced that there is much in what he has
written upon the subject which is erroneous and confusing as
regards the foundations of the science of Probability, and the
philosophical questions which it involves. These errors are
not by any means confined to him, but for various reasons
they will be better discussed in the form of a criticism of his
explicit or implicit expression of them, than in any more independent way.

§ 3.   In the first place then, he always, or almost always,
assumes that there can be but one and the same law of arrangement for the results of our observations, measurements,
and so on, in these statistical enquiries. That is, he assumes that whenever we get a group of such magnitudes
clustering about a mean, and growing less frequent as

---

[1] As regards later statistics on the
same subject the reader can refer to
the Reports of the Anthropometrical
Committee of the British Association
(1879, 1880, 1881, 1883;—especially
this last). These reports seem to
me to represent a great advance on
the results obtained by Quetelet, and
fully to justify the claim of the
Secretary (Mr C. Roberts) that their
statistics are "unique in range and
numbers". They embrace not merely
military recruits—like most of the
previous tables—but almost every
class and age, and both sexes. Moreover they refer not only to stature
but to a number of other physical
characteristics.

they depart from that mean, we shall find that this diminution of frequency takes place according to one invariable law, whatever may be the nature of these magnitudes, and whatever the process by which they may have been obtained.

That such a uniformity as this should prevail amongst many and various classes of phenomena would probably seem surprising in any case. But the full significance of such a fact as this (if indeed it were a fact) only becomes apparent when attention is directed to the profound distinctions in the nature and origin of the phenomena which are thus supposed to be harmonized by being brought under one comprehensive principle. This will be better appreciated if we take a brief glance at some of the principal classes into which the things with which Probability is chiefly concerned may be divided. These are of a three-fold kind.

§ 4. In the first place there are the various combinations, and runs of luck, afforded by games of chance. Suppose a handful, consisting of ten coins, were tossed up a great many times in succession, and the results were tabulated. What we should obtain would be something of the following kind. In a certain proportion of cases, and these the most numerous of all, we should find that we got five heads and five tails; in a somewhat less proportion of cases we should have, as equally frequent results, four heads six tails, and four tails six heads; and so on in a continually diminishing proportion until at length we came down, in a very small relative number of cases, to nine heads one tail, and nine tails one head; whilst the least frequent results possible would be those which gave all heads or all tails[1].

---

[1] As every mathematician knows, the relative numbers of each of these possible throws are given by the successive terms of the expansion of $(1+1)^{10}$, viz. 1, 10, 45, 120, 210, 252, 210, 120, 45, 10, 1.

Here the statistical elements under consideration are, as regards their origin at any rate, optional or brought about by human choice. They would, therefore, be commonly described as being mainly artificial, but their results ultimately altogether a matter of chance.

Again, in the second place, we might take the accurate measurements—i.e. the actual magnitudes themselves,—of a great many natural objects, belonging to the same genus or class; such as the cases, already referred to, of the heights, or other characteristics of the inhabitants of any district. Here human volition or intervention of any kind seem to have little or nothing to do with the matter. It is optional with us to *collect* the measures, but the things measured are quite outside our control. They would therefore be commonly described as being altogether the production of nature, and it would not be supposed that in strictness chance had anything whatever to do with the matter.

In the third place, the result at which we are aiming may be some fixed magnitude, one and the same in each of our successive attempts, so that if our measurements were rigidly accurate we should merely obtain the same result repeated over and over again. But since all our methods of attaining our aims are practically subject to innumerable imperfections, the results actually obtained will depart more or less, in almost every case, from the real and fixed value which we are trying to secure. They will be sometimes more wide of the mark, sometimes less so, the worse attempts being of course the less frequent. If a man aims at a target he will seldom or never hit it precisely in the centre, but his good shots will be more[1]

---

[1] That is they will be more densely aggregated. If a space *the size of the bull's-eye* be examined in each suc- cessive circle, the number of shot marks which it contains will be successively less. The *actual* number

numerous than his bad ones. Here again, then, we have
a series of magnitudes (i.e. the deflections of the shots from
the point aimed at) clustering about a mean, but produced
in a very different way from those of the last two cases.
In this instance the elements would be commonly regarded
as only partially the results of human volition, and chance
therefore as being only a co-agent in the effects produced.
With these must be classed what may be called *estimates*,
as distinguished from measurements.   By the latter are
generally understood the results of a certain amount of
mechanism or manipulation; by the former we may understand those cases in which the magnitude in question is
determined by direct observation or introspection.   The
interest and importance of this class, so far as scientific
principles are concerned, dates mainly from the investigations
of Fechner.   Its chief field is naturally to be found amongst
psychological data.

Other classes of things, besides those alluded to above,
might readily be given. These however are the classes about
which the most extensive statistics are obtainable, or to
which the most practical importance and interest are attached.   The profound distinctions which separate their
origin and character are obvious. If they all really did
display precisely the same law of variation it would be a
most remarkable fact, pointing doubtless to some deep-
seated identity underlying the various ways, apparently
so widely distinct, in which they had been brought about.
The questions now to be discussed are; Is it the case,
with any considerable degree of rigour, that only one law
of distribution does really prevail? and, in so far as this
is so, how does it come to pass?

of shots which strike the bull's-eye
will not be the greatest, since it covers
so much less surface than any of the
other circles.

§ 5. In support of an affirmative answer to the former of these two questions, several different kinds of proof are, or might be, offered.

(I.) For one plan we may make a direct appeal to experience, by collecting sets of statistics and observing what is their law of distribution. As remarked above, this has been done in a great variety of cases, and in some instances to a very considerable extent, by Quetelet and others. His researches have made it abundantly convincing that many classes of things and processes, differing widely in their nature and origin, do nevertheless appear to conform with a considerable degree of accuracy to one and the same[1] law. At least this is made plain for the more

---

[1] Commonly called the exponential law; its equation being of the form $y = Ae^{-hx^2}$. The curve corresponding to it cuts the axis of y at right angles (expressing the fact that near the mean there are a large number of values approximately equal; after a time it begins to slope away rapidly towards the axis of x (expressing the fact that the results soon begin to grow less common as we recede from the mean); and the axis of x is an asymptote in both directions (expressing the fact that no magnitude, however remote from the mean, is strictly impossible; that is, every deviation, however excessive, will have to be encountered at length within the range of a sufficiently long experience). The curve is obviously symmetrical, expressing the fact that equal deviations from the mean, in excess and in defect, tend to occur equally often in the long run.

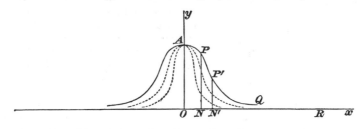

A rough graphic representation of the curve is given above. For the benefit of those unfamiliar with mathematics one or two brief remarks may be here appended concerning some of its properties. (1) It must

central values, for those that is which are situated most nearly about the mean. With regard to the extreme values there is, on the other hand, some difficulty. For instance in the arrangements of the heights of a number of men, these extremes are rather a stumbling-block; indeed it has been proposed to reject them from both ends of the scale on the plea that they are monstrosities, the fact being that their relative numbers do not seem to be by any means those which theory would assign[1]. Such a plan of rejection is however quite unauthorized, for these dwarfs and giants are born into the world like their more normally sized brethren, and have precisely as much right as any others to be included in the formulæ we draw up.

Besides the instance of the heights of men, other classes

not be supposed that all specimens of the curve are similar to one another. The dotted lines are equally specimens of it. In fact, by varying the essentially arbitrary units in which x and y are respectively estimated, we may make the portion towards the vertex of the curve as obtuse or as acute as we please. This consideration is of importance; for it reminds us that, by varying one of these arbitrary units, we could get an 'exponential curve' which should tolerably closely resemble any symmetrical curve of error, provided that this latter recognized and was founded upon the assumption that extreme divergences were excessively rare. Hence it would be difficult, by mere observation, to prove that the law of error in any given case was not exponential; unless the statistics were very extensive, or the actual results departed considerably from the exponential form. (2) It is quite impossible by any graphic representation to give an adequate idea of the excessive rapidity with which the curve after a time approaches the axis of x. At the point R, on our scale, the curve would approach within the fifteen-thousandth part of an inch from the axis of x, a distance which only a very good microscope could detect. Whereas in the hyperbola, e.g. the rate of approach of the curve to its asymptote is continually decreasing, it is here just the reverse; this rate is continually increasing. Hence the two, viz. the curve and the axis of x, appear to the eye, after a very short time, to merge into one another.

[1] As by Quetelet: noted, amongst others, by Herschel, *Essays*, page 409.

of observations of a somewhat similar character have been already referred to as collected and arranged by Quetelet. From the nature of the case, however, there are not many appropriate ones at hand; for when our object is, not to illustrate a law which can be otherwise proved, but to obtain actual direct proof of it, the collection of observations and measurements ought to be made upon such a large scale as to deter any but the most persevering computers from undergoing the requisite labour. Some of the remarks made in the course of the note on the opposite page will serve to illustrate the difficulties which would lie in the way of such a mode of proof.

We are speaking here, it must be understood, only of *symmetrical* curves: if there is asymmetry, i.e. if the Law of Error is different on different sides of the mean,—a comparatively very small number of observations would suffice to detect the fact. But, granted symmetry and rapid decrease of frequency on each side of the mean, we could generally select some one species of the exponential curve which should pretty closely represent our statistics in the neighbourhood of the mean. That is, where the statistics are numerous we could secure agreement; and where we could not secure agreement the statistics would be comparatively so scarce that we should have to continue the observations for a very long time in order to prove the disagreement.

§ 6. Allowing the various statistics such credit as they deserve, for their extent, appropriateness, accuracy and so on, the general conclusion which will on the whole be drawn by almost every one who takes the trouble to consult them, is that they do, in large part, conform approximately to one type or law, at any rate for all except the extreme values. So much as this must be fully admitted. But that they do not, indeed we may say that they cannot, always do so in

the case of the extreme values, will become obvious on
a little consideration. In some of the classes of things to
which the law is supposed to apply, for example, the successions of heads and tails in the throws of a penny, there is
no limit to the magnitude of the fluctuations which may and
will occur. Postulate as long a succession of heads or of tails
as we please, and if we could only live and toss long enough
for it we should succeed in getting it at length. In other
cases, including many of the applications of Probability
to natural phenomena, there can hardly fail to be such
limits. Deviations exceeding a certain range may not be
merely improbable, that is of very rare occurrence, but they
may often from the nature of the case be actually impossible. And even when they are not actually impossible it
may frequently appear on examination that they are only
rendered possible by the occasional introduction of agencies
which are not supposed to be available in the production
of the more ordinary or intermediate values. When, for
instance, we are making observations with any kind of
instrument, the nature of its construction may put an
absolute limit upon the possible amount of error. And even
if there be not an absolute limit under all kinds of usage
it may nevertheless be the case that there is one under
fair and proper usage; it being the case that only when
the instrument is designedly or carelessly tampered with will
any new causes of divergence be introduced which were not
confined within the old limits.

Suppose, for instance, that a man is firing at a mark.
His worst shots must be supposed to be brought about by
a combination of such causes as were acting, or prepared
to act, in every other case; the extreme instance of what
we may thus term 'fair usage' being when a number of
distinct causes have happened to conspire together so as

to tend in the same direction, instead of, as in the other cases, more or less neutralizing one another's work. But the aggregate effect of such causes may well be supposed to be limited. The man will not discharge his shot nearly at right angles to the true line of fire unless some entirely new cause comes in, as by some unusual circumstance having distracted his attention, or by his having had some spasmodic seizure. But influences of this kind were not supposed to have been available before; and even if they were we are taking a bold step in assuming that these occasional great disturbances are subject to the same kind of laws as are the aggregates of innumerable little ones.

We cannot indeed lay much stress upon an example of this last kind, as compared with those in which we can see for certain that there is a fixed limit to the range of error. It is therefore offered rather for illustration than for proof. The enormous, in fact inconceivable magnitude of the numbers expressive of the chance of very rare combinations, such as those in question, has such a bewildering effect upon the mind that one may be sometimes apt to confound the impossible with the higher degrees of the merely mathematically improbable.

§ 7. At the time the first edition of this essay was composed writers on Statistics were, I think, still for the most part under the influence of Quetelet, and inclined to overvalue his authority on this particular subject: of late however attention has been repeatedly drawn to the necessity of taking account of other laws of arrangement than the binomial or exponential.

Mr Galton, for instance,—to whom every branch of the theory of statistics owes so much,—has insisted[1] that the "assumption which lies at the basis of the well-known law of

---

[1] *Proc. R. Soc.* Oct. 21, 1879.

'Frequency of Error'...is incorrect in many groups of vital and social phenomena....For example, suppose we endeavour to match a tint; Fechner's law, in its approximative and simplest form of sensation = log. stimulus, tells us that a series of tints, in which the quantities of white scattered on a black ground are as 1, 2, 4, 8, 16, 32, &c., will appear to the eye to be separated by equal intervals of tint. Therefore, in matching a grey that contains 8 portions of white, we are just as likely to err by selecting one that has 16 portions as one that has 4 portions. In the first case there would be an error in excess, of 8; in the second there would be an error, in deficiency, of 4. Therefore, an error of the same magnitude in excess or in deficiency is not equally probable." The consequences of this assumption are worked out in a remarkable paper by Dr D. McAlister, to which allusion will have to be made again hereafter. All that concerns us here to point out is that when the results of statistics of this character are arranged graphically we do *not* get a curve which is symmetrical on both sides of a central axis.

§ 8.   More recently, Mr F. Y. Edgeworth (in a report of a Committee of the British Association appointed to enquire into the variation of the monetary standard) has urged the same considerations in respect of prices of commodities. He gives a number of statistics " drawn from the prices of twelve commodities during the two periods 1782—1820, 1820—1865. The maximum and minimum entry for each series having been noted, it is found that the number of entries above the 'middle point,' half-way between the maximum and minimum[1], is in every instance less than half the total number of entries in the series. In the twenty-four trials there is not a single exception to the rule, and in very few cases even an approach

[1] We are here considering, remember, the case of a *finite* amount of statistics; so that there are actual limits at each end.

to an exception. We may presume then that the curves are of the lop-sided character indicated by the accompanying diagram." The same facts are also ascertained in respect to *place* variations as distinguished from time variations. To these may be added some statistics of my own, referring to the heights of the barometer taken at the same hour on more than 4000 successive days (v. *Nature*, Sept. 2, 1887). So far as these go they show a marked asymmetry of arrangement.

In fact it appears to me that this want of symmetry ought to be looked for in all cases in which the phenomena under measurement are of a 'one-sided' character; in the sense that they are measured on one side only of a certain fixed point from which their possibility is supposed to start. For not only is it impossible for them to fall below this point: long before they reach it the influence of its proximity is felt in enhancing the difficulty and importance of the same amount of absolute difference.

Look at a table of statures, for instance, with a mean value of 69 inches. A diminution of three feet (were this possible) is much more influential,—counts for much more, in every sense of the term,—than an addition of the same amount; for the former does not double the mean, while the latter more than halves it. Revert to an illustration. If a vast number of petty influencing circumstances of the kind already described were to act upon a swinging *pendulum* we should expect the deflections in each direction to display symmetry; but if they were to act upon a *spring* we should not expect such a result. Any phenomena of which the latter is the more appropriate illustration can hardly be expected to range themselves with symmetry about a mean [1].

---

[1] It must be admitted that experience has not yet (I believe) shown this asymmetry in respect of heights.

§ 9 (II.).   The last remarks will suggest another kind of proof which might be offered to establish the invariable nature of the law of error.   It is of a direct deductive kind, not appealing immediately to statistics, but involving an enquiry into the actual or assumed nature of the causes by which the events are brought about.   Imagine that the event under consideration is brought to pass, in the first place, by some fixed cause, or group of fixed causes.   If this comprised all the influencing circumstances the event would invariably happen in precisely the same way : there would be no errors or deflections whatever to be taken account of.   But now suppose that there were also an enormous number of very small causes which tended to produce deflections ; that these causes acted in entire independence of one another ; and that each of the lot told as often, in the long run, in one direction as in the opposite.   It is easy[1] to see, in a general way, what would follow from these assumptions.   In a very few cases nearly all the causes would tell in the same direction ; in other words, in a very few cases the deflection would be extreme.   In a greater number of cases, however, it would only be the most part of them that would tell in one direction, whilst a few did what they could to counteract the rest ; the result being a comparatively larger number of somewhat smaller deflections.   So on, in increasing numbers, till we approach the middle point.   Here we shall have a very large number of very small deflections : the cases in which the opposed influences just succeed in balancing one another, so that no error whatever is produced, being, though actually infrequent, relatively the most frequent of all.

[1] The above reasoning will probably be accepted as valid at this stage of enquiry.   But in strictness, assumptions are made here, which however justifiable they may be in themselves, involve somewhat of an anticipation.   They demand, and in a future chapter will receive, closer scrutiny and criticism.

Now if all deflections from a mean were brought about in the way just indicated (an indication which must suffice for the present) we should always have one and the same law of arrangement of frequency for these deflections or errors, viz. the exponential[1] law mentioned in § 5.

§ 10. It may be readily admitted from what we know about the production of events that something resembling

---

[1] A definite numerical example of this kind of concentration of frequency about the mean was given in the note to § 4. It was of a binomial form, consisting of the successive terms of the expansion of $(1+1)^m$. Now it may be shown (Quetelet, *Letters*, p. 263; Liagre, *Calcul des Probabilités*, § 34) that the expansion of such a binomial, as m becomes indefinitely great, approaches as its limit the exponential form; that is, if we take a number of equidistant ordinates proportional respectively to 1, m, $\frac{m(m-1)}{1 \cdot 2}$ &c., and connect their vertices, the figure we obtain approximately represents some form of the curve $y = A e^{-hx^2}$, and tends to become identical with it, as m is increased without limit. In other words, if we suppose the errors to be produced by a limited number of finite, equal and independent causes, we have an approximation to the exponential Law of Error, which merges into identity as the causes are increased in number and diminished in magnitude without limit. Jevons has given (*Principles of Science*, p. 381) a diagram drawn to scale, to show how rapid this approximation is. One point must be carefully remembered here, as it is frequently overlooked (by Quetelet, for instance). The coefficients of a binomial of two equal terms—as $(1+1)^m$, in the preceding paragraph—are symmetrical in their arrangement from the first, and very speedily become indistinguishable in (graphical) outline from the final exponential form. But if, on the other hand, we were to consider the successive terms of such a binomial as $(1+4)^m$ (which are proportional to the relative chances of 0, 1, 2, 3,... failures in m ventures, of an event which has one chance in its favour to four against it) we should have an unsymmetrical succession. If however we suppose m to increase without limit, as in the former supposition, the unsymmetry gradually disappears and we tend towards precisely the same exponential form as if we had begun with two equal terms. The only difference is that the position of the vertex of the curve is no longer in the centre: in other words, the likeliest term or event is not an equal number of successes and failures but successes and failures in the ratio of 1 to 4.

these assumptions, and therefore something resembling the consequences which follow from them, is really secured in a very great number of cases.   But although this may prevail approximately, it is in the highest degree improbable that it could ever be secured, even artificially, with anything approaching to rigid accuracy.   For one thing, the causes of deflection will seldom or never be really independent of one another.   Some of them will generally be of a kind such that the supposition that several are swaying in one direction, may affect the capacity of each to produce that full effect which it would have been capable of if it had been left to do its work alone.   In the common example, for instance, of firing at a mark, so long as we consider the case of the tolerably good shots the effect of the wind (one of the causes of error) will be approximately the same whatever may be the precise direction of the bullet.   But when a shot is considerably wide of the mark the wind can no longer be regarded as acting at right angles to the line of flight, and its effect in consequence will not be precisely the same as before.   In other words, the causes here are not strictly independent, as they were assumed to be ; and consequently the results to be attributed to each are not absolutely uninfluenced by those of the others.   Doubtless the effect is trifling here, but I apprehend that if we were carefully to scrutinize the modes in which the several elements of the total cause conspire together, we should find that the assumption of absolute independence was hazardous, not to say unwarrantable, in a very great number of cases.   These brief remarks upon the process by which the deflections are brought about must suffice for the present purpose, as the subject will receive a fuller investigation in the course of the next chapter.

According, therefore, to the best consideration which can at the present stage be afforded to this subject, we may draw a similar conclusion from this deductive line of argument as from the direct appeal to statistics. The same general result seems to be established; namely, that approximately, with sufficient accuracy for all practical purposes, we may say that an examination of the causes by which the deflections are generally brought about shows that they are mostly of such a character as would result in giving us the commonly accepted 'Law of Error,' as it is termed[1]. The two lines of enquiry, therefore, within the limits assigned, afford each other a decided mutual confirmation.

§ 11 (III.). There still remains a third, indirect and mathematical line of proof, which might be offered to establish the conclusion that the Law of Error is always one and the same. It may be maintained that the recognized and universal employment of one and the same method, that known to mathematicians and astronomers as the Method of Least Squares, in all manner of different cases with very satisfactory results, is compatible only with the supposition that the errors to which that method is applied must be grouped according to one invariable law. If all 'laws of error' were not of one and the same type, that is, if the relative frequency of large and small divergences (such as we have been speaking of) were not arranged according to one pattern, how could one method or rule equally suit them all?

In order to preserve a continuity of treatment, some notice must be taken of this enquiry here, though, as in the case of the last argument, any thorough discussion of the

---

[1] 'Law of Error' is the usual technical term for what has been elsewhere spoken of above as a Law of Divergence from a mean. It is in strictness only appropriate in the case of one, namely the third, of the three classes of phenomena mentioned in § 4, but by a convenient generalization it is equally applied to the other two; so that we term the amount of the divergence from the mean an 'error' in every case, however it may have been brought about.

subject is impossible at the present stage. For one thing, it would involve too much employment of mathematics, or at any rate of mathematical conceptions, to be suitable for the general plan of this treatise: I have accordingly devoted a special chapter to the consideration of it.

The main reason, however, against discussing this argument here, is, that to do so would involve the anticipation of a totally different side of the science of Probability from that hitherto treated of. This must be especially insisted upon, as the neglect of it involves much confusion and some error. During these earlier chapters we have been entirely occupied with laying what may be called the physical foundations of Probability. We have done nothing else than establish, in one way or another, the existence of certain groups or arrangements of things which are found to present themselves in nature ; we have endeavoured to explain how they come to pass, and we have illustrated their principal characteristics. But these are merely the foundations of Inference, we have not yet said a word upon the logical processes which are to be erected upon these foundations. We have not therefore entered yet upon the *logic* of chance.

§ 12. Now the way in which the Method of Least Squares is sometimes spoken of tends to conceal the magnitude of this distinction. Writers have regarded it as synonymous with the Law of Error, whereas the fact is that the two are not only totally distinct things but that they have scarcely even any necessary connection with each other. The Law of Error is the statement of a physical fact ; it simply assigns, with more or less of accuracy, the relative frequency with which errors or deviations of any kind are found in practice to present themselves. It belongs therefore to what may be termed the physical foundations of the science. The Method of Least Squares, on the other hand, is not a law at all in the scientific sense of the term. It is simply a rule or direction informing us how we may best proceed to treat any group of these errors which may be set before us, so as to extract the true result at which they have been aiming. Clearly therefore it belongs to the inferential or logical part of the subject.

It cannot indeed be denied that the methods we employ must have some connection with the arrangement of the facts to which they are applied; but the two things are none the less distinct in their nature, and in this case the connection does not seem at all a necessary one, but at most one of propriety and convenience. The Method of Least Squares is usually applied, no doubt, to the most familiar and common form of the Law of Error, namely the exponential form with which we have been recently occupied. But other forms of laws of error may exist, and, if they did, the method in question might equally well be applied to them. I am not asserting that it would necessarily be the best method in every case, but it would be a possible one; indeed we may go further and say, as will be shown in a future chapter, that it would be a good method in almost every case. But its particular merits or demerits do not interfere with its possible employment in every case in which we may choose to resort to it. It will be seen therefore, even from the few remarks that can be made upon the subject here, that the fact that one and the same method is very commonly employed with satisfactory results affords little or no proof that the errors to which it is applied must be arranged according to one fixed law.

§ 13. So much then for the attempt to prove the prevalence, in all cases, of this particular law of divergence. The next point in Quetelet's treatment of the subject which deserves attention as erroneous or confusing, is the doctrine maintained by him and others as to the existence of what he terms a *type*

in the groups of things in question.   This is a not unnatural
consequence from some of the data and conclusions of the
last few paragraphs.   Refer back to two of the three classes
of things already mentioned in § 4.   If it really were the case
that in arranging in order a series of incorrect observations
or attempts of our own, and a collection of natural objects
belonging to some one and the same species or class, we found
that the law of their divergence was in each case identical in
the long run, we should be naturally disposed to apply the
same expression 'Law of Error' to both instances alike,
though in strictness it could only be appropriate to the
former.   When we perform an operation ourselves with a
clear consciousness of what we are aiming at, we may quite
correctly speak of every deviation from this as being an
error; but when Nature presents us with a group of objects
of any kind, it is using a rather bold metaphor to speak in
this case also of a law of error, as if she had been aiming at
something all the time, and had like the rest of us missed
her mark more or less in almost every instance[1].

Suppose we make a long succession of attempts to measure
accurately the precise height of a man, we should from one
cause or another seldom or never succeed in doing so with
absolute accuracy.   But we have no right to assume that these
imperfect measurements of ours would be found so to deviate
according to one particular law of error as to present the
precise counterpart of a series of actual heights of *different*
men, supposing that these latter were assigned with absolute
precision.   What might be the actual law of error in a series
of direct measurements of any given magnitude could hardly
be asserted beforehand, and probably the attempt to deter-

[1] This however seems to be the
purport, either by direct assertion
or by implication, of two elaborate works by Quetelet, viz. his
Physique Sociale, and his *Anthropométrie*.

mine it by experience has not been made sufficiently often to enable us to ascertain it; but upon general grounds it seems by no means certain that it would follow the so-called exponential law. Be this however as it may, it is rather a licence of language to talk as if nature had been at work in the same way as one of us; aiming (ineffectually for the most part) at a given result, that is at producing a man endowed with a certain stature, proportions, and so on, who might therefore be regarded as the typical man.

§ 14. Stated as above, namely, that there is a fixed invariable human type to which all individual specimens of humanity may be regarded as having been meant to attain, but from which they have deviated in one direction or another, according to a law of deviation capable of *à priori* determination, the doctrine is little else than absurd. But if we look somewhat closer at the facts of the case, and the probable explanation of these facts, we may see our way to an important truth. The facts, on the authority of Quetelet's statistics (the great interest and value of which must be frankly admitted), are very briefly as follows: if we take any element of our physical frame which admits of accurate measurement, say the height, and determine this measure in a great number of different individuals belonging to any tolerably homogeneous class of people, we shall find that these heights do admit of an orderly arrangement about a mean, after the fashion which has been already repeatedly mentioned. What is meant by a homogeneous class? is a pertinent and significant enquiry, but applying this condition to any simple cases its meaning is readily stated. It implies that the mean in question will be different according to the nationality of the persons under measurement. According to Quetelet[1], in the case of Englishmen the mean is about

[1] He scarcely, however, professes to give these as an accurate measure

5 ft. 9 in.; for Belgians about 5 ft. 7 in.; for the French about
5 ft. 4 in.   It need hardly be added that these measures are
those of adult males.

§ 15.   It may fairly be asked here what would have
been the consequence, had we, instead of keeping the English
and the French apart, mixed the results of our measurements
of them all together?   The question is an important one, as it
will oblige us to understand more clearly what we mean by
homogeneous classes.   The answer that would usually be
given to it, though substantially correct, is somewhat too decisive and summary.   It would be said that we are here
mixing distinctly heterogeneous elements, and that in consequence the resultant law of error will be by no means of
the simple character previously exhibited.   So far as such an
answer is to be admitted its grounds are easy to appreciate.
In accordance with the usual law of error the divergences
from the mean grow continuously less numerous as they
increase in amount.   Now, if we mix up the French and
English heights, what will follow?   Beginning from the
English mean of 5 feet 9 inches, the heights will at first follow almost entirely the law determined by these English
conditions, for at this point the English data are very numerous, and the French by comparison very few.   But, as we
begin to approach the French mean, the numbers will cease
to show that continual diminution which they should show,
according to the English scale of arrangement, for here the
French data are in turn very numerous, and the English by
comparison few.   The result of such a combination of hetero-

of the mean height, nor does he
always give precisely the same measure.   Practically, none but soldiers
being measured in any great numbers, the English stature did not
afford accurate data on any large
scale.   The statistics given a few
pages further on are probably far
more trustworthy.

geneous elements is illustrated by the figure annexed, of course in a very exaggerated form.

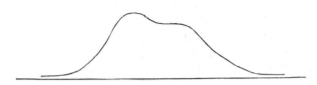

§ 16. In the above case the nature of the heterogeneity, and the reasons why the statistics should be so collected and arranged as to avoid it, seemed tolerably obvious. It will be seen still more plainly if we take a parallel case drawn from artificial proceedings. Suppose that after a man had fired a few thousand shots at a certain spot, say a wafer fixed somewhere on a wall, the position of the spot at which he aims were shifted, and he fired a few thousand more shots at the wafer in its new position. Now let us collect and arrange all the shots of both series in the order of their departure from either of the centres, say the new one. Here we should really be mingling together two discordant sets of elements, either of which, if kept apart from the other, would have been of a simple and homogeneous character. We should find, in consequence, that the resultant law of error betrayed its composite or heterogeneous origin by a glaring departure from the customary form, somewhat after the fashion indicated in the above diagram.

The instance of the English and French heights resembles the one just given, but falls far short of it in the stringency with which the requisite conditions are secured. The fact is we have not here got the most suitable requirements, viz. a group consisting of a few fixed causes supplemented by innumerable little disturbing influences. What we call a nation is really a highly artificial body, the members of which are subject to a considerable number of local or occasional disturbing causes. Amongst Frenchmen were included, presumably, Bretons, Provencals, Alsatians, and so on, thus commingling distinctions which, though less than those between French and English, regarded as wholes, are very far from being insignificant. And to these differences of race must be added other disturbances, also highly important, dependent upon varying climate, food and occupation. It is plain, therefore, that whatever objections exist against confusing together French and English statistics, exist also, though of course in a less degree, against confusing together those of the various provincial and other components which make up the French people.

§ 17. Out of the great variety of important causes which influence the height of men, it is probable that those which most nearly fulfil the main conditions required by the 'Law of Error' are those about which we know the least. Upon the effects of food and employment, observation has something to say, but upon the purely physiological causes by which the height of the parents influences the height of the offspring, we have probably nothing which deserves to be called knowledge. Perhaps the best supposition we can make is one which, in accordance with the saying that 'like breeds like', would assume that the purely physiological causes represent the constant element; that is, given a homogeneous race of people to begin with, who freely intermarry, and are subject to like circumstances of climate, food, and occupation, the standard would remain on the whole constant[1].

In such a case the man who possessed the mean height, mean weight, mean strength, and so on, might then be

---

[1] This statement will receive some explanation and correction in the next chapter.

called, in a sort of way, a 'type'. The deviations from this
type would then be produced by innumerable small influences, partly physiological, partly physical and social, acting
for the most part independently of one another, and resulting in a Law of Error of the usual description. Under such
restrictions and explanations as these, there seems to be no
reasonable objection to speaking of a French or English type
or mean. But it must always be remembered that under
the present circumstances of every political nation, these
somewhat heterogeneous bodies might be subdivided into
various smaller groups, each of which would frequently exhibit the characteristics of such a type in an even more
marked degree.

§ 18. On this point the reports of the Anthropometrical
Committee, already referred to, are most instructive. They
illustrate the extent to which this subdivision could be
carried out, and prove,—if any proof were necessary,—that
the discovery of Quetelet's *homme moyen* would lead us a
long chase. So far as their results go the mean 'English'
stature (in inches) is 67·66. But this is composed of Scotch,
Irish, English and Welsh constituents, the separate means of
these being, respectively; 68·71, 67·90, 67·36, and 66·66.
But these again may be subdivided; for careful observation
shows that the mean English stature is distinctly greater in
certain districts (e.g. the North-Eastern counties) than in
others. Then again the mean of the professional classes is
considerably greater than that of the labourers; and that of
the honest and intelligent is very much greater than that of
the criminal and lunatic constituents of the population.
And, so far as the observations are extensive enough for the
purpose, it appears that every characteristic in respect of the
grouping about a mean which can be detected in the more
extensive of these classes can be detected also in the nar-

rower. Nor is there any reason to suppose that the same
process of subdivision could not be carried out as much
farther as we chose to prolong it.

§ 19. It need hardly be added to the above remarks
that no one who gives the slightest adhesion to the Doctrine
of Evolution could regard the type, in the above qualified
sense of the term, as possessing any real permanence and
fixity. If the constant causes, whatever they may be, remain unchanged, and if the variable ones continue in the
long run to balance one another, the results will continue to
cluster about the same mean. But if the constant ones
undergo a gradual change, or if the variable ones, instead of
balancing each other suffer one or more of their number to
begin to acquire a preponderating influence, so as to put a
sort of bias upon their aggregate effect, the mean will at
once begin, so to say, to shift its ground. And having once
begun to shift, it may continue to do so, to whatever extent
we recognize that Species are variable and Development is a
fact. It is as if the point on the target at which we aim, instead of being fixed, were slowly changing its position as we
continue to fire at it; changing almost certainly to some extent and temporarily, and not improbably to a considerable
extent and permanently.

§ 20. Our examples throughout this chapter have been
almost exclusively drawn from physical characteristics,
whether of man or of inanimate things; but it need not be
supposed that we are necessarily confined to such instances.
Mr Galton, for instance, has proposed to extend the same
principles of calculation to mental phenomena, with a view
to their more accurate determination. The objects to be
gained by so doing belong rather to the inferential part of
our subject, and will be better indicated further on; but
they do not involve any distinct principle. Like other at-

tempts to apply the methods of science in the region of the mind, this proposal has met with some opposition; with very slight reason, as it seems to me. That our mental qualities, if they could be submitted to accurate measurement, would be found to follow the usual Law of Error, may be assumed without much hesitation. The known extent of the correlation of mental and bodily characteristics gives high probability to the supposition that what is proved to prevail, at any rate approximately, amongst most bodily elements which have been submitted to measurement, will prevail also amongst the mental elements.

To what extent such measurements could be carried out practically, is another matter. It does not seem to me that it could be done with much success; partly because our mental qualities are so closely connected with, indeed so run into one another, that it is impossible to isolate them for purposes of comparison[1]. This is to some extent indeed a difficulty in bodily measurements, but it is far more so in those of the mind, where we can hardly get beyond what can be called a good guess. The doctrine, therefore, that mental qualities follow the now familiar law of arrangement can scarcely be grounded upon anything more than a strong analogy. Still this analogy is quite strong enough to justify us in accepting the doctrine and all the conclusions which follow from it, in so far as our estimates and measurements can be regarded as trustworthy. There seems therefore nothing unreasonable in the attempt to establish a system of natural classification of mankind by arranging them into a certain number of groups above and below the average, each group being intended to cor-

[1] I am not speaking here of the now familiar results of Psychophysics, which are mainly occupied with the measurement of perceptions and other simple states of consciousness.

respond to certain limits of excellency or deficiency.[1] All that is necessary for such a purpose is that the rate of departure from the mean should be tolerably constant under widely different circumstances: in this case throughout all the races of man. Of course if the law of divergence is the same as that which prevails in inanimate nature we have a still wider and more natural system of classification at hand, and one which ought to be familiar, more or less, to every one who has thus to estimate qualities.

§ 21. Perhaps one of the best illustrations of the legitimate application of such principles is to be found in Mr Galton's work on *Hereditary Genius.* Indeed the full force and purport of some of his reasonings there can hardly be appreciated except by those who are familiar with the conceptions which we have been discussing in this chapter. We can only afford space to notice one or two points, but the student will find in the perusal, of at any rate the more argumentive parts, of that volume[2] an interesting illustration of the doctrines now under discussion. For one thing it may be safely asserted, that no one unfamiliar with the Law of Error would ever in the least appreciate the excessive

---

[1] Perhaps the best brief account of Mr Galton's method is to be found in a paper in *Mind* (July, 1880) on the statistics of Mental Imagery. The subject under comparison here —viz. the relative power, possessed by different persons, of raising clear visual images of objects no longer present to us—is one which it seems impossible to 'measure', in the ordinary sense of the term. But by arranging all the answers in the order in which the faculty in question seems to be possessed we can, with some approach to accuracy, select the middlemost person in the row and use him as a basis of comparison with the corresponding person in any other batch. And similarly with those who occupy other relative positions than that of the middlemost.

[2] I refer to the introductory and concluding chapters: the bulk of the book is, from the nature of the case, mainly occupied with statistical and biographical details.

rapidity with which the superior degrees of excellence tend
to become scarce. Every one, of course, can see at once, in
a numerical way at least, what is involved in being 'one of a
million'; but they would not at all understand, how very
little extra superiority is to be looked for in the man who is
'one of two million'. They would confound the mere numerical distinction, which seems in some way to imply
double excellence, with the intrinsic superiority, which
would mostly be represented by a very small fractional advantage. To be 'one of ten million' sounds very grand, but
if the qualities under consideration could be estimated in
themselves without the knowledge of the vastly wider area
from which the selection had been made, and in freedom
therefore from any consequent numerical bias, people would
be surprised to find what a very slight comparative superiority was, as a rule, thus obtained.

§ 22. The point just mentioned is an important one in
arguments from statistics. If, for instance, we find a small
group of persons, connected together by blood-relationship,
and all possessing some mental characteristic in marked
superiority, much depends upon the comparative rarity of
such excellence when we are endeavouring to decide whether
or not the common possession of these qualities was accidental. Such a decision can never be more than a rough
one, but if it is to be made at all this consideration must
enter as a factor. Again, when we are comparing one nation
with another[1], say the Athenian with any modern European
people, does the popular mind at all appreciate what sort of
evidence of general superiority is implied by the production,
out of one nation, of such a group as can be composed of
Socrates, Plato, and a few of their contemporaries? In this

---

[1] See Galton's *Hereditary Genius*, pp. 336—350, "On the comparative
worth of different races."

latter case we are also, it should be remarked, employing the
'Law of Error' in a second way; for we are assuming that
where the extremes are great so will also the means be, in
other words we are assuming that every amount of departure
from the mean occurs with a (roughly) calculable degree
of relative frequency.   However generally this truth may
be accepted in a vague way, its evidence can only be appreciated by those who know the reasons which can be given
in its favour.

But the same principles will also supply a caution in
the case of the last example.   They remind us that, for
the mere purpose of comparison, the *average* man of any
group or class is a much better object for selection than
the eminent one.   There may be greater difficulties in the
way of detecting him, but when we have done so we have
got possession of a securer and more stable basis of comparison.   He is selected, by the nature of the case, from
the most numerous stratum of his society; the eminent
man from a thinly occupied stratum.   In accordance therefore with the now familiar laws of averages and of large
numbers the fluctuations amongst the former will generally
be very few and small in comparison with those amongst the
latter.

CHAPTER III.

ON THE CAUSAL PROCESS BY WHICH THE GROUPS OR SERIES OF PROBABILITY ARE BROUGHT ABOUT.

§ 1.   IN discussing the question whether all the various groups and series with which Probability is concerned are of precisely one and the same type, wo made some examination of the process by which they are naturally produced, but we must now enter a little more into the details of this process.   All events are the results of numerous and complicated antecedents, far too numerous and complicated in fact for it to be possible for us to determine or take them all into account.   Now, though it is strictly true that we can never determine them all, there is a broad distinction between the case of Induction, in which we can make out enough of them, and with sufficient accuracy, to satisfy a reasonable certainty, and Probability, in which we cannot do so.   To Induction we shall return in a future chapter, and therefore no more need be said about it here.

We shall find it convenient to begin with a division which, though not pretending to any philosophical accuracy, will serve as a preliminary guide.   It is the simple division into objects, and the agencies which affect them.   All the phenomena with which Probability is concerned (as indeed most of those with which science of any kind is concerned) are the product of certain objects natural and artificial, acting under the influence of certain agencies natural and artificial. In the tossing of a penny, for instance, the objects would be the penny or pence which were successively thrown; the agencies would be the act of throwing, and everything which combined directly or indirectly with this to make any particular face come uppermost. This is a simple and intelligible division, and can easily be so extended in meaning as to embrace every class of objects with which we are concerned.

Now if, in any two or more cases, we had the same object, or objects indistinguishably alike, and if they were exposed to the influence of agencies in all respects precisely alike, we should expect the results to be precisely similar. By one of the applications of the familiar principle of the uniformity of nature we should be confident that exact likeness in the antecedents would be followed by exact likeness in the consequents. If the same penny, or similar pence, were thrown in exactly the same way, we should invariably find that the same face falls uppermost.

§ 2. What we actually find is, of course, very far removed from this. In the case of the objects, when they are artificial constructions, e.g. dice, pence, cards, it is true that they are purposely made as nearly as possible indistinguishably alike. We either use the same thing over and over again or different ones made according to precisely the same model. But in natural objects nothing of the sort prevails. In fact when we come to examine them, we find reproduced in them precisely the same characteristics as those which present themselves in the final result which we were asked to explain, so that unless we examine them a stage further back, as we shall have to do to some extent at any rate, we seem to be merely postulating again the very peculiarity of the phenomena which we were undertaking to explain. They will be found, for instance, to

consist of large classes of objects, throughout all the individual members of which a general resemblance extends.
Suppose that we were considering the length of life. The
objects here are the human beings, or that selected class
of them, whose lives we are considering. The resemblance
existing among them is to be found in the strength and
soundness of their principal vital organs, together with all
the circumstances which collectively make up what we call
the goodness of their constitutions. It is true that most of
these circumstances do not admit of any approach to actual
measurement; but, as was pointed out in the last chapter,
very many of the circumstances which do admit of such
measurement have been measured, and found to display
the characteristics in question. Hence, from the known
analogy and correlation between our various organs, there
can be no reasonable doubt that if we could arrange human
constitutions in general, or the various elements which compose them in particular, in the order of their strength, we
should find just such an aggregate regularity and just such
groupings about the mean, as the final result (viz. in this
case the length of their lives) presents to our notice.

§ 3. It will be observed therefore that for this purpose the existence of natural kinds or groups is necessary.
In our games of chance of course the same die may be
thrown, or a card be drawn from the same pack, as often
as we please; but many of the events which occur to
human beings either cannot be repeated at all, or not often
enough to secure in the case of the single individual any
sufficient statistical uniformity. Such regularity as we trace
in nature is owing, much more than is often suspected,
to the arrangement of things in natural kinds, each of
them containing a large number of individuals. Were each
kind of animals or vegetables limited to a single pair, or

even to but a few pairs, there would not be much scope
left for the collection of statistical tables amongst them.
Or to take a less violent supposition, if the numbers
in each natural class of objects were much smaller than
they are at present, or the differences between their varieties and sub-species much more marked, the consequent
difficulty of extracting from them any sufficient length of
statistical tables, though not fatal, might be very serious.
A large number of objects in the class, together with that
general similarity which entitles the objects to be fairly
comprised in one class, seem to be important conditions
for the applicability of the theory of Probability to any
phenomenon. Something analogous to this excessive paucity
of objects in a class would be found in the attempt to
apply special Insurance offices to the case of those trades
where the numbers are very limited, and the employment
so dangerous as to put them in a class by themselves. If
an insurance society were started for the workmen in
gunpowder mills alone, a premium would have to be charged
to avoid possible ruin, so high as to illustrate the extreme
paucity of appropriate statistics.

§ 4. So much (at present) for the objects. If we turn
to what we have termed the agencies, we find much the
same thing again here. By the adjustment of their relative
intensity, and the respective frequency of their occurrence,
the total effects which they produce are found to be also
tolerably uniform. It is of course conceivable that this
should have been otherwise. It might have been found
that the second group of conditions so exactly corrected the
former as to convert the merely general uniformity into
an absolute one; or it might have been found, on the
other hand, that the second group should aggravate or
disturb the influence of the former to such an extent

as to destroy all the uniformity of its effects. Practically
neither is the case. The second condition simply varies the
details, leaving the uniformity on the whole of precisely
the same general description as it was before. Or if the
objects were supposed to be absolutely alike, as in the case
of successive throws of a penny, it may serve to bring about
a uniformity. Analysis will show these agencies to be
thus made up of an almost infinite number of different
components, but it will detect the same peculiarity that
we have so often had occasion to refer to, pervading almost
all these components. The proportions in which they are
combined will be found to be nearly, though not quite, the
same; the intensity with which they act will be nearly
though not quite equal. And they will all unite and blend
into a more and more perfect regularity as we proceed to
take the average of a larger number of instances.

Take, for instance, the length of life. As we have seen,
the constitutions of a very large number of persons selected
at random will be found to present much the same feature;
general uniformity accompanied by individual irregularity.
Now when these persons go out into the world, they are
exposed to a variety of agencies, the collective influence
of which will assign to each the length of life allotted to
him. These agencies are of course innumerable, and their
mutual interaction complicated beyond all power of analysis
to extricate. Each effect becomes in its turn a cause, is
interwoven inextricably with an indefinite number of other
causes, and reacts upon the final result. Climate, food,
clothing, are some of these agencies, or rather comprise
aggregate groups of them. The nature of a man's work
is also important. One man overworks himself, another
follows an unhealthy trade, a third exposes himself to in-
fection, and so on.

The result of all this interaction between what we have thus called objects and agencies is that the final outcome presents the same general characteristics of uniformity as may be detected separately in the two constituent elements. Or rather, as we shall proceed presently to show, it does so in the great majority of cases.

§ 5. It may be objected that such an explanation as the above does not really amount to anything deserving of the name, for that instead of explaining how a particular state of things is caused it merely points out that the same state exists elsewhere. There is a uniformity discovered in the objects at the stage when they are commonly submitted to calculation; we then grope about amongst the causes of them, and after all only discover a precisely similar uniformity existing amongst these causes. This is to some extent true, for though part of the objection can be removed, it must always remain the case that the foundations of an objective science will rest in the last resort upon the mere fact that things are found to be of such and such a character.

§ 6. This division, into objects and the agencies which affect them, is merely intended for a rough practical arrangement, sufficient to point out to the reader the immediate nature of the causes which bring about our familiar uniformities. If we go back a step further, it might fairly be maintained that they may be reduced to one, namely, to the agencies. The objects, as we have termed them, are not an original creation in the state in which we now find them. No one supposes that whole groups or classes were brought into existence simultaneously, with all their general resemblances and particular differences fully developed. Even if it were the case that the first parents of each natural kind had been specially created, instead

of being developed out of pre-existing forms, it would still
be true that amongst the numbers of each that now present
themselves the characteristic differences and resemblances
are the result of what we have termed agencies. Take, for
instance, a single characteristic only, say the height; what
determines this as we find it in any given group of men?
Partly, no doubt, the nature of their own food, clothing,
employment, and so on, especially in the earliest years of
their life; partly also, very likely, similar conditions and
circumstances on the part of their parents at one time or
another. No one, I presume, in the present state of knowledge, would attempt to enumerate the remaining causes,
or even to give any indication of their exact nature; but
at the same time few would entertain any doubt that
agencies of this general description have been the determining causes at work.

If it be asked again, Into what may these agencies
themselves be ultimately analysed? the answer to this
question, in so far as it involves any detailed examination
of them, would be foreign to the plan of this essay. In so
far as any general remarks, applicable to nearly all classes
alike of such agencies, are called for, we are led back to
the point from which we started in the previous chapter,
when we were discussing whether there is necessarily one
fixed law according to which all our series are formed. We
there saw that every event might be regarded as being
brought about by a comparatively few important causes, of
the kind which comprises all of which ordinary observation
takes any notice, and an indefinitely numerous group of
small causes, too numerous, minute, and uncertain in their
action for us to be able to estimate them or indeed to take
them individually into account at all. The important ones,
it is true, may also in turn be themselves conceived to be

made up of aggregates of small components, but they are
still best regarded as being by comparison simple and distinct, for their component parts act mostly in groups collectively, appearing and disappearing together, so that they
possess the essential characteristics of unity.

§ 7. Now, broadly speaking, it appears to me that the
most suitable conditions for Probability are these : that the
important causes should be by comparison fixed and permanent, and that the remaining ones should on the average
continue to act as often in one direction as in the other.
This they may do in two ways. In the first place we
may be able to predicate nothing more of them than the
mere fact that they act[1] as often in one direction as the
other; what we should then obtain would be merely the
simple statistical uniformity that is described in the first
chapter. But it may be the case, and in practice generally
is so more or less approximately, that these minor causes
act also in independence of one another. What we then
get is a group of uniformities such as was explained and
illustrated in the second chapter. Every possible combination of these causes then occurring with a regular degree of frequency, we find one peculiar kind of uniformity
exhibited, not merely in the mere fact of excess and defect
(of whatever may be the variable quality in question), but
also in every particular amount of excess and defect.
Hence, in this case, we get what some writers term a
'mean' or 'type,' instead of a simple average. For instance, suppose a man throwing a quoit at a mark. Here
our fixed causes are his strength, the weight of the quoit,

---

[1] As stated above, this is really
little more than a re-statement, a
stage further back, of the existence
of the same kind of uniformity as
that which we are called upon to explain in the concrete details presented to us in experience.

and the intention of aiming at a given point. These we must of course suppose to remain unchanged, if we are to obtain any such uniformity as we are seeking. The minor and variable causes are all those innumerable little disturbing influences referred to in the last chapter. It might conceivably be the case that we were only able to ascertain that these acted as often in one direction as in the other; what we should then find was that the quoit tended to fall short of the mark as often as beyond it. But owing to these little causes being mostly independent of one another, and more or less equal in their influence, we find also that every *amount* of excess and defect presents the same general characteristics, and that in a large number of throws the quantity of divergences from the mark, of any given amount, is a tolerably determinate function, according to a regular law, of that amount of divergence[1].

§ 8.   The necessity of the conditions just hinted at will best be seen by a reference to cases in which any of

[1] "It would seem in fact that in coarse and rude observations the errors proceed from a *very few* principal causes, and in consequence our hypothesis [as to the Exponential Law of Error] will probably represent the facts only imperfectly, and the frequency of the errors will only approximate roughly and vaguely to the law which follows from it. But when astronomers, not content with the degree of accuracy they had reached, prosecuted their researches into the remaining sources of error, they found that not three or four, but a *great number* of minor sources of error of nearly co-ordinate importance began to reveal themselves, having been till then masked and overshadowed by the graver errors which had been now approximately removed......There were errors of graduation, and many others in the contraction of instruments ; other errors of their adjustments ; errors (technically so called) of *observation ;* errors from the changes of temperature, of weather, from slight irregular motions and vibrations; in short, the thousand minute disturbing influences with which modern astronomers are familiar." (Extracted from a paper by Mr Crofton in the Vol. of the *Philosophical Transactions* for 1870, p. 177.)

them happen to be missing.   Thus we know that the length
of life is on the whole tolerably regular, and so are the
numbers of those who die in successive years or centuries
of most of the commoner diseases.   But it does not seem
to be the case with all diseases.   What, for instance, of
the Sweating Sickness, the Black Death, the Asiatic
Cholera?   The two former either do not recur, or, if they
do, recur in such a mild form as not to deserve the same
name.   What in fact of any of the diseases which are
epidemic rather than endemic?   All these have their causes
doubtless, and would be produced again by the recurrence
of the conditions which caused them before.   But some of
them apparently do not recur at all.   They seem to have
depended upon such rare conditions that their occurrence
was almost unique.   And of those which do recur the course
is frequently so eccentric and irregular, often so much dependent upon human will or want of will, as to entirely
deprive their results (that is, the annual number of deaths
which they cause) of the statistical uniformity of which we
are speaking.

The explanation probably is that one of the principal
causes in such cases is what we commonly call contagion.
If so, we have at once a cause which so far from being fixed is
subject to the utmost variability.   Stringent caution may
destroy it, carelessness may aggravate it to any extent.   The
will of man, as finding its expression either on the part of
government, of doctors, or of the public, may make of it
pretty nearly what is wished, though against the possibility
of its entrance into any community no precautions can absolutely insure us.

§ 9.   If it be replied that this want of statistical regularity only arises from the fact of our having confined ourselves to too limited a time, and that we should find

irregularity disappear here, as elsewhere, if we kept our
tables open long enough, we shall find that the answer will
suggest another case in which the requisite conditions for
Probability are wanting. Such a reply would only be conclusive upon the supposition that the ways and thoughts of
men are in the long run invariable, or if variable, subject to
periodic changes only. On the assumption of a steady progress in society, either for the better or the worse, the argument falls to the ground at once. From what we know of
the course of the world, these fearful pests of the past may
be considered as solitary events in our history, or at least
events which will not be repeated. No continued uniformity
would therefore be found in the deaths which they occasion,
though the registrar's books were kept open for a thousand
years. The reason here is probably to be sought in the
gradual alteration of those indefinitely numerous conditions
which we term collectively progress or civilization. Every
little circumstance of this kind has some bearing upon the
liability of any one to catch a disease. But when a kind of
slow and steady tide sets in, in consequence of which these
influences no longer remain at about the same average
strength, warring on about equal terms with hostile influences, but on the contrary show a steady tendency to increase their power, the statistics will, with consequent steadiness and permanence, take the impress of such a change.

§ 10. Briefly then, if we were asked where the distinctive characteristics of Probability are most prominently
to be found, and where they are most prominently absent,
we might say that (1) they prevail principally in the properties of natural kinds, both in the ultimate and in the derivative or accidental properties. In all the characteristics of
natural species, in all they do and in all which happens to
them, so far as it depends upon their properties, we seldom

fail to detect this regularity. Thus in men; their height, strength, weight, the age to which they live, the diseases of which they die; all present a well-known uniformity. Life insurance tables offer the most familiar instance of the importance of these applications of Probability.

(2) The same peculiarity prevails again in the force and frequency of most natural agencies. Wind and weather are seen to lose their proverbial irregularity when examined on a large scale. Man's work therefore, when operated on by such agencies as these, even though it had been made in different cases absolutely alike to begin with, afterwards shows only a general regularity. I may sow exactly the same amount of seed in my field every year. The yield may one year be moderate, the next year be abundant through favourable weather, and then again in turn be destroyed by hail. But in the long run these irregularities will be equalized in the result of my crops, because they are equalized in the power and frequency of the productive agencies. The business of underwriters, and offices which insure the crops against hail, would fall under this class; though, as already remarked, there is no very profound distinction between them and the former class.

The reader must be reminded again that this fixity is only temporary, that is, that even here the series belong to the class of those which possess a fluctuating type. Those indeed who believe in the fixity of natural species will have the best chance of finding a series of the really permanent type amongst them, though even they will admit that some change in the characteristic is attainable in length of time. In the case of the principal natural agencies, it is of course incontestable that the present average is referable to the present geological period only. Our average temperature and average rainfall have in former times been widely different from what they now are, and doubtless will be so again.

Any fuller investigation of the process by which, on the Theory of Evolution, out of a primeval simplicity and uniformity the present variety was educed, hardly belongs to the scope of the present work: at most, a few hints must suffice.

§ 11.   The above, then, are instances of natural objects and natural agencies.   There seems reason to believe that it is in such things only, as distinguished from things artificial, that the property in question is to be found.   This is an assertion that will need some discussion and explanation.   Two instances, in apparent opposition, will at once occur to the mind of some readers; one of which, from its great intrinsic importance, and the other, from the frequency of the problems which it furnishes, will demand a few minutes' separate examination.

(1)   The first of these is the already mentioned case of instrumental observations.   In the use of astronomical and other instruments the utmost possible degree of accuracy is often desired, a degree which cannot be reasonably hoped for in any one single observation.   What we do therefore in these cases is to make a large number of successive observations which are naturally found to differ somewhat from each other in their results; by means of these the true value (as explained in a future chapter, on the Method of Least Squares) is to be determined as accurately as possible.   The subjects then of calculation here are a certain number of elements, slightly incorrect elements, given by successive observations.   Are not these observations artificial, or the direct product of voluntary agency?   Certainly not: or rather, the answer depends on what we understand by voluntary. What is really intended and aimed at by the observer, is of

course, perfect accuracy, that is, the true observation, or the voluntary steps and preliminaries on which this observation depends. Whether voluntary or not, this result only can be called intentional. But this result is not obtained. What we actually get in its place is a series of deviations from it, containing results more or less wide of the truth. Now by what are these deviations caused? By just such agencies as we have been considering in some of the earlier sections in this chapter. Heat and its irregular warping influence, draughts of air producing their corresponding effects, dust and consequent friction in one part or another, the slight distortion of the instrument by strains or the slow uneven contraction which continues long after the metal was cast; these and such as these are some of the causes which divert us from the truth. Besides this group, there are others which certainly do depend upon human agency, but which are not, strictly speaking, voluntary. They are such as the irregular action of the muscles, inability to make our various organs and members execute precisely the purposes we have in mind, perhaps different rates in the rapidity of the nervous currents, or in the response to stimuli, in the same or different observers. The effect produced by some of these, and the allowance that has in consequence to be made, are becoming familiar even to the outside world under the name of the 'personal equation' in astronomical, psychophysical, and other observations.

§ 12. (2) The other example, alluded to above, is the stock one of cards and dice. Here, as in the last case, the result is remotely voluntary, in the sense that deliberate volition presents itself at one stage. But subsequently to this stage, the result is produced or affected by so many involuntary agencies that it owes its characteristic properties to these. The turning up, for example, of a particular face of a die is the result of voluntary agency, but it is not an immediate result. That particular face was not chosen, though the fact of its being chosen was the remote consequence of an act of choice. There has been an intermediate chaos of conflicting agencies, which no one can calculate before or distinguish afterwards. These agencies seem to show a uniformity in the long run, and thence to produce a similar uniformity in the result. The drawing of a card from a pack is indeed more directly volitional, as in cutting for partners in a game of whist. But no one continues to do this long without having the pack well shuffled in the interval, whereby a host of involuntary influences are let in.

§ 13. The once startling but now familiar uniformities exhibited in the cases of suicides and misdirected letters, do not belong to the same class. The final resolution, or want of it, which leads to these results, is in each case indeed an important ingredient in the individual's action or omission; but, in so far as volition has anything to do with the results *as a whole*, it instantly disturbs them. If the voice of the Legislature speaks out, or any great preacher or moralist succeeds in deterring, or any impressive example in influencing, our moral statistics are instantly tampered with. Some further discussion will be devoted to this subject in a future chapter; it need only be remarked here that (always excluding such common or general influence as those just mentioned) the average volition, potent as it is in each separate case, is on the whole swayed by non-voluntary conditions, such as those of health, the casualties of employment, &c., in fact the various circumstances which influence the length of a man's life.

§ 14. Such distinctions as those just insisted on may seem to some persons to be needless, but serious errors have occasionally arisen from the neglect of them. The imme-

diate products of man's mind, so far indeed as we can make
an attempt to obtain them, do not seem to possess this
essential characteristic of Probability.   Their characteristic
seems rather to be, either perfect mathematical accuracy or
utter want of it, either law unfailing or mere caprice.   If,
e.g., we find the trees in a forest growing in straight lines,
we unhesitatingly conclude that they were planted by man
as they stand.   It is true on the other hand, that if we find
them not regularly planted, we cannot conclude that they
were not planted by man; partly because the planter may
have worked without a plan, partly because the subsequent
irregularities brought on by nature may have obscured the
plan.   Practically the mind has to work by the aid of imperfect instruments, and is subjected to many hindrances
through various and conflicting agencies, and by these means
the work loses its original properties.   Suppose, for instance,
that a man, instead of producing numerical results by imperfect observations or by the cast of dice, were to select
them at first hand for himself by simply thinking of them
at once; what sort of series would he obtain?   It would be
about as difficult to obtain in this way any such series as
those appropriate to Probability as it would be to keep his
heart or pulse working regularly by direct acts of volition,
supposing that he had the requisite control over these organs.
But the mere suggestion is absurd.   A man must have an
object in thinking, he must think according to a rule or formula; but unless he takes some natural series as a copy, he
will never be able to construct one mentally which shall permanently imitate the originals.   Or take another product of
human efforts, in which the intention can be executed with
tolerable success.   When any one builds a house, there are
many slight disturbing influences at work, such as shrinking
of bricks and mortar, settling of foundations, &c.   But the

effect which these disturbances are able to produce is so inappreciably small, that we may fairly consider that the result obtained is the direct product of the mind, the accurate realization of its intention. What is the consequence? Every house in the row, if designed by one man and at one time, is of exactly the same height, width, &c. as its neighbours; or if there are variations they are few, definite, and regular. The result offers no resemblance whatever to the heights, weights, &c. of a number of men selected at random. The builder probably had some regular design in contemplation, and he has succeeded in executing it.

§ 15. It may be replied that if we extend our observations, say to the houses of a large city, we shall then detect the property under discussion. The different heights of a great number, when grouped together, might be found to resemble those of a great number of human beings under similar treatment. Something of this kind might not improbably be found to be the case, though the resemblance would be far from being a close one. But to raise this question is to get on to different ground, for we were speaking (as remarked above) not of the work of different minds with their different aims, but of that of one mind. In a multiplicity of designs, there may be that variable uniformity, for which we may look in vain in a single design. The heights which the *different* builders contemplated might be found to group themselves into something of the same kind of uniformity as that which prevails in most other things which they should undertake to do independently. We might then trace the action of the same two conditions,—a uniformity in the multitude of their different designs, a uniformity also in the infinite variety of the influences which have modified those designs. But this is a very different thing from saying that the work of one man

will show such a result as this.   The difference is much like
that between the tread of a thousand men who are stepping
without thinking of each other, and their tread when they
are drilled into a regiment.   In the former case there is
the working, in one way or another, of a thousand minds;
in the latter, of one only.

The investigations of this and the former chapter
constitute a sufficiently close examination into the detailed
causes by which the peculiar form of statistical results with
which we are concerned is actually produced, to serve the
purpose of a work which is occupied mainly with the *methods*
of the Science of Probability.   The great importance, however, of certain statistical or sociological enquiries will demand a recurrence in a future chapter to one particular
application of these statistics, viz. to those concerned with
some classes of human actions.

§ 16.   The only important addition to, or modification of,
the foregoing remarks which I have found occasion to make
is due to Mr Galton.   He has recently pointed out,—and was
I believe the first to do so,—that in certain cases some
analysis of the causal processes can be effected, and is in fact
absolutely necessary in order to account for the facts observed.   Take, for instance, the *heights* of the population of
any country.   If the distribution or dispersion of these about
their mean value were left to the unimpeded action of those
myriad productive agencies alluded to above, we should certainly obtain such an arrangement in the posterity of any
one generation as had already been exhibited in the parents.
That is, we should find repeated in the previous stage the
same kind of order as we were trying to account for in the
following stage.

But then, as Mr Galton insists, if such agencies acted
freely and independently, though we should get the same

kind of arrangement or distribution, we should not get the same *degree* of it: there would, on the contrary, be a tendency towards further dispersion. The 'curve of facility' (v. the diagram on p. 29) would belong to the same class, but would have a different modulus. We shall see this at once if we take for comparison a case in which similar agencies work their way without any counteraction whatever. Suppose, for instance, that a large number of persons, whose fortunes were equal to begin with, were to commence gambling or betting continually for some small sum. If we examine their circumstances after successive intervals of time, we should expect to find their fortunes distributed according to the same general law,—i.e. the now familiar law in question,—but we should also expect to find that the poorest ones were slightly poorer, and the richest ones slightly richer, on each successive occasion. We shall see more about this in a future chapter (on *Gambling*), but it may be taken for granted here that there is nothing in the laws of chance to resist this tendency towards intensifying the extremes.

Now it is found, on the contrary, in the case of vital phenomena,—for instance in that of height, and presumably of most of the other qualities which are in any way characteristic of natural kinds,—that there is, through a number of successive generations, a remarkable degree of fixity. The tall men are not taller, and the short men are not shorter, *per cent.* of the population in successive generations: always supposing of course that some general change of circumstances, such as climate, diet, &c. has not set in. There must therefore here be some cause at work which tends, so to say, to draw in the extremes and thus to check the otherwise continually increasing dispersion.

§ 17. The facts were first tested by careful experiment.

At the date of Mr Galton's original paper on the subject[1], there were no available statistics of heights of human beings; so a physical element admitting of careful experiment (viz. the size or weight of certain seeds) was accurately estimated. From these data the actual amount of reversion from the extremes, that is, of the slight pressure continually put upon the extreme members with the result of crowding them back towards the mean, was determined, and this was compared with what theory would require in order to keep the characteristics of the species permanently fixed. Since then, statistics have been obtained to a large extent which deal directly with the heights of human beings.

The general conclusion at which we arrive is that there are several causes at work which are neither slight nor independent. There is, for instance, the observed fact that the extremes are as a rule not equally fertile with the means, nor equally capable of resisting death and disease. Hence as regards their mere numbers, there is a tendency for them somewhat to thin out. Then again there is a distinct positive cause in respect of 'reversion.' Not only are the offspring of the extremes less numerous, but these offspring also tend to cluster about a mean which is, so to say, shifted a little towards the true centre of the whole group; i.e. towards the mean offspring of the mean parents.

§ 18. For a full discussion of these characteristics, and for a variety of most ingenious illustrations of their mode of agency and of their comparative efficacy, the reader may be referred to Mr Galton's original articles. For our present purpose it will suffice to say that these characteristics tend towards maintaining the fixity of species; and that though they do not affect what may be called the general nature of

---

[1] *Typical Laws of Heredity;* read before the Royal Institution, Feb. 9, 1877. See also *Journal of the Anthrop. Inst.* Nov. 1885.

the 'probability curve' or 'law of facility', they do determine
its precise value in the cases in question. If, indeed, it be
asked why there is no need for any such corrective influence
in the case of, say, firing at a mark: the answer is that there
is no opening for it except where a *cumulative* influence is introduced. The reason why the fortunes of our betting party
showed an ever increasing divergency, and why some special
correction was needed in order to avert such a tendency in
the case of vital phenomena, was that the new starting-point
at every step was slightly determined by the results of the
previous step. The man who has lost a shilling one time
starts, next time, worse off by just a shilling; and, but for
the corrections we have been indicating, the man who was
born tall would, so to say, throw off his descendants from a
vantage ground of superior height. The true parallel in the
case of the marksmen would be to suppose that their new
points of aim were always shifted a little in the direction of
the last divergence. The spreading out of the shot-marks
would then continue without limit, just as would the divergence of fortunes of the supposed gamblers.

CHAPTER IV.

ON THE MODES OF ESTABLISHING AND DETERMINING THE EXISTENCE AND NUMERICAL PROPORTIONS OF THE CHARACTERISTIC PROPERTIES OF OUR SERIES OR GROUPS.

§ 1. AT the point which we have now reached, we are supposed to be in possession of series or groups of a certain kind, lying at the bottom, as one may say, and forming the foundation on which the Science of Probability is to be erected. We have described with sufficient particularity the characteristics of such a series, and have indicated the process by which it is, as a rule, actually brought about in nature. The next enquiries which have to be successively made are, how in any particular case we are to establish their existence and determine their special character and properties? and secondly[1], when we have obtained them, in what mode are they to be employed for logical purposes?

The answer to the former enquiry does not seem difficult. Experience is our sole guide. If we want to discover what is in reality a series of *things*, not a series of our own conceptions, we must appeal to the things themselves to obtain it, for we cannot find much help elsewhere. We cannot tell how many persons will be born or die in a year, or how many houses will be burnt or ships wrecked, without actually counting them. When we thus speak of 'experience' we

---

[1] This latter enquiry belongs to what may be termed the more purely logical part of this volume, and is entered on in the course of Chapter VI.

mean to employ the term in its widest signification; we mean experience supplemented by all the aids which inductive or deductive logic can afford. When, for instance, we have found the series which comprises the numbers of persons of any assigned class who die in successive years, we have no hesitation in extending it some way into the future as well as into the past. The justification of such a procedure must be sought in the ordinary canons of Induction. As a special discussion will be given upon the connection between Probability and Induction, no more need be said upon this subject here; but nothing will be found there at variance with the assertion just made, that the series we employ are ultimately obtained by experience only.

§ 2. In many cases it is undoubtedly true that we do not resort to direct experience at all. If I want to know what is my chance of holding ten trumps in a game of whist, I do not enquire how often such a thing has occurred before. If all the inhabitants of the globe were to divide themselves up into whist parties they would have to keep on at it for a great many years, if they wanted to settle the question satisfactorily in that way. What we do of course is to calculate algebraically the proportion of possible combinations in which ten trumps can occur, and take this as the answer to our problem. So again, if I wanted to know the chance of throwing six with a die whose faces were unequal, it would be a question if my best way would not be to calculate geometrically the solid angle subtended at the centre of gravity by the opposite face, and the ratio of this to the whole surface of a sphere would represent sufficiently closely the chance required.

It is quite true that in such examples as the above, especially the former one, nobody would ever think of appealing to statistics. This would be a tedious process to adopt when, as here, the mechanical and other conditions upon which the production of the events depend are comparatively few, determinate, and admit of isolated consideration, whilst the enormous number of combinations which can be constructed out of them causes an enormous consequent multiplicity of ways in which the events can possibly happen. Hence, in practice, *à priori* determination is often easy, whilst *à posteriori* appeal to experience would be not merely tedious but utterly impracticable. This, combined with the frequent simplicity and attractiveness of such examples when deductively treated, has made them very popular, and produced the impression in many quarters that they are the proper typical instances to illustrate the theory of chance. Whereas, had the science been concerned with those kinds of events only which in practice are commonly made subjects of insurance, probably no other view would ever have been taken than that it was based upon direct appeal to experience.

§ 3.   When, however, we look a little closer, we find that there is no occasion for such a sharp distinction as that apparently implied between the two classes of examples just indicated. In such cases as those of dice and cards, even, in which we appear to reason directly from the determining conditions, or possible variety of the events, rather than from actual observation of their occurrence, we shall find that this procedure is only valid by the help of a tacit assumption which can never be determined otherwise than by direct experience. It is, no doubt, an exceedingly natural and obvious assumption, and one which is continually deriving fresh weight from every-day observation, but it is one which ought not to be admitted without consideration. As this is a very important matter, not so much in itself as in connection with the light which it throws upon the theory of the subject, we will enter into a somewhat detailed examination of it.

Let us take a very simple example, that of tossing up a penny. Suppose that I am contemplating a succession of two throws; I can see that the only possible events are[1] *HH.*, *HT.*, *TH.*, *TT.* So much is certain. We are moreover tolerably well convinced from experience that these events occur, in the long run, about equally often. This is of course admitted on all hands. But on the view commonly maintained, it is contended that we might have known the fact beforehand on grounds which are applicable to an indefinite number of other and more complex cases. The form in which this view would generally be advanced is, that we are enabled to state beforehand that the four throws above mentioned are *equally likely.* If in return we ask what is meant by the expression 'equally likely', it appears that there are two and only two possible forms of reply. One of these seeks the explanation in the state of mind of the observer, the other seeks it in some characteristic of the things observed.

(1) It might, for instance, be said on the one hand, that what is meant is that the four events contemplated are equally easy to imagine, or, more accurately, that our expectation or belief in their occurrence is equal. We could hardly be content with this reply, for the further enquiry would immediately be urged, On what ground is this to be believed? What are the characteristics of events of which our expectation is equal? If we consented to give an answer to this further enquiry, we should be led to the second form of reply, to be noticed directly; if we did not consent we should, it seems, be admitting that Probability was only a

---

[1] For the use of those not acquainted with the common notation employed in this subject, it may be remarked that *HH* is simply an abbreviated way of saying that the two successive throws of the penny give head ; *HT* that the first of them gives head, and the second tail ; and so on with the remaining symbols.

portion of Psychology, confined therefore to considering states
of mind in themselves, rather than in their reference to facts,
viz. as being true or false.   We should, that is, be ceasing
to make it a science of inference about things.   This point
will have to be gone into more thoroughly in another chapter; but it is impossible to direct attention too prominently
to the fact that Logic (and therefore Probability as a branch
of Logic) is not concerned with what men *do* believe, but
with what they ought to believe, if they are to believe
correctly.

(2)   In the other form of reply the explanation of the
phrase in question would be sought, not in a state of mind,
but in a quality of the things contemplated.   We might assign
the following as the meaning, viz. that the events really
would occur with equal frequency in the long run.   The
ground of this assertion would probably be found in past experience, and it would doubtless be impossible so to frame
the answer as to exclude the notion of our belief altogether.
But still there is a broad distinction between seeking an
equality in the amount of our belief, as before, and in the
frequency of occurrence of the events themselves, as here.

§ 4.   When we have got as far as this it can readily be
shown that an appeal to experience cannot be long evaded.
For *can* the assertion in question (viz. that the throws of the
penny will occur equally often) be safely made *à priori?*
Those who consider that it can seem hardly to have fully
faced the difficulties which meet them.   For when we begin
to enquire seriously whether the penny will really do what
is expected of it, we find that restrictions have to be introduced.   In the first place it must be an ideal coin, with
its sides equal and fair.   This restriction is perfectly intelligible; the study of solid geometry enables us to idealize a
penny into a circular or cylindrical lamina.   But this condition

by itself is not sufficient, others are wanted as well. The penny was supposed to be tossed up, as we say 'at random.' What is meant by this, and how is this process to be idealized? To ask this is to introduce no idle subtlety; for it would scarcely be maintained that the heads and tails would get their fair chances if, immediately before the throwing, we were so to place the coin in our hands as to start it always with the same side upwards. The difference that would result in consequence, slight as its cause is, would tend in time to show itself in the results. Or, if we persisted in starting with each of the two sides alternately upwards, would the longer repetitions of the same side get their fair chance?

Perhaps it will be replied that if we think nothing whatever about these matters all will come right of its own accord. It may, and doubtless will be so, but this is falling back upon experience. It is here, then, that we find ourselves resting on the experimental assumption above mentioned, and which indeed cannot be avoided. For suppose, lastly, that the circumstances of nature, or my bodily or mental constitution, were such that the same side always *is* started upwards, or indeed that they are started in any arbitrary order of our own? Well, it will be replied, it would not then be a fair trial. If we press in this way for an answer to such enquiries, we shall find that these tacit restrictions are really nothing else than a mode of securing an experimental result. They are only another way of saying, Let a series of actions be performed in such a way as to secure a sequence of a particular kind, viz., of the kind described in the previous chapters.

§ 5. An intermediate way of evading the direct appeal to experience is sometimes found by defining the probability of an event as being measured by the ratio which the

number of cases favourable to the event bears to the total
number of cases which are possible. This seems a somewhat
loose and ambiguous way of speaking. It is clearly not
enough to *count* the number of cases merely, they must also
be *valued*, since it is not certain that each is equally potent
in producing the effect. This, of course, would never be
denied, but sufficient importance does not seem to be attached to the fact that we have really no other way of
valuing them except by estimating the effects which they
actually do, or would produce. Instead of thus appealing to
the proportion of cases favourable to the event, it is far better
(at least as regards the foundation of the science, for we are
not at this moment discussing the practical method of facili-
tating our calculations) to appeal at once to the proportion
of cases in which the event actually occurs.

§ 6. The remarks above made will apply, of course, to
most of the other common examples of chance; the throwing
of dice, drawing of cards, of balls from bags, &c. In the
last case, for instance, one would naturally be inclined to
suppose that a ball which had just been put back would
thereby have a better chance of coming out again next time,
since it will be more in the way for that purpose. How is
this to be prevented? If we designedly thrust it to the
middle or bottom of the others, we may overdo the precaution; and are in any case introducing human design, that
element so essentially hostile to all that we understand by
chance. If we were to trust to a good shake setting matters
right, we may easily be deceived; for shaking the bag can
hardly do more than diminish the disposition of those balls
which were already in each other's neighbourhood, to remain
so. In the consequent interaction of each upon all, the
arrangement in which they start cannot but leave its impress
to some extent upon their final positions. In all such cases,

therefore, if we scrutinize our language, we shall find that any supposed *à priori* mode of stating a problem is little else than a compendious way of saying, Let means be taken for obtaining a given result.   Since it is upon this result that our inferences ultimately rest, it seems simpler and more philosophical to appeal to it at once as the groundwork of our science.

§ 7.   Let us again take the instance of the tossing of a penny, and examine it somewhat more minutely, to see what can be actually proved about the results we shall obtain. We are willing to give the pence fair treatment by assuming that they are perfect, that is, that in the long run they show no preference for either head or tail; the question then remains, Will the repetitions of the same face obtain the proportional shares to which they are entitled by the usual interpretations of the theory?   Putting then, as before, for the sake of brevity, H for head, and HH for heads twice running, we are brought to this issue;—Given that the chance of H is $\frac{1}{2}$, does it follow necessarily that the chance of HH (with two pence) is $\frac{1}{4}$?   To say nothing of 'H ten times' occurring once in 1024 times (with ten pence), need it occur at all?   The mathematicians, for the most part, seem to think that this conclusion follows necessarily from first principles; to me it seems to rest upon no more certain evidence than a reasonable extension by Induction.

Taking then the possible results which can be obtained from a pair of pence, what do we find?   Four different results may follow, namely, (1) HT, (2) HH, (3) TH, (4) TT. If it can be proved that these four are equally probable, that is, occur equally often, the commonly accepted conclusions will follow, for a precisely similar argument would apply to all the larger numbers.

§ 8.   The proof usually advanced makes use of what is

called the Principle of Sufficient Reason.   It takes this form;—Here are four kinds of throws which may happen; once admit that the separate elements of them, namely, H and T, happen equally often, and it will follow that the above combinations will also happen equally often, for no reason can be given in favour of one of them that would not equally hold in favour of the others.

To a certain extent we must admit the validity of the principle for the purpose.   In the case of the throws given above, it would be valid to prove the equal frequency of (1) and (3) and also of (2) and (4); for there is no difference existing between these pairs except what is introduced by our own notation[1].   TH is the same as HT, except in the order of the occurrence of the symbols H and T, which we do not take into account.   But either of the pair (1) and (3) *is* different from either of the pair (2) and (4).   Transpose the notation, and there would still remain here a distinction which the mind can recognize.   A succession of the same thing twice running is distinguished from the conjunction of two different things, by a distinction which does not depend upon our arbitrary notation only, and would remain entirely unaltered by a change in this notation.   The principle therefore of Sufficient Reason, if admitted, would only prove that doublets of the two kinds, for example (2) and (4), occur equally often, but it would not prove that they must each

---

[1] I am endeavouring to treat this rule of Sufficient Reason in a way that shall be legitimate in the opinion of those who accept it, but there seem very great doubts whether a contradiction is not involved when we attempt to extract results from it. If the sides are absolutely alike, how can there be any difference between the terms of the series?   The succession seems then reduced to a dull uniformity, a mere iteration of the same thing many times; the series we contemplated has disappeared. If the sides are not absolutely alike, what becomes of the applicability of the rule?

occur once in four times.   It cannot be proved indeed in this
way that they need ever occur at all.

§ 9.   The formula, then, not being demonstrable *à priori*,
(as might have been concluded,) can it be obtained by experience ? To a certain extent it can ; the present experience
of mankind in pence and dice seems to show that the smaller
successions of throws do really occur in about the proportions
assigned by the theory.   But how nearly they do so no one
can say, for the amount of time and trouble to be expended
before we could feel that we have verified the fact, even for
small numbers, is very great, whilst for large numbers it
would be simply intolerable.   The experiment of throwing
often enough to obtain 'heads ten times' has been actually
performed by two or three persons, and the results are given
by De Morgan, and Jevons[1].   This, however, being only
sufficient on the average to give 'heads ten times' a single
chance, the evidence is very slight; it would take a considerable number of such experiments to set the matter
nearly at rest.

Any such rule, then, as that which we have just been
discussing, which professes to describe what will take place
in a long succession of throws, is only conclusively proved by
experience within very narrow limits, that is, for small repetitions of the same face ; within limits less narrow, indeed,
we feel assured that the rule cannot be flagrantly in error,
otherwise the variation would be almost sure to be detected.
From this we feel strongly inclined to infer that the same
law will hold throughout.   In other words, we are inclined
to extend the rule by Induction and Analogy.   Still there
are so many instances in nature of proposed laws which hold
within narrow limits but get egregiously astray when we

---

[1] *Formal Logic*, p. 185.   *Principles of Science*, p. 208.

attempt to push them to great lengths, that we must give at best but a qualified assent to the truth of the formula.

§ 10.   The object of the above reasoning is simply to show that we cannot be certain that the rule is true.   Let us now turn for a minute to consider the causes by which the succession of heads and tails is produced, and we may perhaps see reasons to make us still more doubtful.

It has been already pointed out that in calculating probabilities *à priori*, as it is called, we are only able to do so by introducing restrictions and suppositions which are in reality equivalent to assuming the expected results.   We use words which in strictness mean, Let a given process be performed; but an analysis of our language, and an examination of various tacit suppositions which make themselves felt the moment they are not complied with, soon show that our real meaning is, Let a series of a given kind be obtained; it is to this series only, and not to the conditions of its production, that all our subsequent calculations properly apply.   The physical process being performed, we want to know whether anything resembling the contemplated series really will be obtained.

Now if the penny were invariably set the same side uppermost, and thrown with the same velocity of rotation and to the same height, &c.—in a word, subjected to the same conditions,—it would always come down with the same side uppermost.   Practically, we know that nothing of this kind occurs, for the individual variations in the results of the throws are endless.   Still there will be an *average* of these conditions, about which the throws will be found, as it were, to cluster much more thickly than elsewhere.   We should be inclined therefore to infer that if the same side were always set uppermost there would really be a departure from the sort of series which we ordinarily expect.   In a very large number of throws we should probably begin to find, under such circumstances, that either head or tail was having a preference shown to it. If so, would not similar effects be found to be connected with the way in which we started each successive *pair* of throws ? According as we chose to make a practice of putting HH or TT uppermost, might there not be a disturbance in the proportion of successions of two heads or two tails ? Following out this train of reasoning, it would seem to point with some likelihood to the conclusion that in order to obtain a series of the kind we expect, we should have to dispose the antecedents in a similar series at the start. The changes and chances produced by the act of throwing might introduce infinite individual variations, and yet there might be found, in the very long run, to be a close similarity between these two series.

§ 11. This is, to a certain extent, only shifting the difficulty, I admit; for the claim formerly advanced about the possibility of proving the proportions of the throws in the former series, will probably now be repeated in favour of those in the latter. Still the question is very much narrowed, for we have reduced it to a series of *voluntary* acts. A man may put whatever side he pleases uppermost. He may act consciously, as I have said, or he may think nothing whatever about the matter, that is, throw at random; if so, it will probably be asserted by many that he will involuntarily produce a series of the kind in question. It may be so, or it may not; it does not seem that there are any easily accessible data by which to decide. All that I am concerned with here is to show the likelihood that the commonly received result does in reality depend upon the fulfilment of a certain condition at the outset, a condition which it is certainly optional with any one to fulfil or not as he pleases. The short successions doubtless will take care of

themselves, owing to the infinite complications produced by
the casual variations in throwing; but the long ones may
suffer, unless their interest be consciously or unconsciously
regarded at the outset.

§ 12.   The advice, 'Only try long enough, and you will
sooner or later get any result that is possible,' is plausible,
but it rests only on Induction and Analogy; mathematics do
not prove it.   As has been repeatedly stated, there are two
distinct views of the subject.   Either we may, on the one
hand, take a series of symbols, call them heads and tails;
H, T, &c.; and make the assumption that each of these, and
each pair of them, and so on, will occur in the long run with
a regulated degree of frequency.   We may then calculate
their various combinations, and the consequences that may
be drawn from the data assumed.   This is a purely algebraical
process; it is infallible; and there is no limit whatever to the
extent to which it may be carried.   This way of looking at
the matter may be, and undoubtedly should be, nothing
more than the counterpart of what I have called the substituted or idealized series which generally has to be introduced
as the basis of our calculation.   The danger to be guarded
against is that of regarding it too purely as an algebraical
conception, and thence of sinking into the very natural
errors both of too readily evolving it out of our own consciousness, and too freely pushing it to unwarranted lengths.

Or on the other hand, we may consider that we are treating of the behaviour of *things;*—balls, dice, births, deaths,
&c.; and drawing inferences about them.   But, then, what
were in the former instance allowable assumptions, become
here propositions to be tested by experience.   Now the whole
theory of Probability as a practical science, in fact as anything more than an algebraical truth, depends of course upon
there being a close correspondence between these two views

of the subject, in other words, upon our substituted series being kept in accordance with the actual series. Experience abundantly proves that, between considerable limits, in the example in question, there does exist such a correspondence. But let no one attempt to enforce our assent to every remote deduction that mathematicians can draw from their formulæ. When this is attempted the distinction just traced becomes prominent and important, and we have to choose our side. Either we go over to the mathematics, and so lose all right of discussion about the things; or else we take part with the things, and so defy the mathematics. We do not question the formal accuracy of the latter within their own province, but either we dismiss them as somewhat irrelevant, as applying to data of whose correctness we cannot be certain, or we take the liberty of remodelling them so as to bring them into accordance with facts.

§ 13. A critic of any doctrine can hardly be considered to have done much more than half his duty when he has explained and justified his grounds for objecting to it. It still remains for him to indicate, if only in a few words, what he considers its legitimate functions and position to be, for it can seldom happen that he regards it as absolutely worthless or unmeaning. I should say, then, that when Probability is thus divorced from direct reference to objects, as it substantially is by not being founded upon experience, it simply resolves itself into the common algebraical or arithmetical doctrine of Permutations and Combinations[1]. The considerations upon which these depend are purely formal and necessary, and can be fully reasoned out without any appeal to experience. We there start from pure considerations of number or magnitude, and we terminate with them,

---

[1] The close connection between these subjects is well indicated in the title of Mr Whitworth's treatise, *Choice and Chance.*

having only arithmetical calculations to connect them together. I wish, for instance, to find the chance of throwing
heads three times running with a penny. All I have to do
is first to ascertain the possible number of throws. Permutations tell me that with two things thus in question (viz.
head and tail) and three times to perform the process, there
are eight possible forms of the result. Of these eight one
only being favourable, the chance in question is pronounced
to be one-eighth.

Now though it is quite true that the actual calculation of
every chance problem must be of the above character, viz. an
algebraical or arithmetical process, yet there is, it seems to
me, a broad and important distinction between a material
science which employs mathematics, and a formal one which
consists of nothing but mathematics. When we cut ourselves off from the necessity of any appeal to experience, we
are retaining only the intermediate or calculating part of the
investigation; we may talk of dice, or pence, or cards, but
these are really only names we choose to give to our symbols.
The H's and T's with which we deal have no bearing on objective occurrences, but are just like the x's and y's with
which the rest of algebra deals. Probability in fact, when so
treated, seems to be absolutely nothing else than a system of
applied Permutations and Combinations.

It will now readily be seen how narrow is the range of
cases to which any purely deductive method of treatment can
apply. It is almost entirely confined to such employments
as games of chance, and, as already pointed out, can only be
regarded as really trustworthy even there, by the help of
various tacit restrictions. This alone would be conclusive
against the theory of the subject being rested upon such a
basis. The experimental method, on the other hand, is, in the
same theoretical sense, of universal application. It would

include the ordinary problems furnished by games of chance, as well as those where the dice are loaded and the pence are not perfect, and also the indefinitely numerous applications of statistics to the various kinds of social phenomena.

§ 14. The particular view of the deductive character of Probability above discussed, could scarcely have intruded itself into any other examples than those of the nature of games of chance, in which the conditions of occurrence are by comparison few and simple, and are amenable to accurate numerical determination. But a doctrine, which is in reality little else than the same theory in a slightly disguised form, is very prevalent, and has been applied to truths of the most purely empirical character. This doctrine will be best introduced by a quotation from Laplace. After speaking of the irregularity and uncertainty of nature as it appears at first sight, he goes on to remark that when we look closer we begin to detect "a striking regularity which seems to suggest a design, and which some have considered a proof of Providence. But, on reflection, it is soon perceived that this regularity is nothing but the development of the respective probabilities of the simple events, which ought to occur more frequently according as they are more probable [1]."

If this remark had been made about the succession of heads and tails in the throwing up of a penny, it would have been intelligible. It would simply mean this : that the constitution of the body was such that we could anticipate with some confidence what the result would be when it was treated in a certain way, and that experience would justify our anticipation in the long run. But applied as it is in a more general form to the facts of nature, it seems really to have but little meaning in it. Let us test it by an instance. Amidst the irregularity of individual births, we find that the

[1] *Essai Philosophique.* Ed. 1825, p. 74.

male children are to the female, in the long run, in about
the proportion of 106 to 100. Now if we were told that
there is nothing in this but "the development of their respective probabilities," would there be anything in such a
statement but a somewhat pretentious re-statement of the
fact already asserted? The probability *is* nothing but that
proportion, and is unquestionably in this case derived from
no other source but the statistics themselves; in the above
remark the attempt seems to be made to invert this process,
and to derive the sequence of events from the mere numerical statement of the proportions in which they occur.

§ 15. It will very likely be replied that by the probability above mentioned is meant, not the mere numerical
proportion between the births, but some fact in our constitution upon which this proportion depends; that just as
there was a relation of equality between the two sides of the
penny, which produced the ultimate equality in the number
of heads and tails, so there may be something in our constitution or circumstances in the proportion of 106 to 100,
which produces the observed statistical result. When this
something, whatever it might be, was discovered, the observed numbers might be supposed capable of being determined beforehand. Even if this were the case, however, it
must not be forgotten that there could hardly fail to be, in
combination with such causes, other concurrent conditions in
order to produce the ultimate result; just as besides the shape
of the penny, we had also to take into account the nature of
the 'randomness' with which it was tossed. What these
may be, no one at present can undertake to say, for the best
physiologists seem indisposed to hazard even a guess upon
the subject[1]. But without going into particulars, one may

[1] An opinion prevailed rather at
one time (quoted and supported by
Quetelet amongst others) that the
relative ages of the parents had

assert with some confidence that these conditions cannot well be altogether independent of the health, circumstances, manners and customs, &c. (to express oneself in the vaguest way) of the parents; and if once these influencing elements are introduced, even as very minute factors, the results cease to be dependent only on fixed and permanent conditions. We are at once letting in other conditions, which, if they also possess the characteristics that distinguish Probability (an exceedingly questionable assumption), must have that fact specially proved about them. That this should be the case indeed seems not merely questionable, but almost certainly impossible; for these conditions partaking of the nature of what we term generally, Progress and Civilization, cannot be expected to show any permanent disposition to hover about an average.

§ 16. The reader who is familiar with Probability is of course acquainted with the celebrated theorem of James Bernoulli. This theorem, of which the examples just adduced are merely particular cases, is generally expressed somewhat as follows:—in the long run all events will tend to occur with a relative frequency proportional to their objective probabilities. With the mathematical proof of this theorem we need not trouble ourselves, as it lies outside the province of this work; but indeed if there is any value in the foregoing criticism, the basis on which the mathematics rest is faulty, owing to there being really nothing which we can with propriety call an objective probability.

If one might judge by the interpretation and uses to

something to do with the sex of the offspring. If this were so, it would quite bear out the above remarks. As a matter of fact, it should be observed, that the proportion of 106 to 100 does not seem by any means universal in all countries or at all times. For various statistical tables on the subject see Quetelet, *Physique Sociale*, Vol. i. 166, 173, 238.

which this theorem is sometimes exposed, we should regard
it as one of the last remaining relics of Realism, which after
being banished elsewhere still manages to linger in the remote province of Probability.   It would be an illustration of
the inveterate tendency to objectify our conceptions, even in
cases where the conceptions had no right to exist at all.   A
uniformity is observed; sometimes, as in games of chance, it
is found to be so connected with the physical constitution of
the bodies employed as to be capable of being inferred beforehand; though even here the connection is by no means
so necessary as is commonly supposed, owing to the fact that
in addition to these bodies themselves we have also to take
into account their relation to the agencies which influence
them.   This constitution is then converted into an 'objective
probability', supposed to develope into the sequence which
exhibits the uniformity.   Finally, this very questionable objective probability is assumed to exist, with the same faculty
of development, in all the cases in which uniformity is observed, however little resemblance there may be between
these and games of chance.

§ 17.   How utterly inappropriate any such conception is
in most of the cases in which we find statistical uniformity,
will be obvious on a moment's consideration.   The observed
phenomena are generally the product, in these cases, of very
numerous and complicated antecedents.   The number of
crimes, for instance, annually committed in any society, is a
function amongst other things, of the strictness of the law,
the morality of the people, their social condition, and the
vigilance of the police, each of these elements being in itself
almost infinitely complex.   Now, as a result of all these
agencies, there is some degree of uniformity; but what has
been called above the change of type, which it sooner or
later tends to display, is unmistakeable.   The average annual

numbers do not show a steady gradual approach towards what might be considered in some sense a limiting value, but, on the contrary, fluctuate in a way which, however it may depend upon causes, shows none of the permanent uniformity which is characteristic of games of chance. This fact, combined with the obvious arbitrariness of singling out, from amongst the many and various antecedents which produced the observed regularity, a few only, which should constitute the objective probability (if we took all, the events being absolutely determined, there would be no occasion for an appeal to probability in the case), would have been sufficient to prevent any one from assuming the existence of any such thing, unless the mistaken analogy of other cases had predisposed him to seek for it.

There is a familiar practical form of the same error, the tendency to which may not improbably be derived from a similar theoretical source. It is that of continuing to accumulate our statistical data to an excessive extent. If the type were absolutely fixed we could not possibly have too many statistics; the longer we chose to take the trouble of collecting them the more accurate our results would be. But if the type is changing, in other words, if some of the principal causes which aid in their production have, in regard to their present degree of intensity, strict limits of time or space, we shall do harm rather than good if we overstep these limits. The danger of stopping too soon is easily seen, but in avoiding it we must not fall into the opposite error of going on too long, and so getting either gradually or suddenly under the influence of a changed set of circumstances.

§ 18. This chapter was intended to be devoted to a consideration, not of the processes by which nature produces the series with which we are concerned, but of the theoretic basis of the methods by which we can determine the existence of such series.   But it is not possible to keep the two enquiries apart, for here, at any rate, the old maxim prevails that to know a thing we must know its causes.   Recur for a minute to the considerations of the last chapter.   We there saw that there was a large class of events, the conditions of production of which could be said to consist of (1) a comparatively few nearly unchangeable elements, and (2) a vast number of independent and very changeable elements.   At least if there were any other elements besides these, we are assumed either to make special allowance for them, or to omit them from our enquiry.   Now in certain cases, such as games of chance, the unchangeable elements may without practical error be regarded as really unchangeable throughout any range of time and space.   Hence, as a result, the deductive method of treatment becomes in their case at once the most simple, natural, and conclusive; but, as a further consequence, the statistics of the events, if we choose to appeal to them, may be collected *ad libitum* with better and better approximation to truth.   On the other hand, in all social applications of Probability, the unchangeable causes can only be regarded as really unchangeable under many qualifications.   We know little or nothing of them directly; they are often in reality numerous, indeterminate, and fluctuating; and it is only under the guarantee of stringent restrictions of time and place, that we can with any safety attribute to them sufficient fixity to justify our theory.   Hence, as a result, the deductive method, under whatever name it may go, becomes totally inapplicable both in theory and practice; and, as a further consequence, the appeal to statistics has to be made with the caution in mind that we shall do mischief rather than good if we go on collecting too many of them.

§ 19.   The results of the last two chapters may be summed up as follows:—We have extended the conception of a series obtained in the first chapter; for we have found that these series are mostly presented to us in groups. These groups are found upon examination to be formed upon approximately the same type throughout a very wide and varied range of experience; the causes of this agreement we discussed and explained in some detail. When, however, we extend our examination by supposing the series to run to a very great length, we find that they may be divided into two classes separated by important distinctions. In one of these classes (that containing the results of games of chance) the conditions of production, and consequently the laws of statistical occurrence, may be practically regarded as absolutely fixed; and the extent of the divergences from the mean seem to know no finite limit. In the other class, on the contrary (containing the bulk of ordinary statistical enquiries), the conditions of production vary with more or less rapidity, and so in consequence do the results. Moreover it is often impossible that variations from the mean should exceed a certain amount. The former we may term *ideal* series. It is they alone which show the requisite characteristics with any close approach to accuracy, and to make the theory of the subject tenable, we have really to substitute one of this kind for one of the less perfect ones of the other class, when these latter are under treatment. The former class have, however, been too exclusively considered by writers on the subject; and conceptions appropriate only to them, and not always even to them, have been imported into the other class. It is in this way that a general tendency to an excessive deductive or *à priori* treatment of the science has been encouraged.

CHAPTER V.

§ 1. THERE is a term of frequent occurrence in treatises on Probability, and which we have already had repeated occasion to employ, viz. the designation *random* applied to an event, as in the expression 'a random distribution'. The scientific conception involved in the correct use of this term is, I apprehend, nothing more than that of aggregate order and individual irregularity (or apparent irregularity), which has been already described in the preceding chapters. A brief discussion of the requisites in this scientific conception, and in particular of the nature and some of the reasons for the departure from the popular conception, may serve to clear up some of the principal remaining difficulties which attend this part of our subject.

The original[1], and still popular, signification of the term is of course widely different from the scientific. What it looks to is the origin, not the results, of the random performance, and it has reference rather to the single action than to a group or series of actions. Thus, when a man

---

[1] According to Prof. Skeat (*Etymological Dictionary*) the earliest known meaning is that of *furious* action, as in a charge of cavalry. The etymology, he considers, is connected with the Teutonic word *rand* (brim), and implies the furious and irregular action of a river full to the brim.

draws a bow 'at a venture', or 'at random', we mean only to point out the aimless character of the performance; we are contrasting it with the definite intention to hit a certain mark. But it is none the less true, as already pointed out, that we can only apply processes of inference to such performances as these when we regard them as being capable of frequent, or rather of indefinitely extended repetition.

Begin with an illustration. Perhaps the best typical example that we can give of the scientific meaning of random distribution is afforded by the arrangement of the drops of rain in a shower. No one can give a guess whereabouts at any instant a drop will fall, but we know that if we put out a sheet of paper it will gradually become uniformly spotted over; and that if we were to mark out any two equal areas on the paper these would gradually tend to be struck equally often.

§ 2. I. Any attempt to draw inferences from the assumption of random arrangement must postulate the occurrence of this particular state of things at some stage or other. But there is often considerable difficulty, leading occasionally to some arbitrariness, in deciding the particular stage at which it ought to be introduced.

(1) Thus, in many of the problems discussed by mathematicians, we look as entirely to the results obtained, and think as little of the actual process by which they are obtained, as when we are regarding the arrangement of the drops of rain. A simple example of this kind would be the following. A pawn, diameter of base one inch, is placed at random on a chess-board, the diameter of the squares of which is one inch and a quarter: find the chance that its base shall lie across one of the intersecting lines. Here we may imagine the pawns to be so to say rained down vertically upon the board,

and the question is to find the ultimate proportion of those which meet a boundary line to the total of those which fall. The problem therefore becomes a merely geometrical one, viz. to determine the ratio of a certain area on the board to the whole area. The determination of this ratio is all that the mathematician ever takes into account.

Now take the following. A straight brittle rod is broken at random in two places: find the chance that the pieces can make a triangle[1]. Since the only condition for making a triangle with three straight lines is that each two shall be greater than the third, the problem seems to involve the same general conception as in the former case. We must conceive such rods breaking at one pair of spots after another,—no one can tell precisely where,—but showing the same ultimate tendency to distribute these spots throughout the whole length uniformly. As in the last case, the mathematician thinks of nothing but this final result, and pays no heed to the process by which it may be brought about. Accordingly the problem is again reduced to one of mensuration, though of a somewhat more complicated character.

§ 3.   (2) In another class of cases we have to contemplate an intermediate process rather than a final result; but the same conception has to be introduced here, though it is now applied to the former stage, and in consequence will not in general apply to the latter.

For instance: a shot is fired at random from a gun whose maximum range (i.e. at 45° elevation) is 3000 yards: what is the chance that the actual range shall exceed 2000 yards? The ultimately uniform (or random) distribution here is commonly assumed to apply to the various directions in which the gun can be pointed; all possible directions above

---

[1] See the problem paper of Jan. 18, 1854, in the Cambridge Mathematical Tripos.

the horizontal being equally represented in the long run. We have therefore to contemplate a surface of uniform distribution, but it will be the surface, not of the ground, but of a hemisphere whose centre is occupied by the man who fires. The ultimate distribution of the bullets on the spots where they strike the ground will not be uniform. The problem is in fact to discover the law of variation of the density of distribution.

The above is, I presume, the treatment generally adopted in solving such a problem. But there seems no absolute necessity for any such particular choice. It is surely open to any one to maintain[1] that his conception of the randomness of the firing is assigned by saying that it is likely that a man should begin by facing towards any point of the compass indifferently, and then proceed to raise his gun to any angle indifferently. The stage of ultimately uniform distribution here has receded a step further back. It is not assigned directly to the surface of an imaginary hemisphere, but to the lines of altitude and azimuth drawn on that surface. Accordingly, the distribution over the hemisphere itself will not now be uniform,—there will be a comparative crowding up towards the pole,—and the ultimate distribution over the ground will not be the same as before.

§ 4.   Difficulties of this kind, arising out of the uncertainty as to what stage should be selected for that of uniform distribution, will occasionally present themselves. For instance: let a book be taken at random out of a bookcase; what is the chance of hitting upon some assigned volume? I hardly know how this question would commonly be treated. If we were to set our man opposite the middle of the shelf

---

[1] As, according to Mr H. Godfray, the majority of the candidates *did* assume when the problem was once proposed in an examination. See the *Educational Times* (Reprint, Vol. VII. p. 99.)

and inquire what would generally happen in practice, supposing him blindfolded, there cannot be much doubt that
the volumes would not be selected equally often. On the
contrary, it is likely that there would be a tendency to increased frequency about a centre indicated by the height
of his shoulder, and (unless he be left-handed) a trifle to the
right of the point exactly opposite his starting point.

If the question were one which it were really worth
while to work out on these lines we should be led a long
way back. Just as we imagined our rifleman's position (on
the second supposition) to be determined by two independent coordinates of assumed continuous and equal facility,
so we might conceive our making the attempt to analyse the
man's movements into a certain number of independent
constituents. We might suppose all the various directions
from his starting point, along the ground, to be equally
likely; and that when he reaches the shelves the random
motion of his hand is to be regulated after the fashion of a
shot discharged at random.

The above would be one way of setting about the statement of the problem. But the reader will understand that
all which I am here proposing to maintain is that in these,
as in every similar case, we always encounter, under this
conception of 'randomness', at some stage or other, this
postulate of ultimate uniformity of distribution over some
assigned magnitude: either time ; or space, linear, superficial,
or solid. But the selection of the stage at which this is to
be applied may give rise to considerable difficulty, and even
arbitrariness of choice.

§ 5. Some years ago there was a very interesting discussion upon this subject carried on in the mathematical part of
the *Educational Times* (see, especially, Vol. VII.). As not
unfrequently happens in mathematics there was an almost

entire accord amongst the various writers as to the assumptions practically to be made in any particular case, and therefore as to the conclusion to be drawn, combined with a very considerable amount of difference as to the axioms and definitions to be employed. Thus Mr M. W. Crofton, with the substantial agreement of Mr Woolhouse, laid it down unhesitatingly that "at random" has "a very clear and definite meaning; one which cannot be better conveyed than by Mr Wilson's definition, *'according to no law';* and in this sense alone I mean to use it." According to any scientific interpretation of 'law' I should have said that where there was no law there could be no inference. But ultimate tendency towards equality of distribution is as much taken for granted by Mr Crofton as by any one else: in fact he makes this a deduction from his definition:—"As this infinite system of parallels are drawn according to no law, they are as thickly disposed along any part of the [common] perpendicular as along any other" (VII. p. 85). Mr Crofton holds that any kind of *unequal* distribution would imply law,—"If the points [on a plane] tended to become denser in any part of the plane than in another, there must be some law attracting them there" (ib. p. 84). The same view is enforced in his paper on *Local Probability* (in the *Phil. Trans.*, Vol. 158). Surely if they tend to become *equally* dense this is just as much a case of regularity or law.

It may be remarked that wherever any serious practical consequences turn upon duly securing the desired randomness, it is always so contrived that no design or awkwardness or unconscious one-sidedness shall disturb the result. The principal case in point here is of course afforded by games of chance. What we want, when we toss a die, is to secure that all numbers from 1 to 6 shall be equally often represented in the long run, but that no person shall be able to predict the individual occurrence. We might, in our statement of a problem, as easily postulate 'a number *thought of* at random' as 'a shot fired at random', but no one would risk his chances of gain and loss on the supposition that this would be done with continued fairness. Accordingly, we construct a die whose sides are accurately alike, and it is found that we may do almost what we like with this, at any previous stage to that of its issue from the dice box on to the table, without interfering with the random nature of the result.

§ 6. II. Another characteristic in which the scientific conception seems to me to depart from the popular or original signification is the following. The area of distribution which we take into account must be a finite or limited one. The necessity for this restriction may not be obvious at first sight, but the consideration of one or two examples will serve to indicate the point at which it makes itself felt. Suppose that one were asked to choose a number at random, not from a finite range, but from the inexhaustible possibilities of enumeration. In the popular sense of the term,—i.e. of uttering a number without pausing to choose,—there is no difficulty. But a moment's consideration will show that no arrangement even tending towards ultimately uniform distribution can be secured in this way. No *average* could be struck with ever increasing steadiness. So with spatial infinity. We can rationally speak of choosing a point at random in a given straight line, area, or volume. But if we suppose the line to have no end, or the selection to be made in infinite space, the basis of ultimate tendency towards what may be called the equally thick deposit of our random points fails us utterly.

Similarly in any other example in which one of the magnitudes is unlimited. Suppose I fling a stick at random in a horizontal plane against a row of iron railings and inquire for the chance of its passing through without touching them. The problem bears some analogy to that of the chessmen, and so far as the motion of translation of the stick is concerned (if we begin with this) it presents no difficulty. But as regards the rotation it is otherwise. For any assigned linear velocity there is a certain angular velocity *below* which the stick may pass through without contact, but *above* which it cannot. And inasmuch as the former range is limited and the latter is unlimited, we encounter the same impossibility as before in endeavouring to conceive a uniform distribution. Of course we might evade this particular difficulty by beginning with an estimate of the angular velocity, when we should have to repeat what has just been said, mutatis mutandis, in reference to the linear velocity.

§ 7.   I am of course aware that there are a variety of problems current which seem to conflict with what has just been said, but they will all submit to explanation. For instance ; What is the chance that three straight lines, taken or drawn at random, shall be of such lengths as will admit of their forming a triangle ? There are two ways in which we may regard the problem. We may, for one thing, start with the assumption of three lines not greater than a certain length *n*, and then determine towards what limit the chance tends as *n* increases unceasingly. Or, we may maintain that the question is merely one of *relative proportion* of the three lines. We may then start with any magnitude we please to represent one of the lines (for simplicity, say, the longest of them), and consider that all possible shapes of a triangle will be represented by varying the lengths of the other two. In either case we get a definite result without need to make an attempt to conceive any random selection from the infinity of possible length.

So in what is called the "three-point problem":—Three points in space are selected at random; find the chance of their forming an acute-angled triangle. What is done is to start with a closed volume,—say a sphere, from its superior simplicity,—find the chance (on the assumption of uniform distribution within this volume); and then conceive the continual enlargement without limit of this sphere. So regarded the problem is perfectly consistent and intelligible, though I fail to see why it should be termed a random selection *in space* rather than in a sphere. Of course if we started with a different volume, say a cube, we should get a different result; and it is therefore contended (e.g. by Mr Crofton in the *Educational Times,* as already referred to) that infinite space is more naturally and appropriately regarded as tended towards by the enlargement of a sphere than by that of a cube or any other figure.

Again: A group of integers is taken at random; show that the number thus taken is more likely to be odd than even. What we do in answering this is to start with any finite number *n,* and show that of all the possible combinations which can be made within this range there are more odd than even. Since this is true irrespective of the magnitude of *n,* we are apt to speak as if we could conceive the selection being made at random from the true infinity contemplated in numeration.

§ 8. Where these conditions cannot be secured then it seems to me that the attempt to assign any finite value to the probability fails. For instance, in the following problem, proposed by Mr J. M. Wilson, "Three straight lines are drawn at random on an infinite plane, and a fourth line is drawn at random to intersect them: find the probability of its passing through the triangle formed by the other three" (*Ed. Times,* Reprint, Vol. v. p. 82), he offers the following solution: "Of the four lines, two must and two must not pass within the triangle formed by the remaining three. Since all are drawn at random, the chance that the last drawn should pass through the triangle formed by the other three is consequently $\frac{1}{2}$."

I quote this solution because it seems to me to illustrate the difficulty to which I want to call attention. As the problem is worded, a triangle is supposed to be assigned by three straight lines. However large it may be, its size bears no finite ratio whatever to the indefinitely larger area outside it; and, so far as I can put any intelligible construction on the supposition, the chance of drawing a fourth random line which should happen to intersect this finite area must be reckoned as zero. The problem Mr Wilson has solved seems to me to be a quite different one, viz. "Given four intersecting straight lines, find the chance that we should, at random, select one that passes through the triangle formed by the other three."

The same difficulty seems to me to turn up in most other attempts to apply this conception of randomness to real infinity. The following seems an exact analogue of the above problem :—A number is selected at random, find the chance that another number selected at random shall be greater than the former ;—the answer surely must be that the chance is unity, viz. certainty, because the range above any assigned number is infinitely greater than that below it. Or, expressed in the only language in which I can understand the term 'infinity', what I mean is this. If the first number be m and I am restricted to selecting up to n $(n > m)$ then the chance of exceeding m is $n - m : n$; if I am restricted to $2n$ then it is $2n - m : 2n$ and so on. That is, however large n and m may be the expression is always intelligible; but, *m being chosen first, n* may be made as much larger than m as we please: i.e. the chance may be made to approach as near to unity as we please.

I cannot but think that there is a similar fallacy in De Morgan's admirably suggestive paper on *Infinity* (*Camb. Phil. Trans.* Vol. 11.) when he is discussing the " three-point problem ":—i.e. given three points taken at random find the chance that they shall form an acute-angled triangle. All that he shows is, that if we start with *one side as given* and consider the subsequent possible positions of the opposite vertex, there are infinitely as many such positions which would form an acute-angled triangle as an obtuse: but, as before, this is solving a different problem.

§ 9.   The nearest approach I can make towards true indefinite randomness, or random selection from true indefiniteness, is as follows.   Suppose a circle with a tangent line extended indefinitely in each direction.   Now from the centre draw radii at random ; in other words, let the semicircumference which lies towards the tangent be ultimately uniformly intersected by the radii.   Let these radii be then produced so as to intersect the tangent line, and consider the distribution of these points of intersection.   We shall obtain in the result *one* characteristic of our random distribution ; i.e. no portion of this tangent, however small or however remote, but will find itself in the position ultimately of any small portion of the pavement in our supposed continual rainfall.   That is, any such elementary patch will become more and more closely dotted over with the points of intersection.   But the other essential characteristic, viz. that of ultimately *uniform* distribution, will be missing.   There will be a special form of distribution,—what in fact will have to be discussed in a future chapter under the designation of a ' law of error ',—by virtue of which the concentration will tend to be greatest at a certain point (that of contact with the circle), and will thin out from here in each direction according to an easily calculated formula. The existence of such a state of things as this is quite opposed to the conception of true randomness.

§ 10. III. Apart from definitions and what comes of them, perhaps the most important question connected with the conception of Randomness is this: How in any given case are we to determine whether an observed arrangement is to be considered a random one or not? This question will have to be more fully discussed in a future chapter, but we are already in a position to see our way through some of the difficulties involved in it.

(1) If the events or objects under consideration are supposed to be continued indefinitely, or if we know enough about the mode in which they are brought about to detect their ultimate tendency,—or even, short of this, if they are numerous enough to be beyond practical counting,—there is no great difficulty. We are simply confronted with a question of fact, to be settled like other questions of fact. In the case of the rain-drops, watch two equal squares of pavement or other surfaces, and note whether they come to be more and more densely uniformly and evenly spotted over: if they do, then the arrangement is what we call a random one. If I want to know whether a tobacco-pipe really breaks at random, and would therefore serve as an illustration of the problem proposed some pages back, I have only to drop enough of them and see whether pieces of all possible lengths are equally represented in the long run. Or, I may argue deductively, from what I know about the strength of materials and the molecular constitution of such bodies, as to whether fractures of small and large pieces are all equally likely to occur.

§ 11. The reader's attention must be carefully directed to a source of confusion here, arising out of a certain cross-

division. What we are now discussing is a question of fact,
viz. the nature of a certain ultimate arrangement; we are
not discussing the particular way in which it is brought
about. In other words, the antithesis is between what is and
what is not random: it is not between what is random and
what is designed. As we shall see in a few moments it is
quite possible that an arrangement which is the result,—if
ever anything were so,—of 'design', may nevertheless present
the unmistakeable stamp of randomness of arrangement.

Consider a case which has been a good deal discussed,
and to which we shall revert again: the arrangement of the
stars. The question here is rather complicated by the fact
that we know nothing about the actual mutual positions of
the stars, all that we can take cognizance of being their apparent or visible places as projected upon the surface of a
supposed sphere. Appealing to what alone we can thus
observe, it is obvious that the arrangement, as a whole, is
not of the random sort. The Milky Way and the other resolvable nebulæ, as they present themselves to us, are as obvious an infraction of such an arrangement as would be the
occurrence here and there of patches of ground in a rain-fall
which received a vast number more drops than the spaces
surrounding them. If we leave these exceptional areas out
of the question and consider only the stars which are visible
by the naked eye or by slight telescopic power, it seems
equally certain that the arrangement *is*, for the most part, a
fairly representative random one. By this we mean nothing
more than the fact that when we mark off any number of
equal areas on the visible sphere these are found to contain
approximately the same number of stars.

The actual arrangement of the stars in space *may* also
be of the same character: that is, the apparently denser
aggregation may be apparent only, arising from the fact that

we are looking through regions which are not more thickly occupied but are merely more extensive. The alternative before us, in fact, is this. If the whole volume, so to say, of the starry heavens is tolerably regular in shape, then the arrangement of the stars is not of the random order; if that volume is very irregular in shape, it is possible that the arrangement within it may be throughout of that order.

§ 12. (2) When the arrangement in question includes but a comparatively small number of events or objects, it becomes much more difficult to determine whether or not it is to be designated a random one. In fact we have to shift our ground, and to decide not by what has been actually observed but by what we have reason to conclude would be observed if we could continue our observation much longer. This introduces what is called 'Inverse Probability', viz. the determination of the nature of a cause from the nature of the observed effect; a question which will be fully discussed in a future chapter. But some introductory remarks may be conveniently made here.

Every problem of Probability, as the subject is here understood, introduces the conception of an ultimate limit, and therefore presupposes an indefinite possibility of repetition. When we have only a finite number of occurrences before us, *direct* evidence of the character of their arrangement fails us, and we have to fall back upon the nature of the agency which produces them. And as the number becomes smaller the confidence with which we can estimate the nature of the agency becomes gradually less.

Begin with an intermediate case. There is a small lawn, sprinkled over with daisies: is this a random arrangement? We feel some confidence that it is so, on mere inspection; meaning by this that (negatively) no trace of any regular pattern can be discerned and (affirmatively) that if we take

any moderately small area, say a square yard, we shall find
much about the same number of the plants included in it.
But we can help ourselves by an appeal to the known agency
of distribution here. We know that the daisy spreads by
seed, and considering the effect of the wind and the continued
sweeping and mowing of the lawn we can detect causes at
work which are analogous to those by which the dealing of
cards and the tossing of dice are regulated.

In the above case the appeal to the process of production
was subsidiary, but when we come to consider the nature of
a very small succession or group this appeal becomes much
more important. Let us be told of a certain succession of
'heads' and 'tails' to the number of ten. The range here is
far too small for decision, and unless we are told whether the
agent who obtained them was tossing or designing we are
quite unable to say whether or not the designation of 'random' ought to be applied to the result obtained. The truth
must never be forgotten that though 'design' is sure to
break down in the long run if it make the attempt to produce directly the semblance of randomness[1], yet for a short
spell it can simulate it perfectly. Any short succession, say
of heads and tails, may have been equally well brought
about by tossing or by deliberate choice.

§ 13. The reader will observe that this question of
randomness is being here treated as simply one of ultimate
statistical fact. I have fully admitted that this is not the
primitive conception, nor is it the popular interpretation,
but to adopt it seems the only course open to us if we are to
draw inferences such as those contemplated in Probability.
When we look to the producing agency of the ultimate
arrangement we may find this very various. It may prove
itself to be (a few stages back) one of conscious deliberate

[1] Vide p. 68.

purpose, as in drawing a card or tossing a die: it may be the outcome of an extremely complicated interaction of many natural causes, as in the arrangement of the flowers scattered over a lawn or meadow: it may be of a kind of which we know literally nothing whatever, as in the case of the actual arrangement of the stars relatively to each other.

This was the state of things had in view when it was said a few pages back that randomness and design would result in something of a cross-division. Plenty of arrangements in which design had a hand, a stage or two back, can be mentioned, which would be quite indistinguishable in their results from those in which no design whatever could be traced. Perhaps the most striking case in point here is to be found in the arrangement of the digits in one of the natural arithmetical constants, such as π or ϵ, or in a table of logarithms. If we look to the process of production of these digits, no extremer instance can be found of what we mean by the antithesis of randomness: every figure has its necessarily pre-ordained position, and a moment's flagging of intention would defeat the whole purpose of the calculator. And yet, if we look to results only, no better instance can be found than one of these rows of digits if it were intended to illustrate what we practically understand by a chance arrangement of a number of objects. Each digit occurs approximately equally often, and this tendency developes as we advance further; the mutual juxtaposition of the digits also shows the same tendency, that is, any digit (say 5) is just as often followed by 6 or 7 as by any of the others. In fact, if we were to take the whole row of hitherto calculated figures, cut off the first five as familiar to us all, and contemplate the rest, no one would have the slightest reason to suppose that these had not come out as the results of a die with ten equal faces.

§ 14. If it be asked *why* this is so, a rather puzzling question is raised. Wherever physical causation is involved we are generally understood to have satisfied the demand implied in this question if we assign antecedents which will be followed regularly by the event before us; but in geometry and arithmetic there is no opening for antecedents. What we then commonly look for is a demonstration, i.e. the re-solution of the observed fact into axioms if possible, or at any rate into admitted truths of wider generality. I do not know that a demonstration can be given as to the existence of this characteristic of statistical randomness in such suc-cessions of digits as those under consideration. But the following remarks may serve to shift the onus of unlikeli-hood by suggesting that the preponderance of analogy is rather in favour of the existence.

Take the well-known constant π for consideration. This stands for a quantity which presents itself in a vast number of arithmetical and geometrical relations; let us take for examination the best known of these, by regarding it as standing for the ratio of the circumference to the diameter of a circle. So regarded, it is nothing more than a simple case of the measurement of a magnitude by an arbitrarily selected unit. Conceive then that we had before us a rod or line and that we wished to measure it with absolute accuracy. We must suppose—if we are to have a suitable analogue to the determination of π to several hundred figures,—that by the application of continued higher magni-fying power we can detect ever finer subdivisions in the graduation. We lay our rod against the scale and find it, say, fall between 31 and 32 inches; we then look at the next division of the scale, viz. that into tenths of an inch. Can we see the slightest reason why the number of these tenths should be other than independent of the number of whole inches? The "piece over" which we are measuring may in fact be regarded as an entirely new piece, which had fallen into our hands after that of 31 inches had been measured and done with; and similarly with every successive piece over, as we proceed to the ever finer and finer divisions.

Similar remarks may be made about most other incommensurable quantities, such as irreducible roots. Conceive two straight lines at right angles, and that we lay off a certain number of inches along each of these from the point of intersection; say two and five inches, and join the extremities of these so as to form the diagonal of a right-angled triangle. If we proceed to measure this diagonal in terms of either of the other lines we are to all intents and purposes extracting a square root. We should expect, rather than otherwise, to find here, as in the case of π, that incommensurability and resultant randomness of order in the digits was the rule, and commensurability was the exception. Now and then, as when the two sides were three and four, we should find the diagonal commensurable with them; but these would be the occasional exceptions, or rather they would be the comparatively finite exceptions amidst the indefinitely numerous cases which furnished the rule.

§ 15. The best way perhaps of illustrating the truly random character of such a row of figures is by appealing to graphical aid. It is not easy here, any more than in ordinary statistics, to grasp the import of mere figures; whereas the arrangement of groups of points or lines is much more readily seized. The eye is very quick in detecting any symptoms of regularity in the arrangement, or any tendency to denser aggregation in one direction than in another. How then are we to dispose our figures so as to force them to display their true character? I should suggest that we set about *drawing a line at random;* and, since we cannot trust our own unaided efforts to do this, that we rely upon the help of such a table of figures to do it for us, and then examine with what sort of efficiency they can perform the task. The problem of drawing *straight* lines at random, under various limitations of direction or intersection, is familiar enough, but I do not know that any one has suggested the drawing of a line whose shape as well as position shall be of a purely random character. For simplicity we suppose the line to be confined to a plane.

The definition of such a line does not seem to involve any particular difficulty. Phrased in accordance with the ordinary language we should describe it as the path (i.e. any path) traced out by a point which at every moment is as likely to move in any one direction as in any other. That we could not ourselves draw such a line, and that we could not get it traced by any physical agency, is certain. The mere inertia of any moving body will always give it a tendency, however slight, to go on in a straight line at each moment, instead of being instantly responsive to instantaneously varying dictates as to its direction of motion. Nor can we conceive or picture such a line in its ultimate or ideal condition. But it is easy to give a graphical approximation to it, and it is easy also to show how this approximation may be carried on as far as we please towards the ideal in question.

We may proceed as follows. Take a sheet of the ordinary ruled paper prepared for the graphical exposition of curves. Select as our starting point the intersection of two of these lines, and consider the eight 'points of the compass' indicated by these lines and the bisections of the contained right angles [1]. For suggesting the random selection amongst

[1] It would of course be more complete to take *ten* alternatives of direction, and thus to omit none of the digits; but this is much more troublesome in practice than to confine ourselves to eight.

these directions let them be numbered from 0 to 7, and
let us say that a line measured due 'north' shall be designated by the figure 0, 'north-east' by 1, and so on.   The
selection amongst these numbers, and therefore directions, at
every corner, might be handed over to a die with eight faces;
but for the purpose of the illustration in view we select the
digits 0 to 7 as they present themselves in the calculated
value of π.   The sort of path along which we should
travel by a series of such steps thus taken at random
may be readily conceived; it is given at the end of this
chapter.

For tho purpose with which this illustration was proposed, viz. the graphical display of tho succossion of digits
in any one of tho incommensurable constants of arithmetic
or geometry, the above may suffice.   After actually testing
some of them in this way they seem to me, so far as the eye,
or the theoretical principles to be presently mentioned, are
any guide, to answer quite fairly to the description of randomness.

§ 16.   As we are on the subject, however, it seems worth
going farther by enquiring how near we could get to the
ideal of randomness of direction.   To carry this out completely two improvements must be made.   For one thing,
instead of confining ourselves to eight directions we must
admit an infinite number.   This would offer no great difficulty; for instead of employing a small number of digits we
should merely have to use some kind of circular teetotum
which would rest indifferently in any direction.   But in the
next place instead of short finite steps we must suppose them
indefinitely short.   It is here that the actual unattainability
makes itself felt.   We are familiar enough with the device,
employed by Newton, of passing from the discontinuous
polygon to the continuous curve.   But we can resort to this

device because the ideal, viz. the curve, is as easily drawn
(and, I should say, as easily conceived or pictured) as any of
the steps which lead us towards it. But in the case before
us it is otherwise. The line in question will remain discontinuous, or rather angular, to the last: for its angles do
not tend even to lose their sharpness, though the fragments
which compose them increase in number and diminish in
magnitude without any limit. And such an ideal is not conceivable as an ideal. It is as if we had a rough body under
the microscope, and found that as we subjected it to higher
and higher powers there was no tendency for the angles to
round themselves off. Our 'random line' must remain as
'spiky' as ever, though the size of its spikes of course
diminishes without any limit.

The case therefore seems to be this. It is easy, in words,
to indicate the conception by speaking of a line which at
every instant is as likely to take one direction as another.
It is easy moreover to draw such a line with any degree
of minuteness which we choose to demand. But it is not
possible to conceive or picture the line in its ultimate form[1].
There is in fact no 'limit' here, intelligible to the understanding or picturable by the imagination (corresponding to
the asymptote of a curve, or the continuous curve to the
incessantly developing polygon), towards which we find ourselves continually approaching, and which therefore we are
apt to conceive ourselves as ultimately attaining The usual
assumption therefore which underlies the Newtonian in-
finitesimal geometry and the Differential Calculus, ceases to
apply here.

§ 17. If we like to consider such a line in one of its
approximate stages, as above indicated, it seems to me that

[1] Any more than we picture the shape of an equiangular spiral *at the
centre.*

some of the usual theorems of Probability, where large numbers are concerned, may safely be applied. If it be asked, for instance, whether such a line will ultimately tend to stray indefinitely far from its starting point, Bernoulli's 'Law of Large Numbers' may be appealed to, in virtue of which we should say that it was excessively unlikely that its divergence should be relatively great. Recur to our graphical illustration, and consider first the resultant deviation of the point (after a great many steps) right or left of the vertical line through the starting point. Of the eight admissible motions at each stage two will not affect this relative position, whilst the other six are equally likely to move us a step to the right or to the left. Our resultant 'drift,' therefore to the right or left will be analogous to the resultant difference between the number of heads and tails after a great many tosses of a penny. Now the well-known outcome of such a number of tosses is that ultimately the *proportional* approximation to the à priori probability, i.e. to equality of heads and tails, is more and more nearly carried out, but that the *absolute* deflection is more and more widely displayed.

Applying this to the case in point, and remembering that the results apply equally to the horizontal and vertical directions, we should say that after any very great number of such 'steps' as those contemplated, the ratio of our distance from the starting point to the whole distance travelled will pretty certainly be small, whereas the actual distance from it would be large. We should also say that the longer we continued to produce such a line the more pronounced would these tendencies become. So far as concerns this test, and that afforded by the general appearance of the lines drawn,—this last, as above remarked, being tolerably trustworthy,—I feel no doubt as to the generally 'random' character of the rows of figures displayed by the incommensurable or irrational ratios in question.

As it may interest the reader to see an actual specimen of such a path I append one representing the arrangement of the eight digits from 0 to 7 in the value of π. The data are taken from Mr Shanks' astonishing performance in the calculation of this constant to 707 places of figures (*Proc. of R. S.*, XXI. p. 319). Of these, after omitting 8 and 9, there remain 568; the diagram represents the course traced out by following the direction of these as the clue to our path. Many of the steps have of course been taken in opposite directions twice or oftener. The result seems to me to furnish a very fair graphical indication of randomness. I have compared it with corresponding paths furnished by rows of figures taken from logarithmic tables, and in other ways, and find the results to be much the same.

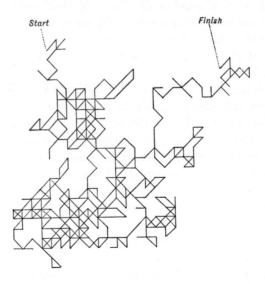

CHAPTER VI[1].

THE SUBJECTIVE SIDE OF PROBABILITY.
MEASUREMENT OF BELIEF.

§ 1. HAVING now obtained a clear conception of a certain kind of series, the next enquiry is, What is to be done with this series? How is it to be employed as a means of making inferences? The general step that we are now about to take might be described as one from the objective to the subjective, from the things themselves to the state of our minds in contemplating them.

The reader should observe that a substitution has, in a great number of cases, already been made as a first stage towards bringing the things into a shape fit for calculation. This substitution, as described in former chapters, is, in a measure, a process of *idealization.* The series we actually meet with are apt to show a changeable type, and the individuals of them will sometimes transgress their licensed irregularity. Hence they have to be pruned a little into shape, as

---

[1] Originally written in somewhat of a spirit of protest against what seemed to me the prevalent disposition to follow De Morgan in taking too subjective a view of the science. In reading it through now I cannot find any single sentence to which I could take distinct objection, though I must admit that if I were writing it entirely afresh I should endeavour to express myself with less emphasis, and I have made alterations in that direction. The reader who wishes to see a view not substantially very different from mine, but expressed with a somewhat opposite emphasis, can refer to Mr F. Y. Edgeworth's article on "The Philosophy of Chance" (*Mind*, Vol. IX.)

natural objects almost always have before they are capable of being accurately reasoned about. The form in which the series emerges is that of a series with a fixed type. This imaginary or ideal series is the basis of our calculation.

§ 2. It must not be supposed that this is at all at variance with the assertion previously made, that Probability is a science of inference about real things; it is only by a substitution of the above kind that we are enabled to reason about the things. In nature nearly all phenomena present themselves in a form which departs from that rigorously accurate one which scientific purposes mostly demand, so we have to introduce an imaginary series, which shall be free from any such defects. The only condition to be fulfilled is, that the substitution is to be as little arbitrary, that is, to vary from the truth as slightly, as possible. This kind of substitution generally passes without notice when natural objects of any kind are made subjects of exact science. I direct distinct attention to it here simply from the apprehension that want of familiarity with the subject-matter might lead some readers to suppose that it involves, in this case, an exceptional deflection from accuracy in the formal process of inference.

It may be remarked also that the adoption of this imaginary series offers no countenance whatever to the doctrine criticised in the last chapter, in accordance with which it was supposed that our series possessed a fixed unchangeable type which was merely the "development of the probabilities" of things, to use Laplace's expression. It differs from anything contemplated on that hypothesis by the fact that it is to be recognized as a necessary substitution of our own for the actual series, and to be kept in as close conformity with facts as possible. It is a mere fiction or artifice necessarily resorted to for the purpose of calculation, and for this purpose only.

This caution is the more necessary, because in the example

that I shall select, and which belongs to the most favourite class of examples in this subject, the substitution becomes accidentally unnecessary. The things, as has been repeatedly pointed out, may sometimes need no trimming, because in the form in which they actually present themselves they *are* almost idealized. In most cases a good deal of alteration is necessary to bring the series into shape, but in some—prominently in the case of games of chance—we find the alterations, for all practical purposes, needless.

§ 3. We start then, from such a series as this, upon the enquiry, What kind of inference can be made about it? It may assist the logical reader to inform him that our first step will be analogous to one class of what are commonly known as *immediate* inferences,—inferences, that is, of the type,—'All men are mortal, therefore any particular man or men are mortal.' This case, simple and obvious as it is in Logic, requires very careful consideration in Probability.

It is obvious that we must be prepared to form an opinion upon the propriety of taking the step involved in making such an inference. Hitherto we have had as little to do as possible with the irregular individuals; we have regarded them simply as fragments of a regular series. But we cannot long continue to neglect all consideration of them. Even if these events in the gross be tolerably certain, it is not only in the gross that we have to deal with them; they constantly come before us a few at a time, or even as individuals, and we have to form some opinion about them in this state. An insurance office, for instance, deals with numbers large enough to obviate most of the uncertainty, but each of their transactions has another party interested in it—What has the man who insures to say to their proceedings? for to him this question becomes an individual one. And even the office itself receives its cases singly, and would

therefore like to have as clear views as possible about these
single cases. Now, the remarks made in the preceding chapters
about the subjects which Probability discusses might seem to
preclude all enquiries of this kind, for was not ignorance of
the individual presupposed to such an extent that even (as
will be seen hereafter) causation might be denied, within
considerable limits, without affecting our conclusions? The
answer to this enquiry will require us to turn now to the
consideration of a totally distinct side of the question, and
one which has not yet come before us. Our best introduction
to it will be by the discussion of a special example.

§ 4. Let a penny be tossed up a very great many
times; we may then be supposed to know for certain this
fact (amongst many others) that in the long run head and
tail will occur about equally often. But suppose we consider
only a moderate number of throws, or fewer still, and so
continue limiting the number until we come down to three
or two, or even one? We have, as the extreme cases, certainty or something undistinguishably near it, and utter
uncertainty. Have we not, between these extremes, all
gradations of belief? There is a large body of writers, including some of the most eminent authorities upon this
subject, who state or imply that we are distinctly conscious of
such a variation of the amount of our belief, and that this
state of our minds can be measured and determined with
almost the same accuracy as the external events to which
they refer. The principal mathematical supporter of this
view is De Morgan, who has insisted strongly upon it in all
his works on the subject. The clearest exposition of his
opinions will be found in his *Formal Logic,* in which work he
has made the view which we are now discussing the basis of
his system. He holds that we have a certain amount of belief
of every proposition which may be set before us, an amount

which in its nature admits of determination, though we may practically find it difficult in any particular case to determine it. He considers, in fact, that Probability is a sort of sister science to Formal Logic[1], speaking of it in the following words : "I cannot understand why the study of the effect, which partial belief of the premises produces with respect to the conclusion, should be separated from that of the consequences of supposing the former to be absolutely true[2]". In other words, there is a science—Formal Logic—which investigates the rules according to which one proposition can be necessarily inferred from another; in close correspondence with this there is a science which investigates the rules according to which the amount of our belief of one proposition varies with the amount of our belief of other propositions with which it is connected.

The same view is also supported by another high authority, the late Prof. Donkin, who says (*Phil. Mag.* May, 1851), " It will, I suppose, be generally admitted, and has often been more or less explicitly stated, that the subject-matter of calculation in the mathematical theory of Probabilities is *quantity of belief.*"

§ 5. Before proceeding to criticise this opinion, one remark may be made upon it which has been too frequently overlooked. It should be borne in mind that, even were this view of the subject not actually incorrect, it might be objected to as insufficient for the purpose of a definition, on the ground that variation of belief is not confined to Probability. It is a property with which that science is concerned, no doubt, but it is a property which meets us in other directions as

[1] In the ordinary signification of this term. As De Morgan uses it he makes Formal Logic *include* Probability, as one of its branches, as indicated in his title " Formal Logic, or the Calculus of Inference, necessary and probable."

[2] *Formal Logic.* Preface, page v.

well. In every case in which we extend our inferences by
Induction or Analogy, or depend upon the witness of others,
or trust to our own memory of the past, or come to a conclusion through conflicting arguments, or even make a long and
complicated deduction by mathematics or logic, we have a
result of which we can scarcely feel as certain as of the premises from which it was obtained. In all these cases then
we are conscious of varying quantities of belief, but are the
laws according to which the belief is produced and varied the
same? If they cannot be reduced to one harmonious scheme,
if in fact they can at best be brought to nothing but a number
of different schemes, each with its own body of laws and rules,
then it is vain to endeavour to force them into one science.

This opinion is strengthened by observing that most of
the writers who adopt the definition in question do practically dismiss from consideration most of the above-mentioned
examples of diminution of belief, and confine their attention
to classes of events which have the property discussed in
Chap. I., viz. 'ignorance of the few, knowledge of the many.'
It is quite true that considerable violence has to be done to
some of these examples, by introducing exceedingly arbitrary
suppositions into them, before they can be forced to assume
a suitable form. But still there is little doubt that, if we
carefully examine the language employed, we shall find that
in almost every case assumptions are made which virtually
imply that our knowledge of the individual is derived from
propositions given in the typical form described in Chap. I.
This will be more fully proved when we come to consider
some common misapplications of the science.

§ 6. Even then, if the above-mentioned view of the
subject were correct, it would yet, I consider, be insufficient
for the purpose of a definition; but it is at least very doubtful
whether it is correct. Before we could properly assign to

the belief side of the question the prominence given to it by
De Morgan and others, certainly before the science could be
defined from that side, it would be necessary, it appears, to
establish the two following positions, against both of which
strong objections can be brought.

(1)   That our belief of every proposition is a thing which
      we can, strictly speaking, be said to measure; that
      there must be a certain amount of it in every case,
      which we can realize somehow in consciousness and
      refer to some standard so as to pronounce upon its
      value.

(2)   That the value thus apprehended is the correct one
      according to tho theory, viz that it is the exact
      fraction of full conviction that it should be.   This
      statement will perhaps seem somewhat obscure at
      first; it will be explained presently.

§ 7.   (I) Now, in the first place, as regards the difficulty
of obtaining any measure of the amount of our belief.   One
source of this difficulty is too obvious to have escaped notice;
this is the disturbing influence produced on the quantity of
belief by any strong emotion or passion.   A deep interest in
the matter at stake, whether it excite hope or fear, plays great
havoc with the belief-meter, so that we must assume the
mind to be quite unimpassioned in weighing the evidence.
This is noticed and acknowledged by Laplace and others;
but these writers seem to me to assume it to be the only
source of error, and also to be of comparative unimportance.
Even if it were the only source of error I cannot see that it
would be unimportant.   We experience hope or fear in so
very many instances, that to omit such influences from consideration would be almost equivalent to saying that whilst
we profess to consider the whole quantity of our belief we
will in reality consider only a portion of it.   Very strong

feelings are, of course, exceptional, but we should nevertheless find that the emotional element, in some form or other,
makes itself felt on almost every occasion. It is very seldom
that we cannot speak of our surprise or expectation in reference to any particular event. Both of these expressions, but
especially the former, seem to point to something more than
mere belief. It is true that the word 'expectation' is generally defined in treatises on Probability as equivalent to
belief; but it seems doubtful whether any one who attends
to the popular use of the terms would admit that they were
exactly synonymous. Be this however as it may, the emotional element is present upon almost every occasion, and its
disturbing influence therefore is constantly at work.

§ 8. Another cause, which co-operates with the former,
is to be found in the extreme complexity and variety of the
evidence on which our belief of any proposition depends.
Hence it results that our actual belief at any given moment
is one of the most fugitive and variable things possible, so
that we can scarcely ever get sufficiently clear hold of it to
measure it. This is not confined to the times when our
minds are in a turmoil of excitement through hope or fear.
In our calmest moments we shall find it no easy thing to
give a precise answer to the question, How firmly do I hold
this or that belief? There may be one or two prominent
arguments in its favour, and one or two corresponding objections against it, but this is far from comprising all the
causes by which our state of belief is produced. Because
such reasons as these are all that can be practically introduced into oral or written controversies, we must not conclude that it is by these only that our conviction is influenced.
On the contrary, our conviction generally rests upon a sort
of chaotic basis composed of an infinite number of inferences
and analogies of every description, and these moreover dis-

torted by our state of feeling at the time, dimmed by the
degree of our recollection of them afterwards, and probably
received from time to time with varying force according to
the way in which they happen to combine in our consciousness at the moment. To borrow a striking illustration from
Abraham Tucker, the substructure of our convictions is not
so much to be compared to the solid foundations of an ordinary building, as to the piles of the houses of Rotterdam
which rest somehow in a deep bed of soft mud. They bear
their weight securely enough, but it would not be easy to
point out accurately the dependence of the different parts
upon one another. Directly we begin to think of the amount
of our belief, we have to think of the arguments by which it
is produced—in fact, these arguments will intrude themselves
without our choice.   As each in turn flashes through the
mind, it modifies the strength of our conviction ; we are like
a person listening to the confused hubbub of a crowd, where
there is always something arbitrary in the particular sound
we choose to listen to.   There may be reasons enough to
suffice abundantly for our ultimate choice, but on examination we shall find that they are by no means apprehended
with the same force at different times.   The belief produced
by some strong argument may be very decisive at the moment, but it will often begin to diminish when the argument
is not actually before the mind. It is like being dazzled by
a strong light; the impression still remains, but begins almost immediately to fade away.   I think that this is the
case, however we try to limit the sources of our conviction.

§ 9.   (II)   But supposing that it were possible to strike
a sort of average of this fluctuating state, should we find this
average to be of the amount assigned by theory ?   In other
words, is our natural belief in the happening of two different
events in direct proportion to the frequency with which those

events happen in the long run ?   There is a lottery with 100
tickets and ten prizes; is a man's belief that he will get a
prize fairly represented by one-tenth of certainty?   The mere
reference to a lottery should be sufficient to disprove this.
Lotteries have flourished at all times, and have never failed
to be abundantly supported, in spite of the most perfect conviction, on the part of many, if not of most, of those who put
into them, that in the long run all will lose.   Deductions
should undoubtedly be made for those who act from super-
stitious motives, from belief in omens, dreams, and so on.
But apart from these, and supposing any one to come forti-
fied by all that mathematics can do for him, it is difficult to
believe that his natural impressions about single events would
be always what they should be according to theory.   Are
there many who can honestly declare that they would have
no desire to buy a single ticket?   They would probably say
to themselves that the sum they paid away was nothing
worth mentioning to lose, and that there was a chance of
gaining a great deal; in other words, they are not apportioning their belief in the way that theory assigns.

What bears out this view is, that the same persons who
would act in this way in single instances would often not
think of doing so in any but single instances.   In other
words, the natural tendency here is to attribute too great an
amount of belief where it is or should be small; i.e. to de-
preciate the risk in proportion to the contingent advantage.
They would very likely, when argued with, attach disparag-
ing epithets to this state of feeling, by calling it an un-
accountable fascination, or something of that kind, but of
its existence there can be little doubt.   We are speaking
now of what is the natural tendency of our minds, not of
that into which they may at length be disciplined by educa-
tion and thought.   If, however, educated persons have suc-

ceeded for the most part in controlling this tendency in games of chance, the spirit of reckless speculation has scarcely yet been banished from commerce. On examination, this tendency will be found so prevalent in all ages, ranks, and dispositions, that it would be inadmissible to neglect it in order to bring our supposed instincts more closely into accordance with the commonly received theories of Probability.

§ 10. There is another aspect of this question which has been often overlooked, but which seems to deserve some attention. Granted that we have an instinct of credence, why should it be assumed that this must be just of that intensity which subsequent experience will justify? Our instincts are implanted in us for good purposes, and are intended to act immediately and unconsciously. They are, however, subject to control, and have to be brought into accordance with what we believe to be true and right. In other departments of psychology we do not assume that every spontaneous prompting of nature is to be left just as we find it, or even that on the average, omitting individual variations, it is set at that pitch that will be found in the end to be the best when we come to think about it and assign its rules. Take, for example, the case of resentment. Here we have an instinctive tendency, and one that on the whole is good in its results. But moralists are agreed that almost all our efforts at self-control are to be directed towards subduing it and keeping it in its right direction. It is assumed to be given as a sort of rough protection, and to be set, if one might so express oneself, at too high a pitch to be deliberately and consciously acted on in society. May not something of this kind be the case also with our belief? I only make a passing reference to this point here, as on the theory of Probability adopted in this work it does not appear to be at all material to the science. But it seems

a strong argument against the expediency of commencing
the study of the science from the subjective side, or even of
assigning any great degree of prominence to this side.

That men *do* not believe in exact accordance with this
theory must have struck almost every one, but this has
probably been considered as mere exception and irregularity;
the assumption being made that on the average, and in far
the majority of cases, they do so believe. As stated above,
it is very doubtful whether the tendency which has just
been discussed is not so widely prevalent that it might with
far more propriety be called the rule than the exception.
And it may be better that this should be so : many good
results may follow from that cheerful disposition which induces a man sometimes to go on trying after some great
good, the chance of which he overvalues. He will keep on
through trouble and disappointment, without serious harm
perhaps, when the cool and calculating bystander sees plainly
that his 'measure of belief' is much higher than it should
be. So, too, the tendency also so common, of underrating
the chance of a great evil may also work for good. By many
men death might be looked upon as an almost infinite evil,
at least they would so regard it themselves; suppose they
kept this contingency constantly before them at its right
value, how would it be possible to get through the practical
work of life ? Men would be stopping indoors because if
they went out they might be murdered or bitten by a mad
dog. To say this is not to advocate a return to our instincts ;
indeed when we have once reached the critical and conscious
state, it is hardly possible to do so ; but it should be noticed
that the advantage gained by correcting them is at best but
a balanced one[1]. What is most to our present purpose, it

[1] An illustration of the points
here insisted on has recently [1876]
been given in a quarter where few
would have expected it; I allude, as

suggests the inexpediency of attempting to found an exact theory on what may afterwards prove to be a mere instinct, unauthorized in its full extent by experience.

§ 11. It may be replied, that though people, as a matter of fact, do not apportion belief in this exact way, yet they *ought* to do so. The purport of this remark will be examined presently; it need only be said here that it grants all that is now contended for. For it admits that the degree of our belief is capable of modification, and may need it. But in accordance with what is the belief to be modified? obviously in accordance with experience; it cannot be trusted to by itself, but the fraction at which it is to be rated must be determined by the comparative frequency of the events to which it refers. Experience then furnishing the standard, it is surely most reasonable to start from this experience, and to found the theory of our processes upon it.

If we do not do this, it should be observed that we are detaching Probability altogether from the study of things external to us, and making it nothing else in effect than a portion of Psychology. If we refuse to be controlled by experience, but confine our attention to the laws according to which belief is naturally or instinctively compounded and distributed in our minds, we have no right then to appeal to experience afterwards even for illustrations, unless under the

many readers will readily infer, to J. S. Mill's exceedingly interesting Essays on Theism. It is not within our province here to criticise any of their conclusions, but they have expressed in a very significant way the conviction entertained by him that beliefs which are not justified by evidence, and possibly may not be capable of justification (those for instance of immortality and the existence of the Deity), may nevertheless not only continue to exist in cultivated minds, but may also be profitably encouraged there, at any rate in the shape of hopes, for certain supposed advantages attendant on their retention, irrespective even of their truth.

express understanding that we do not guarantee its accuracy. Our belief in some single events, for example, might be correct, and yet that in a compound of several (if derived merely from our instinctive laws of belief) very possibly might not be correct, but might lead us into practical mistakes if we determined to act upon it. Even if the two were in accordance, this accordance would have to be proved, which would lead us round, by what I cannot but think a circuitous process, to the point which has been already chosen for commencing with.

§ 12. De Morgan seems to imply that the doctrine criticised above finds a justification from the analogy of Formal Logic. If the laws of necessary inference can be studied apart from all reference to external facts (except by way of illustration), why not those of probable inference? There does not, however, seem to be much force in any such analogy. Formal Logic, at any rate under its modern or Kantian mode of treatment, is based upon the assumption that there are laws of thought as distinguished from laws of things, and that these laws of thought can be ascertained and studied without taking into account their reference to any particular object. Now so long as we are confined to necessary or irreversible laws, as is of course the case in ordinary Formal Logic, this assumption leads to no special difficulties. We mean by this, that no conflict arises between these subjective and objective necessities. The two exist in perfect harmony side by side, the one being the accurate counterpart of the other. So precise is the correspondence between them, that few persons would notice, until study of metaphysics had called their attention to such points, that there were these two sides to the question. They would make their appeal to either with equal confidence, saying indifferently, 'the thing must be so,' or, 'we cannot conceive its being

otherwise.' In fact it is only since the time of Kant that
this mental analysis has been to any extent appreciated and
accepted. And even now the dominant experience school of
philosophy would not admit that there are here two really
distinct sides to the phenomenon ; they maintain either that
the subjective necessity is nothing more than the consequence by inveterate association of the objective uniformity,
or else that this so-called necessity (say in the Law of Contradiction) is after all merely verbal, merely a different way of
saying the same thing over again in other words. Whatever
the explanation adopted, the general result is that fallacies,
as real acts of thought, are impossible within the domain of
pure logic ; error within that province is only possible by a
momentary lapse of attention, that is of consciousness.

§ 13. But though this perfect harmony between subjective and objective uniformities or laws may exist within
the domain of pure logic, it is far from existing within that
of probability. The moment we make the *quantity* of our
belief an integral part of the subject to be studied, any such
invariable correspondence ceases to exist. In the former
case, we could not consciously think erroneously even though
we might try to do so ; in the latter, we not only can believe
erroneously but constantly do so. Far from the quantity of
our belief being so exactly adjusted in conformity with the
facts to which it refers that we cannot even in imagination
go astray, we find that it frequently exists in excess or defect
of that which subsequent judgment will approve. Our instincts of credence are unquestionably in frequent hostility
with experience ; and what do we do then ? We simply
modify the instincts into accordance with the things. We
are constantly performing this practice, and no cultivated
mind would find it possible to do anything else. No man
would think of divorcing his belief from the things on which

it was exercised, or would suppose that the former had anything else to do than to follow the lead of the latter.   Hence
it results that that separation of the subjective necessity from
the objective, and that determination to treat the former
as a science apart by itself, for which a plausible defence
could be made in the case of pure logic, is entirely inadmissible in the case of probability.   However we might
contrive to '*think*' aright without appeal to facts, we cannot *believe* aright without incessantly checking our proceedings by such appeals.   Whatever then may be the
claims of Formal Logic to rank as a separate science, it
does not appear that it can furnish any support to the
theory of Probability at present under examination.

§ 14.   The point in question is sometimes urged as
follows.   Suppose a man with two, and only two, alternatives before him, one of which he knows must involve
success and the other failure.   He knows nothing more
about them than this, and he is forced to act.   Would he
not regard them with absolutely similar and equal feelings
of confidence, without the necessity of referring them to any
real or imaginary series ?   If so, is not this equivalent to
saying that his belief of either, since one of them must
come to pass, is equal to that of the other, and therefore that
his belief of each is one-half of full confidence ?   Similarly
if there are more than two alternatives: let it be supposed
that there are any number of them, amongst which no
distinctions whatever can be discerned except in such particulars as we know for certain will not affect the result ;
should we not feel equally confident in respect of each of
them ? and so here again should we not have a fractional
estimate of our absolute amount of belief ? It is thus
attempted to lay the basis of a pure science of Probability,
determining the distribution and combination of our belief

hypothetically; viz. *if* the contingencies are exactly alike, then our belief is so apportioned, the question whether the contingencies are equal being of course decided as the objective data of Logic or Mathematics are decided.

To discuss this question fully would require a statement at some length of the reasons in favour of the objective or material view of Logic, as opposed to the Formal or Conceptualist. I shall have to speak on this subject in another chapter, and will not therefore enter upon it here. But one conclusive objection which is applicable more peculiarly to Probability may be offered at once. To pursue the line of enquiry just indicated, is, as already remarked, to desert the strictly logical ground, and to take up that appropriate to psychology; the proper question, in all these cases, being not what *do* men believe, but what ought they to believe? Admitting, as was done above, that in the case of Formal Logic these two enquiries, or rather those corresponding to them, practically run into one, owing to the fact that men cannot consciously 'think' wrongly; it cannot be too strongly insisted on that in Probability the two are perfectly separable and distinct. It is of no use saying what men do or will believe, we want to know what they will be right in believing; and this can never be settled without an appeal to the phenomena themselves.

§ 15. But apart from the above considerations, this way of putting the case does not seem to me at all conclusive. Take the following example. A man[1] finds himself on the

---

[1] It is necessary to take an example in which the man is forced to act, or we should not be able to shew that he has any belief on the subject at all. He may declare that he neither knows nor cares anything about the matter, and that there-fore there is nothing of the nature of belief to be extracted out of his mental condition. He very likely would take this ground if we asked him, as De Morgan does, with a slightly different reference (*Formal Logic*, p. 183), whether he considers

sands of the Wash or Morecambe Bay, in a dense mist, when
the spring-tide is coming in ; and knows therefore that to
be once caught by the tide would be fatal. He hears a
church-bell at a distance, but has no means of knowing
whether it is on the same side of the water with himself or
on the opposite side. He cannot tell therefore whether by
following its sound he will be led out into the mid-stream
and be lost, or led back to dry land and safety. Here there
can be no repetition of the event, and the cases are indistinguishably alike, to him, in the only circumstances which
can affect the issue : is not then his prospect of death, it
will be said, necessarily equal to one-half ? A proper analysis
of his state of mind would be a psychological rather than
a logical enquiry, and in any case, as above remarked, the
decision of this question does not touch our logical position.
But according to the best introspection I can give I should
say that what really passes through the mind in such a case
is something of this kind: In most doubtful positions and
circumstances we are accustomed to decide our conduct by
a consideration of the relative advantages and disadvantages
of each side, that is by the observed or inferred frequency
with which one or the other alternative has succeeded. In
proportion as these become more nearly balanced, we are
more frequently mistaken in the individual cases ; that is, it
becomes more and more nearly what would be called ' a
mere toss up' whether we are right or wrong. The case
in question seems merely the limiting case, in which it has

that there are volcanoes on the unseen
side of the moon larger than those
on the side turned towards us; or,
with Jevons (*Principles of Science,*
Ed. ii. p. 212) whether he considers
that a Platythliptic Coefficient is
positive. These do not therefore
seem good instances to illustrate the
position that we always entertain a
certain degree of belief on every
question which can be stated, and
that utter inability to give a reason
in favour of either alternative corresponds to half belief.

been contrived that there shall be no appreciable difference between the alternatives, by which to decide in favour of one or other, and we accordingly feel no confidence in the particular result. Having to decide, however, we decide according to the precedent of similar cases which have occurred before. To stand still and wait for better information is certain death, and we therefore appeal to and employ the only rule we know of; or rather we feel, or endeavour to feel, as we have felt before when acting in the presence of alternatives as nearly balanced as possible. But I can neither perceive in my own case, nor feel convinced in that of others, that this appeal, in a case which cannot be repeated[1], to a rule acted on and justified in cases which can be and are repeated, at all forces us to admit that our state of mind is the same in each case.

§ 16. This example serves to bring out very clearly a point which has been already mentioned, and which will have to be insisted upon again, viz. that all which Probability discusses is the statistical frequency of events, or, if we prefer so to put it, the quantity of belief with which any one of these events should be individually regarded, but leaves all the subsequent conduct dependent upon that frequency, or that belief, to the choice of the agents. Suppose there are two travellers in the predicament in question: shall they keep together, or separate in opposite directions? In either case alike the chance of safety to each is the same, viz. one-half, but clearly their circumstances must decide which course it is preferable to adopt. If they are husband and wife, they will probably prefer to remain together; if they are sole depositaries of an important state secret, they may decide to part. In other words, we have to select here between the two alternatives of the certainty of a single loss, and the even chance

---

[1] Except indeed on the principles indicated further on in §§ 24, 25.

of a double loss; alternatives which the common mathematical statement of their chances has a decided tendency to make us regard as indistinguishable from one another. But clearly the decision must be grounded on the desires, feelings, and conscience of the agents. Probability cannot say a word upon this question. As I have pointed out elsewhere, there has been much confusion on this matter in applications of the science to betting, and in the discussion of the Petersburg problem.

We have thus examined the doctrine in question with a minuteness which may seem tedious, but in consequence of the eminence of its supporters it would have been presumptuous to have rejected it without the strongest grounds. The objections which have been urged might be summarised as follows:—the amount of our belief of any given proposition, supposing it to be in its nature capable of accurate determination (which does not seem to be the case), depends upon a great variety of causes, of which statistical frequency—the subject of Probability—is but one. That even if we confine our attention to this one cause, the natural amount of our belief is not necessarily what theory would assign, but has to be checked by appeal to experience. The subjective side of Probability therefore, though very interesting and well deserving of examination, seems a mere appendage of the objective, and affords in itself no safe ground for a science of inference.

§ 17. The conception then of the science of Probability as a science of the laws of belief seems to break down at every point. We must not however rest content with such merely negative criticism. The degree of belief we entertain of a proposition may be hard to get at accurately, and when obtained may be often wrong, and may need therefore to be checked by an appeal to the objects of belief. Still in

popular estimation we do seem to be able with more or less
accuracy to form a graduated scale of intensity of belief.
What we have to examine now is whether this be possible,
and, if so, what is the explanation of the fact?

   That it is generally believed that we can form such a
scale scarcely admits of doubt.   There is a whole vocabulary
of common expressions such as, 'I feel almost sure,' 'I do not
feel quite certain,' 'I am less confident of this than of that,'
and so on.   When we make use of any one of these phrases
we seldom doubt that we have a distinct meaning to convey
by means of it.   Nor do we feel much at a loss, under any
given circumstances, as to which of these expressions we
should employ in preference to the others.   If we were asked
to arrange in order, according to the intensity of the belief
with which we respectively hold them, things broadly marked
off from one another, we could do it from our consciousness
of belief alone, without a fresh appeal to the evidence upon
which the belief depended.   Passing over the looser propositions which are used in common conversation, let us take but
one simple example from amongst those which furnish numerical data.   Do I not feel more certain that some one will die
this week in the whole town, than in the particular street in
which I live? and if the town is known to contain a population one hundred times greater than that in the street, would
not almost any one be prepared to assert on reflection that
he felt a hundred times more sure of the first proposition
than of the second?   Or to take a non-numerical example, are
we not often able to say unhesitatingly which of two propositions we believe the most, and to some rough degree how
much more we believe one than the other, at a time when all
the evidence upon which each rests has faded from the
mind, so that each has to be judged, as we may say, solely on
its own merits?

Here then a problem proposes itself. If popular opinion, as illustrated in common language, be correct,—and very considerable weight must of course be attributed to it,—there does exist something which we call partial belief in reference to any proposition of the numerical kind described above. Now what we want to do is to find some test or justification of this belief, to obtain in fact some intelligible answer to the question, Is it correct? We shall find incidentally that the answer to this question will throw a good deal of light upon another question nearly as important and far more intricate, viz. What is the meaning of this partial belief?

§ 18. We shall find it advisable to commence by ascertaining how such enquiries as the above would be answered in the case of ordinary full belief. Such a step would not offer the slightest difficulty. Suppose, to take a simple example, that we have obtained the following proposition,—whether by induction, or by the rules of ordinary deductive logic, does not matter for our present purpose,—that a certain mixture of oxygen and hydrogen is explosive. Here we have an inference, and consequent belief of a proposition. Now suppose there were any enquiry as to whether our belief were correct, what should we do? The simplest way of settling the matter would be to find out by a distinct appeal to experience whether the proposition was true. Since we are reasoning about things, the justification of the belief, that is, the test of its correctness, would be most readily found in the truth of the proposition. If by any process of inference I have come to believe that a certain mixture will explode, I consider my belief to be justified, that is to be correct, if under proper circumstances the explosion always does occur; if it does not occur the belief was wrong.

Such an answer, no doubt, goes but a little way, or rather no way at all, towards explaining what is the nature of belief in itself; but it is sufficient for our present purpose, which is merely that of determining what is meant by the correctness of our belief, and by the test of its correctness. In all inferences about things, in which the *amount* of our belief is not taken into account, such an explanation as the above is quite sufficient; it would be the ordinary one in any question of science. It is moreover perfectly intelligible, whether the conclusion is particular or universal. Whether we believe that 'some men die', or that 'all men die', our belief may with equal ease be tested by the appropriate train of experience.

§ 19. But when we attempt to apply the same test to *partial* belief, we shall find ourselves reduced to an awkward perplexity. A difficulty now emerges which has been singularly overlooked by those who have treated of the subject. As a simple example will serve our purpose, we will take the case of a penny. I am about to toss one up, and I therefore half believe, to adopt the current language, that it will give head. Now it seems to be overlooked that if we appeal to the event, as we did in the case last examined, our belief must inevitably be wrong, and therefore the test above mentioned will fail. For the thing must either happen or not happen: i.e. in this case the penny must either give head, or not give it; there is no third alternative. But whichever way it occurs, our half-belief, so far as such a state of mind admits of interpretation, must be wrong. If head does come, I am wrong in not having expected it enough; for I only half believed in its occurrence. If it does not happen, I am equally wrong in having expected it too much; for I half believed in its occurrence, when in fact it did not occur at all.

The same difficulty will occur in every case in which we attempt to justify our state of partial belief in a single contingent event. Let us take another example, slightly differing from the last. A man is to receive £1 if a die gives six, to pay 1*s*. if it gives any other number. It will generally be admitted that he ought to give 2*s*. 6*d*. for the chance, and that if he does so he will be paying a fair sum. This example only differs from the last in the fact that instead of simple belief in a proposition, we have taken what mathematicians call 'the *value* of the expectation'. In other words, we have brought into greater prominence, not merely the belief, but the conduct which is founded upon the belief. But precisely the same difficulty recurs here. For appealing to the event,—the single event, that is,—we see that one or other party must lose his money without compensation. In what sense then can such an expectation be said to be a fair one?

§ 20. A possible answer to this, and so far as appears the only possible answer, will be, that what we really mean by saying that we half believe in the occurrence of head is to express our conviction that head will certainly happen on the average every other time. And similarly, in the second example, by calling the sum a fair one it is meant that in the long run neither party will gain or lose. As we shall recur presently to the point raised in this form of answer, the only notice that need be taken of it at this point is to call attention to the fact that it entirely abandons the whole question in dispute, for it admits that this partial belief does not in any strict sense apply to the individual event, since it clearly cannot be justified there. At such a result indeed we cannot be surprised; at least we cannot on the theory adopted throughout this Essay. For bearing in mind that the employment of Probability postulates ignorance of the single event, it is not easy to see how we are to justify any other opinion or statement about the single event than a confession of such ignorance.

§ 21. So far then we do not seem to have made the slightest approximation to a solution of the particular question now under examination. The more closely we have analysed special examples, the more unmistakeably are we brought to the conclusion that in the individual instance no justification of anything like quantitative belief is to be found; at least none is to be found in the same sense in which we expect it in ordinary scientific conclusions, whether Inductive or Deductive. And yet we have to face and account for the fact that common impressions, as attested by a whole vocabulary of common phrases, are in favour of the existence of this quantitative belief. How are we to account for this? If we appeal to an example again, and analyse it somewhat more closely, we may yet find our way to some satisfactory explanation.

In our previous analysis (§ 18) we found it sufficient to stop at an early stage, and to give as the justification of our belief the fact of the proposition being true. Stopping however at that stage, we have found this explanation fail altogether to give a justification of partial belief; fail, that is, when applied to the individual instance. The two states of belief and disbelief correspond admirably to the two results of the event happening and not happening respectively, and unless for psychological purposes we saw no reason to analyse further; but to partial belief there is nothing corresponding in the result, for the event cannot partially happen in such cases as we are concerned with. Suppose then we advance a step further in the analysis, and ask again what is meant by the proposition being true? This introduces us, of course, to a very long and intricate path; but in the short distance along it which we shall advance, we shall not, it is to be hoped, find any very serious difficulty. As before, we will illustrate the analysis by first applying it to the case of ordinary full belief.

§ 22. Whatever opinion then may be held about the essential nature of belief, it will probably be admitted that a

readiness to act upon the proposition believed is an inseparable accompaniment of that state of mind.   There can be no
alteration in our belief (at any rate in the case of sane persons)
without a possible alteration in our conduct, nor anything in
our conduct which is not connected with something in our
belief.   We will first take an example in connection with the
penny, in which there is full belief; we will analyse it a step
further than we did before, and then attempt to apply the
same analysis to an example of a similar kind, but one in
which the belief is partial instead of full.

Suppose that I am about to throw a penny up, and contemplate the prospect of its falling upon one of its sides and
not upon its edge.   We feel perfectly confident that it will
do so.   Now whatever else may be implied in our belief, we
certainly mean this; that we are ready to stake our conduct
upon its falling thus.   All our betting, and everything else
that we do, is carried on upon this supposition.   Any risk
whatever that might ensue upon its falling otherwise will be
incurred without fear.   This, it must be observed, is equally
the case whether we are speaking of a single throw or of a
long succession of throws.

But now let us take the case of a penny falling, not upon
one side or the other, but upon a given side, *head.*   To a
certain extent this example resembles the last.   We are perfectly ready to stake our conduct upon what comes to pass in
the long run.   When we are considering the result of a large
number of throws, we are ready to act upon the supposition
that head comes every other time.   If e.g. we are betting
upon it, we shall not object to paying £1 every time that
head comes, on condition of receiving £1 every time that
head does not come.   This is nothing else than the *transla-*
tion, as we may call it, into practice, of our belief that head
and tail occur equally often.

Now it will be obvious, on a moment's consideration, that our conduct is capable of being slightly varied: of being varied, that is, in form, whilst it remains identical in respect of its results. It is clear that to pay £1 every time we lose, and to get £1 every time we gain, comes to precisely the same thing, in the case under consideration, as to pay ten shillings every time without exception, and to receive £1 every time that head occurs. It is so, because heads occur, on the average, every other time. In the long run the two results coincide; but there is a marked difference between the two cases, considered individually. The difference is two-fold. In the first place we depart from the notion of a payment every other time, and come to that of one made every time. In the second place, what we pay every time is half of what we get in the cases in which we do get anything. The difference may seem slight; but mark the effect when our conduct is translated back again into the subjective condition upon which it depends, viz. into our belief. It is in consequence of such a translation, as it appears to me, that the notion has been acquired that we have an accurately determinable amount of belief as to every such proposition. To have losses and gains of equal amount, and to incur them equally often, was the experience connected with our belief that the two events, head and tail, would occur equally often. This was quite intelligible, for it referred to the long run. To find that this could be commuted for a payment made every time without exception, a payment, observe, of half the amount of what we occasionally receive, has very naturally been interpreted to mean that there must be a state of half-belief which refers to each individual throw.

§ 23. One such example, of course, does not go far towards establishing a theory. But the reader will bear in mind that almost all our conduct tends towards the same result; that it is not in betting only, but in every course of action in which we have to count the events, that such a numerical apportionment of our conduct is possible. Hence, by the ordinary principles of association, it would appear exceedingly likely that, not exactly a numerical condition of mind, but rather numerical associations, become inseparably connected with each particular event which we know to occur in a certain proportion of times. Once in six times a die gives ace; a knowledge of this fact, taken in combination with all the practical results to which it leads, produces, one cannot doubt, an inseparable notion of one-sixth connected with each *single* throw. But it surely cannot be called belief to the amount of one-sixth; at least it admits neither of justification nor explanation in these single cases, to which alone the fractional belief, if such existed, ought to apply.

It is in consequence, I apprehend, of such association that we act in such an unhesitating manner in reference to any single contingent event, even when we have no expectation of its being repeated. A die is going to be thrown up once, and once only. I bet 5 to 1 against ace, not, as is commonly asserted, because I feel one-sixth part of certainty in the occurrence of ace; but because I know that such conduct would be justified in the long run of such cases, and I apply to the solitary individual the same rule that I should apply to it if I knew it were one of a long series. This accounts for my conduct being the same in the two cases; by association, moreover, we probably experience very similar feelings in regard to them both.

§ 24. And here, on the view of the subject adopted in this Essay, we might stop. We are bound to explain the 'measure of our belief' in the occurrence of a single event when we judge solely from the statistical frequency with which such events occur, for such a series of events was our starting-point; but we are not bound to inquire whether in every case in which persons have, or claim to have, a certain measure of belief there must be such a series to which to refer it, and by which to justify it. Those who start from the subjective side, and regard Probability as the science of quantitative belief, are obliged to do this, but we are free from the obligation.

Still the question is one which is so naturally raised in connection with this subject, that it cannot be altogether passed by. I think that to a considerable extent such a justification as that mentioned above will be found applicable in other cases. The fact is that we are very seldom called upon to decide and act upon a single contingency which cannot be viewed as being one of a series. Experience introduces us, it must be remembered, not merely to a succession of events neatly arranged in a single series (as we have hitherto assumed them to be for the purpose of illustration), but to an infinite number belonging to a vast variety of different series. A man is obliged to be acting, and therefore exercising his belief about one thing or another, almost the whole of every day of his life. Any one person will have to decide in his time about a multitude of events, each one of which may never recur again within his own experience. But by the very fact of there being a multitude, though they are all of different kinds, we shall still find that order is maintained, and so a course of conduct can be justified. In a plantation of trees we should find that there is order of a certain kind if we measure them in any one direction, the trees being on an average about the same distance from each other. But a somewhat similar order would be found if we were to examine them in any other direction whatsoever. So in nature generally; there is regularity in a succession of events of the same kind. But there may also be regularity if we form a series by taking successively a number out of totally distinct kinds.

It is in this circumstance that we find an extension of the practical justification of the measure of our belief. A man, say, buys a life annuity, insures his life on a railway journey, puts into a lottery, and so on. Now we may make a series out of these acts of his, though each is in itself a single event which he may never intend to repeat. His conduct, and therefore his belief, measured by the result in each individual instance, will not be justified, but the reverse, as shewn in § 19. Could he indeed repeat each kind of action often enough it would be justified; but from this, by the conditions of life, he is debarred. Now it is perfectly conceivable that in the new series, formed by his successive acts of different kinds, there should be no regularity. As a matter of fact, however, it is found that there is regularity. In this way the equalization of his gains and losses, for which he cannot hope in annuities, insurances, and lotteries taken separately, may yet be secured to him out of these events taken collectively. If in each case he values his chance at its right proportion (and acts accordingly) he will in the course of his life neither gain nor lose. And in the same way if, whenever he has the alternative of different courses of conduct, he acts in accordance with the estimate of his belief described above, i.e. chooses the event whose chance is the best, he will in the end gain more in this way than by any other course. By the existence, therefore, of these *cross-series*, as we may term them, there is an immense addition to the number of actions which may be fairly considered to belong to those courses of conduct which offer many successive opportunities of equalizing gains and losses. All these cases then may be regarded as admitting of justification in the way now under discussion.

§ 25. In the above remarks it will be observed that we

have been giving what is to be regarded as a justification of his belief from the point of view of the individual agent himself. If we suppose the existence of an enlarged fellow-feeling, the applicability of such a justification becomes still more extensive. We can assign a very intelligible sense to the assertion that it is 999 to 1 that I shall not get a prize in a lottery, even if this be stated in the form that my belief in my so doing is represented by the fraction $\frac{1}{1000}$th of certainty. Properly it means that in a very large number of throws I should gain once in 1000 times. If we include other contingencies of the same kind, as described in the last section, each individual may be supposed to reach to something like this experience within the limits of his own life. He could not do it in this particular line of conduct alone, but he could do it in this line combined with others. Now introduce the possibility of each man feeling that the gain of others offers some analogy to his own gains, which we may conceive his doing except in the case of the gains of those against whom he is directly competing, and the above justification becomes still more extensively applicable.

The following would be a fair illustration to test this view. I know that I must die on some day of the week, and there are but seven days. My belief, therefore, that I shall die on a Sunday is one-seventh. Here the contingent event is clearly one that does not admit of repetition; and yet would not the belief of every man have the value assigned it by the formula? It would appear that the same principle will be found to be at work here as in the former examples. It is quite true that I have only the opportunity of dying once myself, but I am a member of a class in which deaths occur with frequency, and I form my opinion upon evidence drawn from that class. If, for example, I had insured my life for £1000, I should feel a certain propriety in demanding

£7000 in case the office declared that it would only pay in the event of my dying on a Sunday. *I*, indeed, for my own private part, might not find the arrangement an equitable one; but mankind at large, in case they acted on such a principle, might fairly commute their aggregate gains in such a way, whilst to the Insurance Office it would not make any difference at all.

§ 26.   The results of the last few sections might be summarised as follows :—the different amounts of belief which we entertain upon different events, and which are recognized by various phrases in common use, have undoubtedly some meaning.   But the greater part of their meaning, and certainly their only justification, are to be sought in the *series* of corresponding events to which they belong; in regard to which it may be shewn that far more events are capable of being referred to a series than might be supposed at first sight.   The test and justification of belief are to be found in conduct; in this test applied to the series as a whole, there is nothing peculiar, it differs in no way from the similar test when we are acting on our belief about any single event. But so applied, from the nature of the case it is applied successively to each of the individuals of the series; here our *conduct* generally admits of being separately considered in reference to each particular event; and this has been understood to denote a certain amount of belief which should be a fraction of certainty.   Probably on the principles of association, a peculiar condition of mind is produced in reference to each single event.   And these associations are not unnaturally retained even when we contemplate any one of these single events isolated from any series to which it belongs.   When it is found alone we treat it, and feel towards it, as we do when it is in company with the rest of the series.

§ 27.   We may now see, more clearly than we could

before, why it is that we are free from any necessity of assuming the existence of causation, in the sense of necessary invariable sequence, in the case of the events which compose our series. Against such a view it might very plausibly be urged, that we constantly talk of the probability of a single event; but how can this be done, it may reasonably be said, if we once admit the possibility of that event occurring fortuitously? Take an instance from human life; the average duration of the lives of a batch of men aged thirty will be about thirty-four years. We say therefore to any individual of them, Your expectation of life is thirty-four years. But how can this be said if we admit that the train of events composing his life is liable to be destitute of all regular sequence of cause and effect? To this it may be replied that the denial of causation enables us to say neither more nor less than its assertion, in reference to the length of the individual life, for of this we are ignorant in each case alike. By assigning, as above, an expectation in reference to the individual, we *mean* nothing more than to make a statement about the average of his class. Whether there be causation or not in these individual cases does not affect our knowledge of the average, for this by supposition rests on independent experience. The legitimate inferences are the same on either hypothesis, and of equal value. The only difference is that on the hypothesis of non-causation we have forced upon our attention the impropriety of talking of the 'proper' expectation of the individual, owing to the fact that all knowledge of its amount is formally impossible; on the other hypothesis the impropriety is overlooked from the fact of such knowledge being only practically unattainable. As a matter of fact the amount of our knowledge is the same in each case; it is a knowledge of the average, and of that only[1].

---

[1] For a fuller discussion of this, see the Chapter on Causation.

§ 28. We may conclude, then, that the limits within which we are thus able to justify the amount of our belief are far more extensive than might appear at first sight. Whether every case in which persons feel an amount of belief short of perfect confidence could be forced into the province of Probability is a wider question. Even, however, if the belief could be supposed capable of justification on its principles, its rules could never in such cases be made use of. Suppose, for example, that a father were in doubt whether to give a certain medicine to his sick child. On the one hand, the doctor declared that the child would die unless the medicine were given; on the other, through a mistake, the father cannot feel quite sure that the medicine he has is the right one. It is conceivable that some mathematicians, in their conviction that everything has its definite numerical probability, would declare that the man's belief had some 'value' (if they could only find out what it is), say nine-tenths; by which they would mean that in nine cases out of ten in which he entertained a belief of that particular value he proved to be right. So with his belief and doubt on the other side of the question. Putting the two together, there is but one course which, as a prudent man and a good father, he can possibly follow. It may be so, but when (as here) the identification of an event in a series depends on purely subjective conditions, as in this case upon the degree of vividness of his conviction, of which no one else can judge, no test is possible, and therefore no proof can be found.

§ 29. So much then for the attempts, so frequently made, to found the science on a subjective basis; they can lead, as it has here been endeavoured to show, to no satisfactory result. Still our belief is so inseparably connected with our action, that something of a defence can be made for the attempts described above; but when it is attempted, as is often the case, to import other sentiments besides pure belief, and to find a justification for them also in the results of our science, the confusion becomes far worse. The following extract from Archbishop Thomson's *Laws of Thought* (§ 122, Ed. II.) will show what kind of applications of the science are contemplated here: " In applying the doctrine of chances to that subject in connexion with which it was invented—games of chance,—the principles of what has been happily termed ' moral arithmetic' must not be forgotten. Not only would it be difficult for a gamester to find an antagonist on terms, as to fortune and needs, precisely equal, but also it is impossible that with such an equality the advantage of a considerable gain should balance the harm of a serious loss. ' If two men,' says Buffon, ' were to determine to play for their whole property, what would be the effect of this agreement? The one would only double his fortune, and the other reduce his to naught. What proportion is there between the loss and the gain? The same that there is between all and nothing. The gain of the one is but a moderate sum,—the loss of the other is numerically infinite, and morally so great that the labour of his whole life may not perhaps suffice to restore his property.'"

As moral advice this is all very true and good. But if it be regarded as a contribution to the science of the subject it is quite inappropriate, and seems calculated to cause confusion. The doctrine of chances pronounces upon certain kinds of events in respect of number and magnitude; it has absolutely nothing to do with any particular person's feelings about these relations. We might as well append a corollary to the rules of arithmetic, to point out that although it is very true that twice two are four it does not follow that four horses will give twice as much pleasure to the owner as two will. If two men play on equal terms their chances are

equal; in other words, if they were often to play in this
manner each would lose as frequently as he would gain. That
is all that Probability can say; what under the circumstances
may be the determination and opinions of the men in question, it is for them and them alone to decide. There are
many persons who cannot bear mediocrity of any kind, and
to whom the prospect of doubling their fortune would out-
weigh a greater chance of losing it altogether. They alone
are the judges.

If we will introduce such a balance of pleasure and pain
the individual must make the calculation for himself. The
supposition is that total ruin is very painful, partial loss
painful in a less proportion than that assigned by the ratio
of the losses themselves; the inference is therefore drawn
that on the average more pain is caused by occasional great
losses than by frequent small ones, though the money value
of the losses in the long run may be the same in each case.
But if we suppose a country where the desire of spending
largely is very strong, and where owing to abundant production loss is easily replaced, the calculation might incline the
other way. Under such circumstances it is quite possible
that more happiness might result from playing for high than
for low stakes. The fact is that all emotional considerations
of this kind are irrelevant; they are, at most, mere applications of the theory, and such as each individual is alone
competent to make for himself. Some more remarks will be
made upon this subject in the chapter upon Insurance and
Gambling.

§ 30. It is by the introduction of such considerations as
these that the Petersburg Problem has been so perplexed.
Having already given some description of this problem we
will refer to it very briefly here. It presents us with a
sequence of sets of throws for each of which sets I am to

receive something, say a shilling, as the minimum receipt. My receipts increase in proportion to the rarity of each particular kind of set, and each kind is observed or inferred to grow more rare in a certain definite but unlimited order. By the wording of the problem, properly interpreted, I am supposed never to stop. Clearly therefore, however large a fee I pay for each of these sets, I shall be sure to make it up in time. The mathematical expression of this is, that I ought always to pay an infinite sum. To this the objection is opposed, that no sensible man would think of advancing even a large finite sum, say £50. Certainly he would not; but why? Because neither he nor those who are to pay him would be likely to live long enough for him to obtain throws good enough to remunerate him for one-tenth of his outlay; to say nothing of his trouble and loss of time. We must not suppose that the problem, as stated in the ideal form, will coincide with the practical form in which it presents itself in life. A carpenter might as well object to Euclid's second postulate, because his plane came to a stop in six feet on the plank on which he was at work. Many persons have failed to perceive this, and have assumed that, besides enabling us to draw numerical inferences about the members of a series, the theory ought also to be called upon to justify all the opinions which average respectable men might be inclined to form about them, as well as the conduct they might choose to pursue in consequence. It is obvious that to enter upon such considerations as these is to diverge from our proper ground. We are concerned, in these cases, with the actions of men only, as given in statistics; with the emotions they experience in the performance of these actions we have no direct concern whatever. The error is the same as if any one were to confound, in political economy, value in use with value in exchange, and object to measuring the value of a loaf by its cost of production, because bread is worth more to a man when he is hungry than it is just after his dinner.

§ 31. One class of emotions indeed ought to be excepted, which, from the apparent uniformity and consistency with which they show themselves in different persons and at different times, do really present some better claim to consideration. In connection with a science of inference they can never indeed be regarded as more than an accident of what is essential to the subject, but compared with other emotions they seem to be inseparable accidents.

The reader will remember that attention was drawn in the earlier part of this chapter to the compound nature of the state of mind which we term belief. It is partly intellectual, partly also emotional; it professes to rest upon experience, but in reality the experience acts through the distorting media of hopes and fears and other disturbing agencies. So long as we confine our attention to the *state of mind* of the person who believes, it appears to me that these two parts of belief are quite inseparable. Indeed, to speak of them as two parts may convey a wrong impression; for though they spring from different sources, they so entirely merge in one result as to produce what might be called an indistinguishable compound. Every kind of inference, whether in probability or not, is liable to be disturbed in this way. A timid man may honestly believe that he will be wounded in a coming battle, when others, with the same experience but calmer judgments, see that the chance is too small to deserve consideration. But such a man's belief, if we look only to that, will not differ in its nature from sound belief. His conduct also in consequence of his belief will by itself afford no ground of discrimination; he will make his will as sincerely as a man who is unmistakeably on

his death-bed.   The only resource is to check and correct
his belief by appealing to past and current experience[1].   This
was advanced as an objection to the theory on which probability is regarded as concerned primarily with laws of belief.
But on the view taken in this Essay in which we are supposed to be concerned with laws of inference about things,
error and difficulty from this source vanish.   Let us bear clearly
in mind that we are concerned with inferences about things,
and whatever there may be in belief which does not depend
on experience will disappear from notice.

§ 32.   These emotions then can claim no notice as an
integral portion of any science of inference, and should in
strictness be rigidly excluded from it.   But if any of them
are uniform and regular in their production and magnitude,
they may be fairly admitted as accidental and extraneous
accompaniments.   This is really the case to some extent
with our surprise.   This emotion does show a considerable
degree of uniformity.   The rarer any event is the more am I,
in common with most other men, surprised at it when it does
happen.   This surprise may range through all degrees, from
the most languid form of interest up to the condition which
we term 'being startled'.   And since the surprise seems
to be pretty much the same, under similar circumstances,
at different times, and in the case of different persons, it is
free from that extreme irregularity which is found in most
of the other mental conditions which accompany the con-

---

[1] The best example I can recall
of the distinction between judging
from the subjective and the objective side, in such cases as these,
occurred once in a railway train.
I met a timid old lady who was
in much fear of accidents.   I endeavoured to soothe her on the
usual statistical ground of the extreme rarity of such events.   She
listened patiently, and then replied,
"Yes, Sir, that is all very well; but
I don't see how the real danger will
be a bit the less because I don't believe in it."

templation of unexpected events. Hence our surprise, though,
as stated above, having no proper claim to admission into
the science of Probability, is such a constant and regular
accompaniment of that which Probability is concerned with,
that notice must often be taken of it. References will occasionally be found to this aspect of the question in the
following chapters.

It may be remarked in passing, for the sake of further
illustration of the subject, that this emotional accompaniment of surprise, to which we are thus able to assign something like a fractional value, differs in two important respects
from the commonly accepted fraction of belief. In the first
place, it has what may be termed an independent existence;
it is intelligible by itself. The belief, as we endeavoured to
show, needs explanation and finds it in our consequent conduct. Not so with the emotion; this stands upon its own
footing, and may be examined in and by itself. Hence, in
the second place, it is as applicable, and as capable of any kind
of justification, in relation to the *single event*, as to a series of
events. In this respect, as will be remembered, it offers a
complete contrast to our state of belief about any one contingent event. May not these considerations help to account
for the general acceptance of the doctrine, that we have a
certain definite and measurable amount of belief about these
events? I cannot help thinking that what is so obviously
true of the emotional portion of the belief, has been unconsciously transferred to the other or intellectual portion of the
compound condition, to which it is not applicable, and where
it cannot find a justification.

§ 33. A further illustration may now be given of the
subjective view of Probability at present under discussion.

An appeal to common language is always of service, as

the employment of any distinct word is generally a proof
that mankind have observed some distinct properties in the
things, which have caused them to be singled out and have
that name appropriated to them. There is such a class of
words assigned by popular usage to the kind of events of
which Probability takes account. If we examine them we
shall find, I think, that they direct us unmistakeably to the
two-fold aspect of the question,—the objective and the subjective, the quality in the events and the state of our minds
in considering them,—that have occupied our attention
during the former chapters.

The word 'extraordinary', for instance, seems to point to
the observed fact, that events are arranged in a sort of ordo
or rank. No one of them might be so exactly placed that
we could have inferred its position, but when we take a great
many into account together, running our eye, as it were,
along the line, we begin to see that they really do for the
most part stand in order. Those which stand away from the
line have this divergence observed, and are called extraordinary, the rest ordinary, or in the line. So too 'irregular' and 'abnormal' are doubtless used from the appearance of things, when examined in large numbers, being that
of an arrangement by rule or measure. This only holds
when there are a good many; we could not speak of the
single events being so arranged. Again the word 'law', in
its philosophical sense, has now become quite popularised.
How the term became introduced is not certain, but
there can be little doubt that it was somewhat in this
way:—The effect of a law, in its usual application to
human conduct, is to produce regularity where it did not
previously exist; when then a regularity began to be perceived in nature, the same word was used, whether the cause
was supposed to be the same or not. In each case there

was the same generality of agreement, subject to occasional deflection[1].

On the other hand, observe the words 'wonderful', 'unexpected', 'incredible'. Their connotation describes states of mind simply; they are of course not confined to Probability, in the sense of statistical frequency, but imply simply that the events they denote are such as from some cause we did not expect would happen, and at which therefore, when they do happen, we are surprised.

Now when we bear in mind that these two classes of words are in their origin perfectly distinct;—the one denoting simply events of a certain character; the other, though also denoting events, *connoting* simply states of mind;—and yet that they are universally applied to the same events, so as to be used as perfectly synonymous, we have in this a striking illustration of the two sides under which Probability may be viewed, and of the universal recognition of a close connection between them. The words are popularly used as synonymous, and we must not press their meaning too far; but if it were to be observed, as I am rather inclined to think it could, that the application of the words which denote mental states is wider than that of the others, we should have an illustration of what has been already observed, viz. that the province of Probability is not so extensive as that over which variation of belief might be observed. Probability only considers the case in which this variation is brought about in a certain definite statistical way.

§ 34. It will be found in the end both interesting and important to have devoted some attention to this subjective

[1] This would still hold of *empirical* laws which may be capable of being broken: we now have very much shifted the word, to denote an *ultimate* law which it is supposed cannot be broken.

side of the question. In the first place, as a mere speculative inquiry the quantity of our belief of any proposition
deserves notice. To study it at all deeply would be to tres-
pass into the province of Psychology, but it is so intimately
connected with our own subject that we cannot avoid all
reference to it. We therefore discuss the laws under which
our expectation and surprise at isolated events increases or
diminishes, so as to account for these states of mind in any
individual instance, and, if necessary, to correct them when
they vary from their proper amount.

But there is another more important reason than this.
It is quite true that when the subjects of our discussion in
any particular instance lie entirely within the province
of Probability, they may be treated without any reference
to our belief. We may or we may not employ this side of
the question according to our pleasure. If, for example, I
am asked whether it is more likely that A. B. will die this
year, than that it will rain to-morrow, I may calculate the
chance (which really is at bottom the same thing as my
belief) of each, find them respectively, one-sixth and one-
seventh, say, and therefore decide that my 'expectation' of
the former is the greater, viz. that this is the more likely
event. In this case the process is precisely the same whether
we suppose our belief to be introduced or not; our mental
state is, in fact, quite immaterial to the question. But, in
other cases, it may be different. Suppose that we are comparing two things, of which one is wholly alien to Probability, in the sense that it is hopeless to attempt to assign
any degree of numerical frequency to it, the only ground
they have in common may be the amount of belief to which
they are respectively entitled. We cannot compare the
frequency of their occurrence, for one may occur too seldom
to judge by, perhaps it may be unique. It has been already

said, that our belief of many events rests upon a very complicated and extensive basis. My belief may be the product
of many conflicting arguments, and many analogies more or
less remote; these proofs themselves may have mostly faded
from my mind, but they will leave their effect behind them
in a weak or strong conviction. At the time, therefore, I
may still be able to say, with some degree of accuracy,
though a very slight degree, what amount of belief I entertain upon the subject. Now we cannot compare things that
are heterogeneous: if, therefore, we are to decide between
this and an event determined naturally and properly by
Probability, it is impossible to appeal to chances or frequency
of occurrence. The measure of belief is the only common
ground, and we must therefore compare this quantity in each
case. The test afforded will be an exceedingly rough one,
for the reasons mentioned above, but it will be better than
none; in some cases it will be found to furnish all we want.

Suppose, for example, that one letter in a million is lost
in the Post Office, and that in any given instance I wish to
know which is more likely, that a letter has been so lost, or
that my servant has stolen it? If the latter alternative
could, like the former, be stated in a numerical form, the
comparison would be simple. But it cannot be reduced to
this form, at least not consciously and directly. Still, if we
could feel that our belief in the man's dishonesty was greater
than one-millionth, we should then have homogeneous things
before us, and therefore comparison would be possible.

§ 35. We are now in a position to give a tolerably accurate definition of a phrase which we have frequently been
obliged to employ, or incidentally to suggest, and of which
the reader may have looked for a definition already, viz. the
probability of an event, or what is equivalent to this, the
chance of any given event happening. I consider that these

terms presuppose a series; within the indefinitely numerous class which composes this series a smaller class is distinguished by the presence or absence of some attribute or attributes, as was fully illustrated and explained in a previous chapter.   These larger and smaller classes respectively are commonly spoken of as instances of the 'event,' and of 'its happening in a given particular way.'   Adopting this phraseology, which with proper explanations is suitable enough, we may define the probability or chance (the terms are here regarded as synonymous) of the event happening in that particular way as the numerical fraction which represents the proportion between the two different classes in the long run.   Thus, for example, let the probability be that of a given infant living to be eighty years of age.   The larger series will comprise all infants, the smaller all who live to eighty.   Let the proportion of the former to the latter be 9 to 1; in other words, suppose that one infant in ten lives to eighty.   Then the chance or probability that any given infant will live to eighty is the numerical fraction $\frac{1}{10}$.   This assumes that the series are of indefinite extent, and of the kind which we have described as possessing a fixed type. If this be not the case, but the series be supposed terminable, or regularly or irregularly fluctuating, as might be the case, for instance, in a society where owing to sanitary or other causes the average longevity was steadily undergoing a change, then in so far as this is the case the series ceases to be a subject of science.   What we have to do under these circumstances, is to substitute a series of the right kind for the inappropriate one presented by nature, choosing it, of course, with as little deflection as possible from the observed facts.   This is nothing more than has to be done, and invariably is done, whenever natural objects are made subjects of strict science.

§ 36. A word or two of explanation may be added about
the expression employed above, 'the proportion in the long
run.' The run must be supposed to be very long indeed, in
fact never to stop. As we keep on taking more terms of the
series we shall find the proportion still fluctuating a little,
but its fluctuations will grow less. The proportion, in fact,
will gradually approach towards some fixed numerical value,
what mathematicians term its *limit*. This fractional value
is the one spoken of above. In the cases in which deductive
reasoning is possible, this fraction may be obtained without
direct appeal to statistics, from reasoning about the conditions under which the events occur, as was explained in
the fourth chapter.

Here becomes apparent the full importance of the distinction so frequently insisted on, between the actual irregular
series before us and the substituted one of calculation, and
the meaning of the assertion (Ch. I. § 13), that it was in the
case of the latter only that strict scientific inferences could
be made. For how can we have a 'limit' in the case of
those series which ultimately exhibit irregular fluctuations?
When we say, for instance, that it is an even chance that
a given person recovers from the cholera, the meaning of
this assertion is that in the long run one half of the persons
attacked by that disease do recover. But if we examined
a sufficiently extensive range of statistics, we might find
that the manners and customs of society had produced such
a change in the type of the disease or its treatment, that we
were no nearer approaching towards a fixed limit than we
were at first. The conception of an ultimate limit in the
ratio between the numbers of the two classes in the series
necessarily involves an absolute fixity of the type. When
therefore nature does not present us with this absolute fixity,
as she seldom or never does except in games of chance (and

not demonstrably there), our only resource is to introduce such a series, in other words, as has so often been said, to substitute a series of the right kind.

§ 37. The above, which may be considered tolerably complete as a definition, might equally well have been given in the last chapter. It has been deferred however to the present place, in order to connect with it at once a proposition involving the conceptions introduced in this chapter; viz. the state of our own minds, in reference to the amount of belief we entertain in contemplating any one of the events whose probability has just been described. Reasons were given against the opinion that our belief admitted of any exact apportionment like the numerical one just mentioned. Still, it was shown that a reasonable explanation could be given of such an expression as, 'my belief is $\frac{1}{10}$th of certainty', though it was an explanation which pointed unmistakeably to a series of events, and ceased to be intelligible, or at any rate justifiable, when it was not viewed in such a relation to a series. In so far, then, as this explanation is adopted, we may say that our belief is in proportion to the above fraction. This referred to the purely intellectual part of belief which cannot be conceived to be separable, even in thought, from the things upon which it is exercised. With this intellectual part there are commonly associated various emotions. These we can to a certain extent separate, and, when separated, can measure with that degree of accuracy which is possible in the case of other emotions. They are moreover intelligible in reference to the individual events. They will be found to increase and diminish in accordance, to some extent, with the fraction which represents the scarcity of the event. The emotion of surprise does so with some degree of accuracy.

The above investigation describes, though in a very brief

form, the amount of truth which appears to me to be contained in the assertion frequently made, that the fraction expressive of the probability represents also the fractional part of full certainty to which our belief of the individual event amounts. Any further analysis of the matter would seem to belong to Psychology rather than to Probability.

CHAPTER VII.

THE RULES OF INFERENCE IN PROBABILITY.

§ 1. In the previous chapter, an investigation was made into what may be called, from the analogy of Logic, Immediate Inferences. Given that nine men out of ten, of any assigned age, live to forty, what could be inferred about the prospect of life of any particular man ? It was shown that, although this step was very far from being so simple as it is frequently supposed to be, and as the corresponding step really is in Logic, there was nevertheless an intelligible sense in which we might speak of the amount of our belief in any one of these 'proportional propositions,' as they may succinctly be termed, and justify that amount. We must now proceed to the consideration of inferences more properly so called, I mean inferences of the kind analogous to those which form the staple of ordinary logical treatises. In other words, having ascertained in what manner particular propositions could be inferred from the general propositions which included them, we must now examine in what cases one general proposition can be inferred from another. By a general proposition here is meant, of course, a general proposition of the statistical kind contemplated in Probability. The rules of such inference being very few and simple, their consideration will not detain us long. From the data now in our possession we are able to deduce the rules of probability given in ordinary treatises upon the science. It would be more correct to say that we are able to deduce *some* of these rules, for, as will appear on examination, they are of two very different kinds, resting on entirely distinct grounds. They might be divided into those which are formal, and those which are more or less experimental. This may be otherwise expressed by saying that, from the kind of series described in the first chapters, some rules will follow necessarily by the mere application of arithmetic; whilst others either depend upon peculiar hypotheses, or demand for their establishment continually renewed appeals to experience, and extension by the aid of the various resources of Induction. We shall confine our attention at present principally to the former class; the latter can only be fully understood when we have considered the connection of our science with Induction.

§ 2. The fundamental rules of Probability strictly so called, that is the formal rules, may be divided into two classes,—those obtained by addition or subtraction on the one hand, corresponding to what are generally termed the connection of exclusive or incompatible events[1]; and those obtained by multiplication or division, on the other hand, corresponding to what are commonly termed dependent events. We will examine these in order.

(1) We can make inferences by simple addition. If, for instance, there are two distinct properties observable in various members of the series, which properties do not occur in the same individual; it is plain that in any batch the number that are of one kind or the other will be equal to the sum of those of the two kinds separately. Thus 36.4 infants

---

[1] It might be more accurate to speak of 'incompatible hypotheses with respect to any individual case', or 'mutually exclusive classes of events'.

in 100 live to over sixty, 35.4 in 100 die before they are
ten[1]; take a large number, say 10,000, then there will be
about 3640 who live to over sixty, and about 3540 who do
not reach ten; hence the total number who do not die within
the assigned limits will be about 2820 altogether. Of course
if these proportions were accurately assigned, the resultant
sum would be equally accurate: but, as the reader knows, in
Probability this proportion is merely the limit towards which
the numbers tend in the long run, not the precise result
assigned in any particular case. Hence we can only venture
to say that this is the limit towards which we tend as the
numbers become greater and greater.

This rule, in its general algebraic form, would be expressed in the language of Probability as follows:—If the
chances of two exclusive or incompatible events be re-
spectively $\dfrac{1}{m}$ and $\dfrac{1}{n}$ the chance of one or other of them
happening will be $\dfrac{1}{m} + \dfrac{1}{n}$ or $\dfrac{m+n}{mn}$. Similarly if there were
more than two events of the kind in question. On the prin-
ciples adopted in this work, the rule, when thus algebraically
expressed, means precisely the same thing as when it is
expressed in the statistical form. It was shown at the conclusion of the last chapter that to say, for example, that the
chance of a given event happening in a certain way is $\dfrac{1}{6}$, is
only another way of saying that in the long run it does tend
to happen in that way once in six times.

It is plain that a sort of corollary to this rule might be

---

[1] The examples, of this kind, referring to human mortality are taken
from the Carlisle tables. These
differ considerably, as is well known,
from other tables, but we have the
high authority of De Morgan for regarding them as the best representative of the average mortality of the
English middle classes at the present
day.

obtained, in precisely the same way, by subtraction instead of addition. Stated generally it would be as follows:—If the chance of one or other of two incompatible events be $\dfrac{1}{m}$ and the chance of one alone be $\dfrac{1}{n}$, the chance of the remaining one will be $\dfrac{1}{m} - \dfrac{1}{n}$ or $\dfrac{n - m}{nm}$.

For example, if the chance of any one dying in a year is $\dfrac{1}{10}$, and his chance of dying of some particular disease is $\dfrac{1}{100}$, his chance of dying of any other disease is $\dfrac{9}{100}$.

The reader will remark here that there are two apparently different modes of stating this rule, according as we speak of 'one or other of two or more events happening,' or of 'the same event happening in one or other of two or more ways.' But no confusion need arise on this ground; either way of speaking is legitimate, the difference being merely verbal, and depending (as was shown in the first chapter, § 8) upon whether the distinctions between the 'ways' are or are not too deep and numerous to entitle the event to be conventionally regarded as the same.

We may also here point out the justification for the common doctrine that certainty is represented by unity, just as any given degree of probability is represented by its appropriate fraction. If the statement that an event happens once in m times, is equivalently expressed by saying that its chance is $\dfrac{1}{m}$, it follows that to say that it happens m times in m times, or every time without exception, is equivalent to saying that its chance is $\dfrac{m}{m}$ or 1. Now an event that happens every time is of course one of whose occurrence we are certain; hence the fraction which represents the 'chance' of an event which is certain becomes unity.

It will be equally obvious that given that the chance that an event will happen is $\frac{1}{m}$, the chance that it will not happen is $1 - \frac{1}{m}$ or $\frac{m-1}{m}$.

§ 3. (2) We can also make inferences by multiplication or division. Suppose that the two events, instead of being incompatible, are connected together in the sense that one is contingent upon the occurrence of the other. Let us be told that a given proportion of the members of the series possess a certain property, and a given proportion again of these possess another property, then the proportion of the whole which possess both properties will be found by multiplying together the two fractions which represent the above two proportions. Of the inhabitants of London, twenty-five in a thousand, say, will die in the course of the year; we suppose it to be known also that one death in five is due to fever; we should then infer that one in 200 of the inhabitants will die of fever in the course of the year. It would of course be equally simple, by division, to make a sort of converse inference. Given the total mortality per cent. of the population from fever, and the proportion of fever cases to the aggregate of other cases of mortality, we might have inferred, by dividing one fraction by the other, what was the total mortality per cent. from all causes.

The rule as given above is variously expressed in the language of Probability. Perhaps the simplest and best statement is that it gives us the rule of dependent events. That is; if the chance of one event is $\frac{1}{m}$, and the chance that if it happens another will also happen is $\frac{1}{n}$, then the chance

of the latter is $\dfrac{1}{mn}$. In this case it is assumed that the latter
is so entirely dependent upon the former that though it does
not always happen with it, it certainly will not happen without it; the necessity of this assumption however may be
obviated by saying that what we are speaking of in the
latter case is the *joint* event, viz. both together if they are
simultaneous events, or the latter *in consequence of* the
former, if they are successive.

§ 4.   The above inferences are necessary, in the sense in
which arithmetical inferences are necessary, and they do not
demand for their establishment any arbitrary hypothesis.
We assume in them no more than is warranted, and in fact
necessitated by the data actually given to us, and make our
inferences from these data by the help of arithmetic.   In the
simple examples given above nothing is required beyond
arithmetic in its most familiar form, but it need hardly be
added that in practice examples may often present themselves which will require much profounder methods than
these.   It may task all the resources of that higher and more
abstract arithmetic known as algebra to extract a solution.
But as the necessity of appeal to such methods as these does
not touch the principles of this part of the subject we need
not enter upon them here.

§ 5.   The formula next to be discussed stands upon a
somewhat different footing from the above in respect of its
cogency and freedom from appeal to experience, or to hypothesis.   In the two former instances we considered cases in
which the data were supposed to be given under the conditions
that the properties which distinguished the different kinds of
events whose frequency was discussed, were respectively
known to be disconnected and known to be connected.   Let
us now suppose that no such conditions are given to us.

One man in ten, say, has black hair, and one in twelve
is short-sighted; what conclusions could we then draw as
to the chance of any given man having one only of these
two attributes, or neither, or both? It is clearly possible
that the properties in question might be inconsistent with
one another, so as never to be found combined in the same
person; or all the short-sighted might have black hair; or
the properties might be allotted[1] in almost any other proportion whatever. If we are perfectly ignorant upon these
points, it would seem that no inferences whatever could be
drawn about the required chances.

Inferences however *are* drawn, and practically, in most
cases, quite justly drawn. An escape from the apparent
indeterminateness of the problem, as above described, is
found by assuming that, not merely will one-tenth of the
whole number of men have black hair (for this was given as
one of the data), but also that one-tenth alike of those who
are and who are not short-sighted have black hair. Let us
take a batch of 1200, as a sample of the whole. Now, from
the data which were originally given to us, it will easily be
seen that in every such batch there will be on the average
120 who have black hair, and therefore 1080 who have not.
And here in strict right we ought to stop, at least until we
have appealed again to experience; but we do not stop here.
From data which we assume, we go on to infer that of the
120, 10 (i.e. one-twelfth of 120) will be short-sighted, and
110 (the remainder) will not. Similarly we infer that of the

---

[1] I say, *almost* any proportion, because, as may easily be seen, arithmetic imposes certain restrictions
upon the assumptions that can be
made. We could not, for instance,
suppose that all the black-haired

men are short-sighted, for in any
given batch of men the former are
more numerous. But the range of
these restrictions is limited, and
their existence is not of importance
in the above discussion.

1080, 90 are short-sighted, and 990 are not. On the whole, then, the 1200 are thus divided:—black-haired short-sighted, 10; short-sighted without black hair, 90; black-haired men who are not short-sighted, 110; men who are neither short-sighted nor have black hair, 990.

This rule, expressed in its most general form, in the language of Probability, would be as follows:—If the chances of a thing being p and q are respectively $\dfrac{1}{m}$ and $\dfrac{1}{n}$, then the chance of its being both p and q is $\dfrac{1}{mn}$, p and not q is $\dfrac{n-1}{mn}$, q and not p is $\dfrac{m-1}{mn}$, not p and not q is $\dfrac{(m-1)(n-1)}{mn}$, where p and q are independent. The sum of these chances is obviously unity; as it ought to be, since one or other of the four alternatives must necessarily exist.

§ 6. I have purposely emphasized the distinction between the inference in this case, and that in the two preceding, to an extent which to many readers may seem unwarranted. But it appears to me that where a science makes use, as Probability does, of two such very distinct sources of conviction as the necessary rules of arithmetic and the merely more or less cogent ones of Induction, it is hardly possible to lay too much stress upon the distinction. Few will be prepared to deny that very arbitrary assumptions have been made by many writers on the subject, and none will deny that in the case of what are called 'inverse probabilities' assumptions are sometimes made which are at least decidedly open to question. The best course therefore is to make a pause and stringent enquiry at the point at which the possibility of such error and doubtfulness first exhibits itself. These remarks apply to some of the best writers on the subject; in the case of inferior writers, or those who appeal to

Probability without having properly mastered its principles, we may go further. It would really not be asserting too much to say that they seem to think themselves justified in assuming that where we know nothing about the distribution of the properties alluded to we must assume them to be distributed as above described, and therefore apportion our belief in the same ratio. This is called 'assuming the events to be independent,' the supposition being made that the rule will certainly follow from this independence, and that we have a right, if we know nothing to the contrary, to assume that the events are independent.

The validity of this last claim has already been discussed in the first chapter; it is only another of the attempts to construct *à priori* the series which experience will present to us, and one for which no such strong defence can be made as for the equality of heads and tails in the throws of a penny. But the meaning to be assigned to the 'independence' of the events in question demands a moment's consideration.

The circumstances of the problem are these. There are two different qualities, by the presence and absence respectively of each of which, amongst the individuals of a series, two distinct pairs of classes of these individuals are produced. For the establishment of the rule under discussion it was found that one supposition was both necessary and sufficient, namely, that the division into classes caused by each of the above distinctions should subdivide each of the classes created by the other distinction in the same ratio in which it subdivides the whole. If the independence be granted and so defined as to mean this, the rule of course will stand, but, without especial attention being drawn to the point, it does not seem that the word would naturally be so understood.

§ 7.   The above, then, being the fundamental rules of

inference in probability, the question at once arises, What is their relation to the great body of formulæ which are made use of in treatises upon the science, and in practical applications of it ? The reply would be that these formulæ, in so far as they properly belong to the science, are nothing else in reality than applications of the above fundamental rules. Such applications may assume any degree of complexity, for owing to the difficulty of particular examples, in the form in which they actually present themselves, recourse must sometimes be made to the profoundest theorems of mathematics. Still we ought not to regard these theorems as being anything else than convenient and necessary abbreviations of arithmetical processes, which in practice have become too cumbersome to be otherwise performed.

This explanation will account for some of the rules as they are ordinarily given, but by no means for all of them. It will account for those which are demonstrable by the certain laws of arithmetic, but not for those which in reality rest only upon inductive generalizations. And it can hardly be doubted that many rules of the latter description have become associated with those of the former, so that in popular estimation they have been blended into one system, of which all the separate rules are supposed to possess a similar origin and equal certainty. Hints have already been frequently given of this tendency, but the subject is one of such extreme importance that a separate chapter (that on Induction) must be devoted to its consideration.

§ 8. In establishing the validity of the above rules, we have taken as the basis of our investigations, in accordance with the general scheme of this work, the statistical frequency of the events referred to; but it was also shown that each formula, when established, might with equal propriety be expressed in the more familiar form of a fraction representing the 'chance' of the occurrence of the particular event. The question may therefore now be raised, Can those writers who (as described in the last chapter) take as the primary subject of the science not the degree of statistical frequency, but the quantity of belief, with equal consistency make this the basis of their rules, and so also regard the fraction expressive of the chance as a merely synonymous expression ? De Morgan maintains that whereas in ordinary logic we suppose the premises to be absolutely true, the province of Probability is to study 'the effect which partial belief of the premises produces with respect to the conclusion.' It would appear therefore as if in strictness we ought on this view to be able to determine this consequent diminution at first hand, from introspection of the mind, that is of the conceptions and beliefs which it entertains; instead of making any recourse to statistics to tell us how much we ought to believe the conclusion.

Any readers who have concurred with me in the general results of the last chapter, will naturally agree in the conclusion that nothing deserving the name of logical science can be extracted from any results of appeal to our consciousness as to the quantity of belief we entertain of this or that proposition. Suppose, for example, that one person in 100 dies on the sea passage out to India, and that one in 9 dies during a 5 years residence there. It would commonly be said that the chance that any one, who is now going out, has of living to start homewards 5 years hence, is $\frac{88}{100}$; for his chance of getting there is $\frac{99}{100}$; and of his surviving, if he gets there, $\frac{8}{9}$; hence the result or dependent event is got by multiplying these fractions together, which gives $\frac{88}{100}$. Here the real basis of the reasoning is statistical, and the processes or results are merely translated afterwards into fractions. But can we say the same when we look at the belief side of

the question ? I quite admit the psychological fact that we
have degrees of belief, more or less corresponding to the
frequency of the events to which they refer. In the above example, for instance, we should undoubtedly admit on enquiry
that our belief in the man's return was affected by each of
the risks in question, so that we had less expectation of it
than if he were subject to either risk separately ; that is, we
should in some way compound the risks. But what I cannot
recognise is that we should be able to perform the process
with any approach to accuracy without appeal to the statistics, or that, even supposing we could do so, we should
have any guarantee of the correctness of the result without similar appeal. It appears to me in fact that but little
meaning, and certainly no security, can be attained by so
regarding the process of inference. The probabilities expressed as degrees of belief, just as those which are expressed
as fractions, must, when we are put upon our justification,
first be translated into their corresponding facts of statistical
frequency of occurrence of the events, and then the inferences must be drawn and justified there. This part of
the operation, as we have already shown, is mostly carried
on by the ordinary rules of arithmetic. When we have
obtained our conclusion we may, if we please, translate it
back again into the subjective form, just as we can and do
for convenience into the fractional, but I do not see how the
process of inference can be conceived as taking place in that
form, and still less how any proof of it can thus be given. If
therefore the process of inference be so expressed it must be
regarded as a symbolical process, symbolical of such an inference about things as has been described above, and it
therefore seems to me more advisable to state and expound
it in this latter form.

On Inverse Probability and the Rules required for it.

§ 9. It has been already stated that the only fundamental rules of inference in Probability are the two described
in §§ 2, 3, but there are of course abundance of derivative
rules, the nature and use of which are best obtained from the
study of any manual upon the subject. One class of these
derivative rules, however, is sufficiently distinct in respect of
the questions to which it may give rise, to deserve special
examination It involves the distinction commonly recognised as that between Direct and Inverse Probability. It is
thus introduced by De Morgan :—

"In the preceding chapter we have calculated the chances
of an event, knowing the circumstances under which it is to
happen or fail. We are now to place ourselves in an inverted
position : we know the event, and ask what is the probability
which results from the event in favour of any set of circumstances under which the same might have happened[1]." The
distinction might therefore be summarily described as that
between finding an effect when we are given the causes, and
finding a cause when we are given effects.

On the principles of the science involved in the definition
which was discussed and adopted in the earlier chapters of
this work, the reader will easily infer that no such distinction
as this can be regarded as fundamental. One common feature
was traced in all the objects which were to be referred to
Probability, and from this feature the possible rules of

---

[1] *Essay on Probabilities*, p. 53. I
have been reminded that in his article on Probability in the *Encyclo-*
pædia Metropolitana he has stated
that such rules involve no new principle.

inference can be immediately derived.   All other distinctions are merely those of arrangement or management.

But although the distinction is not by any means fundamental, it is nevertheless true that the practical treatment of such problems as those principally occurring in Inverse Probability, does correspond to a very serious source of ambiguity and perplexity.   The arbitrary assumptions which appear in Direct Probability are not by any means serious; but those which invade us in a large proportion of the problems offered by Inverse Probability are both serious and inevitable.

§ 10.   This will be best seen by the examination of special examples; as any, however simple, will serve our purpose, let us take the two following :—

(1)   A ball is drawn from a bag containing nine black balls and one white: what is the chance of its being the white ball ?

(2)   A ball is drawn from a bag containing ten balls, and is found to be white; what is the chance of there having been but that one white ball in the bag ?

The class of which the first example is a simple instance has been already abundantly discussed.   The interpretation of it is as follows: If balls be continually drawn and replaced, the proportion of white ones to the whole number drawn will tend towards the fraction $\frac{1}{10}$.   The contemplated action is a single one, but we view it as one of the above series; at least our opinion is formed upon that assumption. We conclude that we are going to take one of a series of events which may appear individually fortuitous, but in which, in the long run, those of a given kind are one-tenth of the whole; this kind (white) is then singled out by anticipation.   By stating that its chance is $\frac{1}{10}$, we merely mean to assert this physical fact, together with such other mental facts, emotions, inferences, &c., as may be properly associated with it.

§ 11. Have we to interpret the second example in a different way ? Here also we have a single instance, but the nature of the question would seem to decide that the only series to which it can properly be referred is the following :—Balls are continually drawn from *different* bags each containing ten, and are always found to be white ; what is ultimately the proportion of cases in which they will be found to have been taken from bags with only one white ball in them ? Now it may be readily shown[1] that time has nothing to do with the question ; omitting therefore the consideration of this element, we have for the two series from which our opinions in these two examples respectively are to be formed :—(1) balls of different colours presented to us in a given ultimate ratio ; (2) bags with different contents similarly presented. From these data respectively we have to assign their due weight to our anticipations of (1) a white ball ; (2) a bag containing but one white ball. So stated the problems would appear to be formally identical.

When, however, we begin the practical work of solving them we perceive a most important distinction.   In the first example there is not much that is arbitrary ; balls would under such circumstance really come out more or less accurately in the proportion expected.   Moreover, in case it should be objected that it is difficult to prove that they will do so, it does not seem an unfair demand to say that the balls are to be ' well-mixed ' or ' fairly distributed,' or to introduce any of the other conditions by which, under the semblance of judging *à priori*, we take care to secure our prospect of a

---

[1] This point will be fully discussed in a future chapter, after the general stand-point of an objective system of logic has been explained and illustrated.

series of the desired kind. But we cannot say the same in the case of the second example.

§ 12. The line of proof by which it is generally attempted to solve the second example is of this kind;—It is shown that there being one white ball for certain in the bag, the only possible antecedents are of ten kinds, viz. bags, each of which contains ten balls, but in which the white balls range respectively from one to ten in number. This of course imposes limits upon the kind of terms to be found in our series. But we want more than such limitations, we must know the proportions in which these terms are ultimately found to arrange themselves in the series. Now this requires an experience about bags which may not, and indeed in a large proportion of similar cases, cannot, be given to us. If therefore we are to solve the question at all we must make an assumption; let us make the following;—*that each of the bags described above occurs equally often,*—and see what follows. The bags being drawn from equally often, it does not follow that they will each yield equal numbers of white balls. On the contrary they will, as in the last example, yield them in direct proportion to the number of such balls which they contain. The bag with one white and nine black will yield a white ball once in ten times; that with two white, twice; and so on. The result of this, it will be easily seen, is that in 100 drawings there will be obtained on the average 55 white balls and 45 black. Now with those drawings that do not yield white balls we have, by the question, nothing to do, for that question postulated the drawing of a white ball as an accomplished fact. The series we want is therefore composed of those which do yield white. Now what is the additional attribute which is found in some members, and in some members only, of this series, and which we mentally anticipate? Clearly it is the attribute of having been drawn from a bag which only contained one of these white balls.   Of these there is, out of the 55 drawings, but one.   Accordingly the required chance is $\frac{1}{55}$.   That is to say, the white ball will have been drawn from the bag containing only that one white, once in 55 times.

§ 13.   Now, with the exception of the passage in italics, the process here is precisely the same as in the other example ; it is somewhat longer only because we are not able to appeal immediately to experience, but are forced to try to deduce what the result will be, though the validity of this deduction itself rests, of course, ultimately upon experience. But the above passage is a very important one.   It is scarcely necessary to point out how arbitrary it is.

For *is* the supposition, that the different specified kinds of bags are equally likely, the most reasonable supposition under the circumstances in question ?   One man may think it is, another may take a contrary view.   In fact in an excellent manual[1] upon the subject a totally different supposition is made, at any rate in one example ; it is taken for granted in that instance, not that every possible number of black and white balls respectively is equally likely, but that every possible way of getting each number is equally likely, whence it follows that bags with an intermediate number of black and white balls are far more likely than those with an extreme number of either.   On this supposition five black and five white being obtainable in 252 ways against the ten ways of obtaining one white and nine black, it follows that the chance that we have drawn from a bag of the latter description is much less than on the hypothesis first made.   The chance, in fact, becomes now $\frac{1}{512}$ instead of $\frac{1}{55}$.   In the one case each distinct result is considered

[1] Whitworth's *Choice and Chance*, Ed. II., p. 123.   See also Boole's *Laws of Thought*, p. 370.

equally likely, in the other every distinct way of getting each result.

§ 14. Uncertainties of this kind are peculiarly likely to arise in these inverse probabilities, because when we are merely given an effect and told to look out for the chance of some assigned cause, we are often given no clue as to the relative prevalence of these causes, but are left to determine them on general principles. Give us either their actual prevalence in statistics, or the conditions by which such prevalence is brought about, and we know what to do; but without the help of such data we are reduced to guessing. In the above example, if we had been told how the bag had been originally filled, that is by what process, or under what circumstances, we should have known what to do. If it had been filled at random from a box containing equal numbers of black and white balls, the supposition in Mr Whitworth's example is the most reasonable; but in the absence of any such information as this we are entirely in the dark, and the supposition made in § 12 is neither more nor less trustworthy and reasonable than many others, though it doubtless possesses the merit of superior simplicity[1]. If the reader will recur to Ch. v. §§ 4, 5, he will find this particular difficulty fully explained. Everybody practically admits that a certain characteristic arrangement or distribution has to be introduced at some prior stage; and that, as soon as this stage has been selected, there are no further theoretic difficulties to be encountered. But when we come to decide, in examples of the class in question, at what stage it is most reasonable

---

[1] Opinions differ about the defence of such suppositions, as they do about the nature of them. Some writers, admitting the above assumption to be doubtful, call it the most impartial hypothesis. Others regard it as a sort of mean hypothesis.

to make our postulate, we are often left without any very definite or rational guidance.

§ 15. When, however, we take what may be called, by comparison with the above purely artificial examples, instances presented by nature, much of this uncertainty will disappear, and then all real distinction between direct and inverse probability will often vanish. In such cases the causes are mostly determined by tolerably definite rules, instead of being a mere cloud-land of capricious guesses. We may either find their relative frequency of occurrence by reference to tables, or may be able to infer it by examination of the circumstances under which they are brought about. Almost any simple example would then serve to illustrate the fact that under such circumstances the distinction between direct and inverse probability disappears altogether, or merely resolves itself into one of *time*, which, as will be more fully shown in a future chapter, is entirely foreign to our subject.

It is not of course intended to imply that difficulties similar to those mentioned above do not occasionally invade us here also. As already mentioned, they are, if not inherent in the subject, at any rate almost unavoidable in comparison with the simpler and more direct procedure of determining what is likely to follow from assigned conditions. What is meant is that so long as we confine ourselves within the comparatively regular and uniform field of natural sequences and coexistences, statistics of causes may be just as readily available as those of effects. There will not be much more that is arbitrary in the one than in the other. But of course this security is lost when, as will be almost immediately noticed, what may be called metaphysical rather than natural causes are introduced into the enquiry.

For instance, it is known that in London about 20 people

die per thousand each year. Suppose it also known that of every 100 deaths there are about 4 attributable to bronchitis. The odds therefore against any unknown person dying of bronchitis in a given year are 1249 to 1. Exactly the same statistics are available to solve the inverse problem :—A man is dead, what is the chance that he died of bronchitis ? Here, since the man's death is taken for granted, we do not require to know the general average mortality. All that we want is the proportional mortality from the disease in question as given above. If Probability dealt only with inferences founded in this way upon actual statistics, and these tolerably extensive, it is scarcely likely that any distinction such as this between direct and inverse problems would ever have been drawn.

§ 16. Considered therefore as a contribution to the theory of the subject, the distinction between Direct and Inverse Probability must be abandoned. When the appropriate statistics are at hand the two classes of problems become identical in method of treatment, and when they are not we have no more right to extract a solution in one case than in the other. The discussion however may serve to direct renewed attention to another and far more important distinction. It will remind us that there is one class of examples to which the calculus of Probability is rightfully applied, because statistical data are all we have to judge by ; whereas there are other examples in regard to which, if we will insist upon making use of these rules, we may either be deliberately abandoning the opportunity of getting far more trustworthy information by other means, or we may be obtaining solutions about matters on which the human intellect has no right to any definite quantitative opinion.

§ 17. The nearest approach to any practical justification of such judgments that I remember to have seen is afforded

by cases of which the following example is a specimen:—
" Of 10 cases treated by Lister's method, 7 did well and 3
suffered from blood-poisoning: of 14 treated with ordinary
dressings, 9 did well and 5 had blood-poisoning; what are
the odds that the success of Lister's method was due to
chance ?[1]". Or, to put it into other words, a short experience
has shown an actual superiority in one method over the
other: what are the chances that an indefinitely long experience, under similar conditions, will confirm this superiority ?

The proposer treated this as a ' bag and balls' problem,
analogous to the following: 10 balls from one bag gave
7 white and 3 black, 14 from another bag gave 9 white and
5 black: what is the chance that the actual ratio of white to
black balls was greater in the former than in the latter ?—
this actual ratio being of course considered a true indication
of what would be the ultimate proportions of white and black
drawings.   This seems to me to be the only reasonable way
of treating the problem, if it is to be considered capable of
numerical solution at all.

Of course the inevitable assumption has to be made here
about the equal prevalence of the different possible kinds of
bag,—or, as the supporters of the justice of the calculation
would put it, of the obligation to assume the equal *à priori*
likelihood of each kind,—but I think that in this particular
example the arbitrariness of the assumption is less than
usual.   This is because the problem discusses simply a
balance between two extremely similar cases, and there is a
certain set-off against each other of the objectionable assump-

---

[1] *Educational Times;* Reprint, Vol.
xxxvii. p. 40. The question was
proposed by Dr Macalister and gave
rise to considerable controversy. As
usual with problems of this inverse
kind hardly any two of the writers
were in agreement as to the assumptions to be made, or therefore as to
the numerical estimate of the odds.

tions on each side. Had *one* set of experiments only been
proposed, and had we been asked to evaluate the probability
of continued repetition of them confirming their verdict, I
should have felt all the scruples I have already mentioned.
But here we have got two sets of experiments carried on
under almost exactly similar circumstances, and there is
therefore less arbitrariness in assuming that their unknown
conditions are tolerably equally prevalent.

§ 18. Examples of the description commonly introduced
seem objectionable enough, but if we wish to realize to its
full extent the vagueness of some of the problems submitted to this Inverse Probability, we have not far to seek. In
natural as in artificial examples, where statistics are unattainable the enquiry becomes utterly hopeless, and all attempts
at laying down rules for calculation must be abandoned.
Take, for instance, the question which has given rise to some
discussion[1], whether such and such groups of stars are or are
not to be regarded as the results of an accidental distribution ; or the still wider and vaguer question, whether such and
such things, or say the world itself, have been produced by
chance ?

In cases of this kind the insuperable difficulty is in determining what sense exactly is to be attached to the words
' accidental ' and ' random ' which enter into the discussion.
Some account was given, in the fourth chapter, of their
scientific and conventional meaning in Probability. There
seem to be the same objections to generalizing them out of
such relation, as there is in metaphysics to talking of the
Infinite or the Absolute. Infinite magnitude, or infinite

[1] See Todhunter's *History*, pp.
333, 4.

There is an interesting discussion
upon this question by the late J. D.
Forbes in a paper in the *Philosophical Magazine* for Dec. 1850. It was
replied to in a subsequent number by
Prof. Donkin.

power, one can to some extent comprehend, or at least one may understand what is being talked about, but '*the* infinite' seems to me a term devoid of meaning. So of anything supposed to have been produced at random: tell us the nature of the agency, the limits of its randomness and so on, and we can venture upon the problem, but without such data we know not what to do. The further consideration of such a problem might, I think, without arrogance be relegated to the Chapter on Fallacies. Accordingly any further remarks which I have to make upon the subject will be found there, and at the conclusion of the chapter on Causation and Design.

CHAPTER VIII.

THE RULE OF SUCCESSION[1].

§ 1. In the last chapter we discussed at some length the nature of the kinds of inference in Probability which correspond to those termed, in Logic, immediate and mediate inferences. We ascertained what was the meaning of saying, for example, that the chance of any given man A. B. dying in a year is $\frac{1}{3}$, when concluded from the general proposition that one man out of three in his circumstances dies. We also discussed the nature and evidence of rules of a more completely inferential character. But to stop at this point would be to take a very imperfect view of the subject. If Probability is a science of real inference about things, it must surely lead up to something more than such merely formal conclusions; we must be able, if not by means of it, at any rate by some means, to step beyond the limits of what has been actually observed, and to draw conclusions about what is as yet unobserved. This leads at once to the question, What is the connection of Probability with Induction? This is a question into which it will be necessary to enter now with some minuteness.

That there is a close connection between Probability and Induction, must have been observed by almost every one

---

[1] A word of apology may be offered here for the introduction of a new name. The only other alternative would have been to entitle the rule one of *Induction*. But such a title I cannot admit, for reasons which will be almost immediately explained.

who has treated of either subject; I have not however seen any account of this connection that seemed to me to be satisfactory.   An explicit description of it should rather be sought in treatises upon the narrower subject, Probability; but it is precisely here that the most confusion is to be found.   The province of Probability being somewhat narrow, incursions have been constantly made from it into the adjacent territory of Induction.   In this way, amongst the arithmetical rules discussed in the last chapter, others have been frequently introduced which ought not in strictness to be classed with them, as they rest on an entirely different basis.

§ 2.   The origin of such confusion is easy of explanation; it arises, doubtless, from the habit of laying undue stress upon the *subjective* side of Probability, upon that which treats of the quantity of our belief upon different subjects and the variations of which that quantity is susceptible.   It has been already urged that this variation of belief is at most but a constant accompaniment of what is really essential to Probability, and is moreover common to other subjects as well.   By defining the science therefore from this side these other subjects would claim admittance into it; some of these, as Induction, have been accepted, but others have been somewhat arbitrarily rejected.   Our belief in a wider proposition gained by Induction is, prior to verification, not so strong as that of the narrower generalization from which it is inferred.   This being observed, a so-called rule of probability has been given by which it is supposed that this diminution of assent could in many instances be calculated.

But *time* also works changes in our conviction; our belief in the happening of almost every event, if we recur to it long afterwards, when the evidence has faded from the mind, is

less strong than it was at the time. Why are not rules of
oblivion inserted in treatises upon Probability? If a man is
told how firmly he ought to expect the tide to rise again,
because it has already risen ten times, might he not also ask
for a rule which should tell him how firm should be his belief
of an event which rests upon a ten years' recollection?[1] The
infractions of a rule of this latter kind could scarcely be more
numerous and extensive, as we shall see presently, than those
of the former confessedly are. The fact is that the agencies,
by which the strength of our conviction is modified, are so
indefinitely numerous that they cannot all be assembled into
one science; for purposes of definition therefore the quantity
of belief had better be omitted from consideration, or at any
rate regarded as a mere appendage, and the science, defined
from the other or statistical side of the subject, in which,
as has been shown, a tolerably clear boundary-line can be
traced.

§ 3. Induction, however, from its importance does merit
a separate discussion; a single example will show its bearing
upon this part of our subject. We are considering the prospect of a given man, A.B. living another year, and we find
that nine out of ten men of his age do survive. In forming
an opinion about his surviving, however, we shall find that
there are in reality two very distinct causes which aid in
determining the strength of our conviction; distinct, but in
practice so intimately connected that we are very apt to
overlook one, and attribute the effect entirely to the other.

(I) There is that which strictly belongs to Probability;

---

[1] John Craig, in his often named
work, *Theologiæ Christianæ Prin-
cipia Mathematica* (Lond. 1699) attempted something in this direction
when he proposed to solve such
problems as:—Quando evanescet pro-
babilitas cujusvis Historiæ, cujus sub-
jectum est transiens, vivâ tantum
voce transmissæ, determinare.

that which (as was explained in Chap. VI.) measures our belief of the individual case as deduced from the general proposition. Granted that nine men out of ten of the kind to which A. B. belongs do live another year, it obviously does not follow at all necessarily that *he* will. We describe this state of things by saying, that our belief of his surviving is diminished from certainty in the ratio of 10 to 9, or, in other words, is measured by the fraction $\frac{9}{10}$.

(II) But are we certain that nine men out of ten like him *will* live another year? we know that they have so survived in time past, but will they continue to do so? Since A. B. is still alive it is plain that this proposition is to a certain extent assumed, or rather obtained by Induction. We cannot however be as certain of the inductive inference as we are of the data from which it was inferred. Here, therefore, is a second cause which tends to diminish our belief; in practice these two causes always accompany each other, but in thought they can be separated.

The two distinct causes described above are very liable to be confused together, and the class of cases from which examples are necessarily for the most part drawn increases this liability. The step from the statement 'all men have died in a certain proportion' to the inference 'they will continue to die in that proportion' is so slight a step that it is unnoticed, and the diminution of conviction that should accompany it is unsuspected. In what are called *à priori* examples the step is still slighter. We feel so certain about the permanence of the laws of mechanics, that few people would think of regarding it as an inference when they believe that a die will in the long run turn up all its faces equally often, because other dice have done so in time past.

§ 4. It has been already pointed out (in Chapter VI.)

that, so far as concerns that definition of Probability which
regards it as the science which discusses the degree and
modifications of our belief, the question at issue seems to be
simply this:—Are the causes alluded to above in (II) capable
of being reduced to one simple coherent scheme, so that any
universal rules for the modification of assent can be obtained
from them ?   If they are, strong grounds will have been
shown for classing them with (I), in other words, for considering them as rules of probability.   Even then they
would be rules practically of a very different kind, contingent instead of necessary (if one may use these terms without committing oneself to any philosophical system), but this
objection might perhaps be overruled by the greater simplicity secured by classing them together.   This view is, with
various modifications, generally adopted by writers on Probability, or at least, as I understand the matter, implied by
their methods of definition and treatment.   Or, on the other
hand, must these causes be regarded as a vast system, one
might almost say a chaos, of perfectly distinct agencies;
which may indeed be classified and arranged to some extent,
but from which we can never hope to obtain any rules of
perfect generality which shall not be subject to constant
exception ?   If so, but one course is left; to exclude them
all alike from Probability.   In other words, we must assume
the general proposition, viz. that which has been described
throughout as our starting-point, to be given to us; it may
be obtained by any of the numerous rules furnished by
Induction, or it may be inferred deductively, or given by our
own observation; its value may be diminished by its depending upon the testimony of witnesses, or its being recalled by
our own memory.   Its real value may be influenced by
these causes or any combinations of them; but all these are
preliminary questions with which we have nothing directly

to do.   We assume our statistical proposition to be true, neglecting the diminution of its value by the process of attainment; we take it up first at this point and then apply our rules to it.   We receive it in fact, if one may use the expression, *ready-made*, and ask no questions about the process or completeness of its manufacture.

§ 5.   It is not to be supposed, of course, that any writers have seriously attempted to reduce to one system of calculation all the causes mentioned above, and to embrace in one formula the diminution of certainty to which the inclusion of them subjects us.   But on the other hand, they have been unwilling to restrain themselves from all appeal to them. From an early period in the study of the science attempts have been made to proceed, by the Calculus of Probability, from the observed cases to adjacent and similar cases.   In practice, as has been already said, it is not possible to avoid some extension of this kind.   But it should be observed. that in these instances the divergence from the strict ground of experience is not in reality recognized, at least not as a part of our logical procedure.   We have, it is true, wandered somewhat beyond it, and so obtained a wider proposition than our data strictly necessitated, and therefore one of less certainty.   Still we assume the conclusion given by induction to be equally certain with the data, or rather omit all notice of the divergence from consideration.   It is assumed that the unexamined instances will resemble the examined, an assumption for which abundant warrant may exist; the theory of the calculation rests upon the supposition that there will be no difference between them, and the practical error is insignificant simply because this difference is small.

§ 6.   But the rule we are now about to discuss, and which may be called the Rule of Succession, is of a very different kind.   It not only recognizes the fact that we are

leaving the ground of past experience, but takes the consequences of this divergence as the express subject of its calculation.   It professes to give a general rule for the measure of
expectation that we should have of the reappearance of a
phenomenon that has been already observed any number of
times.   This rule is generally stated somewhat as follows:
"To find the chance of the recurrence of an event already
observed, divide the number of times the event has been
observed, increased by one, by the same number increased
by two."

§ 7.   It will be instructive to point out the origin of
this rule; if only to remind the reader of the necessity of
keeping mathematical formulæ to their proper province,
and to show what astonishing conclusions are apt to
be accepted on the supposed warrant of mathematics.
Revert then to the example of Inverse Probability on p.
182. We saw that under certain assumptions, it would
follow that when a single white ball had been drawn
from a bag known to contain 10 balls which were white
or black, the chance could be determined that there was
only one white ball in it.   Having done this we readily
calculate 'directly' the chance that this white ball will
be drawn next time.   Similarly we can reckon the chances
of there being two, three, &c. up to ten white balls in it,
and determine on each of these suppositions the chance
of a white ball being drawn next time.   Adding these
together we have the answer to the question:—a white
ball has been drawn once from a bag known to contain
ten balls, white or black; what is the chance of a second
time drawing a white ball?

So far only arithmetic is required.   For the next step we
need higher mathematics, and by its aid we solve this
problem:—A white ball has been drawn m times from a

bag which contains any number, we know not what, of
balls each of which is white or black, find the chance of
the next drawing also yielding a white ball. The answer is

$$\frac{m+1}{m+2}.$$

Thus far mathematics. Then comes in the physical
assumption that the universe may be likened to such a bag
as the above, in the sense that the above rule may be
applied to solve this question:—an event has been observed
to happen m times in a certain way, find the chance that
it will happen in that way next time. Laplace, for instance,
has pointed out that at the date of the writing of his *Essai
Philosophique*, the odds in favour of the sun's rising again
(on the old assumption as to the age of the world) were
1,826,214 to 1. De Morgan says that a man who standing
on the bank of a river has seen ten ships pass by with flags
should judge it to be 11 to 1 that the next ship will also
carry a flag.

§ 8. It is hard to take such a rule as this seriously, for
there does not seem to be even that moderate confirmation
of it which we shall find to hold good in the case of the
application of abstract formulæ to the estimation of the
evidence of witnesses. If however its validity is to be discussed there appear to be two very distinct lines of enquiry
along which we may be led.

(1) In the first place we may take it for what it professes to be, and for what it is commonly understood to
be, viz. a rule which assigns the measure of expectation
we ought to entertain of the recurrence of the event under
the circumstances in question. Of course, on the view
adopted in this work, we insist on enquiring whether it is
really true that on the average events do thus repeat their
performance in accordance with this law. Thus tested, no

one surely would attempt to defend such a formula. So
far from past occurrence being a ground for belief in future
recurrence, there are (as will be more fully pointed out
in the Chapter on Fallacies) plenty of cases in which the
direct contrary holds good. Then again a rule of this kind
is subject to the very serious perplexity to be explained
in our next chapter, arising out of the necessary arbitrariness
of such inverse reference. That is, when an event has
happened but a few times, we have no certain guide; and
when it has happened but once [1], we have no guide whatever,
as to the class of cases to which it is to be referred. In
the example above, about the flags, why did we stop short at
this notion simply, instead of specifying the size, shape, &c.
of the flags?

De Morgan, it must be remembered, only accepts this
rule in a qualified sense. He regards it as furnishing a
minimum value for the amount of our expectation. He
terms it "the rule of probability of a *pure induction,*" and
says of it, "The probabilities shown by the above rules
are merely *minima* which may be augmented by other
sources of knowledge." That is, he recognizes only those
instances in which our belief in the Uniformity of Nature
and in the existence of special laws of causation comes in

[1] When $m=1$ the fraction becomes
$\frac{2}{3}$; *i.e.* the odds are 2 to 1 in favour
of recurrence. And there are writers
who accept this result. For instance,
Jevons (*Principles of Science* p. 258)
says "Thus on the first occasion on
which a person sees a shark, and
notices that it is accompanied by a
little pilot fish, the odds are 2 to 1
that the next shark will be so accompanied." To say nothing of the fact
that recognizing and naming the fish
implies that they have often been
seen before, how many of the observed characteristics of that single
'event' are to be considered essential?
Must the pilot precede; and at the
same distance? Must we consider
the latitude, the ocean, the season,
the species of shark, as matter also
of repetition on the next occasion?
and so on. I cannot see how the
Inductive problem can be even in-
telligibly stated, for quantitative
purposes, on the first occurrence of
any event.

to supplement that which arises from the mere frequency
of past occurrence. This however does not meet those cases
in which past occurrence is a positive ground of disbelief in
future recurrence.

§ 9. (2) There is however another and very different
view which might be taken of such a rule. It is one, an
obscure recognition of which has very likely had much to
do with the acceptance which the rule has received.

What we might suppose ourselves to be thus expressing
is,—not the measure of rational expectation which might be
held by minds sufficiently advanced to be able to classify
and to draw conscious inferences, but,—the law according to
which the primitive elements of belief were started and
developed. Of course such an interpretation as this would
be equivalent to quitting the province of Logic altogether
and crossing over into that of Psychology; but it would be a
perfectly valid line of enquiry. We should be attempting
nothing more than a development of the researches of
Fechner and his followers in psycho-physical measurement.
Only then we ought, like them, not to start with any analogy
of a ballot box and its contents, but to base our enquiry
on careful determination of the actual mental phenomena
experienced. We know how the law has been determined
in accordance with which the intensity of the feeling of
light varies with that of its objective source. We see how it
is possible to measure the growth of *memory* according to
the number of repetitions of a sentence or a succession
of mere syllables. In this latter case, for instance, we just
try experiments, and determine how much better a man can
remember any utterances after eight hearings than after
seven[1].

---

[1] See in *Mind* (x. 454) Mr Jacob's
account of the researches of Herr
Ebbinghaus as described in his work
Ueber das Gedächtniss.

Now this case furnishes a very close parallel to our supposed attempt to measure the increase of intensity of belief after repeated recurrence. That is, if it were possible to experiment in this order of mental phenomena, we ought simply to repeat a phenomenon a certain number of times and then ascertain by actual introspection or by some simple test, how fast the belief was increasing. Thus viewed the problem seems to me a hopeless one. The difficulties are serious enough, when we are trying to measure our simple sensations, of laying aside the effects of past training, and of attempting, as it were, to leave the mind open and passive to mere reception of stimuli. But if we were to attempt in this way to measure our belief these difficulties would become quite insuperable. We can no more divest ourselves of past training here than we can of intelligence or thought. I do not see how any one could possibly avoid classing the observed recurrences with others which he had experienced, and of being thus guided by special analogies and inductions instead of trusting solely to De Morgan's 'pure induction'. The same considerations tend to rebut another form of defence for the rule in question. It is urged, for instance, that we may at least resort to it in those cases in which we are in entire ignorance as to the number and nature of the antecedents. This is a position to which I can hardly conceive it possible that we should ever be reduced. However remote or exceptional may be the phenomenon selected we may yet bring it into relation with some accepted generalizations and thus draw our conclusions from these rather than from purely *à priori* considerations.

§ 10. Since then past acquisitions cannot be laid aside or allowed for, the only remaining resource would be to experiment upon the infant mind. One would not like

to pronounce that any line of enquiry is impossible; but
the difficulties would certainly be enormous. And interesting
as the facts would be, supposing that we had succeeded
in securing them, they would not be of the slightest importance in Logic. However the question were settled:—
whether, for instance, we proved that the sentiment or
emotion of belief grew up slowly and gradually from a sort
of zero point under the impress of repetition of experience;
or whether we proved that a single occurrence produced
complete belief in the repetition of the event, so that
experience gradually untaught us and weakened our convictions;—in no case would the mature mind gain any aid
as to what it ought to believe.

I cannot but think that some such view as this must
occasionally underlie the acceptance which this rule has received. For instance, Laplace, though unhesitatingly adopting it as a real, that is, objective rule of inference, has gone
into so much physiological and psychological matter towards
the end of his discussion (*Essai philosophique*) as to suggest
that what he had in view was the natural history of belief
rather than its subsequent justification.

Again, the curious doctrine adopted by Jevons, that the
principles of Induction rest entirely upon the theory of
Probability,—a very different doctrine from that which is
conveyed by saying that all knowledge of facts is *probable*
only, i.e. not necessary,—seems unintelligible except on some
such interpretation. We shall have more to say on this
subject in our next chapter. It will be enough here to
remark that in our present reflective and rational stage
we find that every inference in Probability involves some
appeal to, or support from, Induction, but that it is impossible to base either upon the other. However far back
we try to push our way, and however disposed we might be

to account for our ultimate beliefs by Association, it seems
to me that so long as we consider ourselves to be dealing
with rules of inference we must still distinguish between
Induction and Probability.

CHAPTER IX.

INDUCTION AND ITS CONNECTION WITH PROBABILITY.

§ 1. WE were occupied, during the last chapter, with the examination of a rule, the object of which was to enable us to make inferences about instances as yet unexamined It was professedly, therefore, a rule of an inductive character. But, in the form in which it is commonly expressed, it was found to fail utterly. It is reasonable therefore to enquire at this point whether Probability is entirely a formal or deductive science, or whether, on the other hand, we are able, by means of it, to make valid inferences about instances as yet unexamined. This question has been already in part answered by implication in the course of the last two chapters. It is proposed in the present chapter to devote a fuller investigation to this subject, and to describe, as minutely as limits will allow, the nature of the connection between Probability and Induction. We shall find it advisable for clearness of conception to commence our enquiry at a somewhat early stage. We will travel over the ground, however, as rapidly as possible, until we approach the boundary of what can properly be termed Probability.

§ 2. Let us then conceive some one setting to work to investigate nature, under its broadest aspect, with the view of systematizing the facts of experience that are known, and thence (in case he should find that this is possible) discover-

ing others which are at present unknown. He observes a
multitude of phenomena, physical and mental, contemporary
and successive. He enquires what connections are there
between them ? what rules can be found, so that some of
these things being observed I can infer others from them ?
We suppose him, let it be observed, deliberately resolving to
investigate the things themselves, and not to be turned
aside by any prior enquiry as to there being laws under
which the mind is compelled to judge of the things. This
may arise either from a disbelief in the existence of any
independent and necessary mental laws, and a consequent
conviction that the mind is perfectly competent to observe
and believe anything that experience offers, and should
believe nothing else, or simply from a preference for investigations of the latter kind. In other words, we suppose him
to reject Formal Logic, and to apply himself to a study of
objective existences.

It must not for a moment be supposed that we are here
doing more than conceiving a fictitious case for the purpose
of more vividly setting before the reader the nature of the
inductive process, the assumptions it has to make, and the
character of the materials to which it is applied. It is not
psychologically possible that any one should come to the study
of nature with all his mental faculties in full perfection, but
void of all materials of knowledge, and free from any bias as
to the uniformities which might be found to prevail around
him. In practice, of course, the form and the matter—the
laws of belief or association, and the objects to which they
are applied—act and react upon one another, and neither
can exist in any but a low degree without presupposing the
existence of the other. But the supposition is perfectly legitimate for the purpose of calling attention to the requirements of such a system of Logic, and is indeed nothing more

than what has to be done at almost every step in psychological enquiry[1].

§ 3. His task at first might be conceived to be a slow and tedious one. It would consist of a gradual accumulation of individual instances, as marked out from one another by various points of distinction, and connected with one another by points of resemblance. These would have to be respectively distinguished and associated in the mind, and the consequent results would then be summed up in general propositions, from which inferences could afterwards be drawn. These inferences could, of course, contain no new facts, they would only be repetitions of what he or others had previously observed. All that we should have so far done would have been to make our classifications of things and then to appeal to them again. We should therefore be keeping well within the province of ordinary logic, the processes of which (whatever their ultimate explanation) may of course always be expressed, in accordance with Aristotle's Dictum, as ways of determining whether or not we can show that one given class is included wholly or partly within another, or excluded from it, as the case may be.

§ 4. But a very short course of observation would suggest the possibility of a wide extension of his information. Experience itself would soon detect that events were connected together in a regular way; he would ascertain that there are 'laws of nature.' Coming with no *à priori* necessity of believing in them, he would soon find that as a matter

---

[1] Some of my readers may be familiar with a very striking digression in Buffon's Natural History (*Natural Hist. of Man*, § viii.), in which he supposes the first man in full possession of his faculties, but with all his experience to gain, and speculates on the gradual acquisition of his knowledge. Whatever may be thought of his particular conclusions the passage is very interesting and suggestive to any student of Psychology.

of fact they do exist, though he could not feel any certainty as to the extent of their prevalence. The discovery of this arrangement in nature would at once alter the plan of his proceedings, and set the tone to the whole range of his methods of investigation. His main work now would be to find out by what means he could best discover these laws of nature.

An illustration may assist. Suppose I were engaged in breaking up a vast piece of rock, say slate, into small pieces. I should begin by wearily working through it inch by inch. But I should soon find the process completely changed owing to the existence of *cleavage*. By this arrangement of things a very few blows would do the work—not, as I might possibly have at first supposed, to the extent of a few inches— but right through the whole mass. In other words, by the process itself of cutting, as shown in experience, and by nothing else, a constitution would be detected in the things that would make that process vastly more easy and extensive. Such a discovery would of course change our tactics. Our principal object would thenceforth be to ascertain the extent and direction of this cleavage.

Something resembling this is found in Induction. The discovery of laws of nature enables the mind to dart with its inferences from a few facts completely through a whole class of objects, and thus to acquire results the successive individual attainment of which would have involved long and wearisome investigation, and would indeed in multitudes of instances have been out of the question. We have no demonstrative proof that this state of things is universal; but having found it prevail extensively, we go on with the resolution at least to try for it everywhere else, and we are not disappointed. From propositions obtained in this way, or rather from the original facts on which these propositions rest, we can make *new* inferences, not indeed with absolute certainty, but with a degree of conviction that is of the utmost practical use. We have gained the great step of being able to make trustworthy generalizations. We conclude, for instance, not merely that John and Henry die, but that all men die.

§ 5. The above brief investigation contains, it is hoped, a tolerably correct outline of the nature of the Inductive inference, as it presents itself in Material or Scientific Logic. It involves the distinction drawn by Mill, and with which the reader of his *System of Logic* will be familiar, between an inference drawn *according* to a formula and one drawn *from* a formula. We do in reality make our inference from the data afforded by experience directly to the conclusion ; it is a mere arrangement of convenience to do so by passing through the generalization. But it is one of such extreme convenience, and one so necessarily forced upon us when we are appealing to our own past experience or to that of others for the grounds of our conclusion, that practically we find it the best plan to divide the process of inference into two parts. The first part is concerned with establishing the generalization ; the second (which contains the rules of ordinary logic) determines what conclusions can be drawn from this generalization.

§ 6. We may now see our way to ascertaining the province of Probability and its relation to kindred sciences. Inductive Logic gives rules for discovering such generalizations as those spoken of above, and for testing their correctness. If they are expressed in universal propositions it is the part of ordinary logic to determine what inferences can be made from and by them; if, on the other hand, they are expressed in proportional propositions, that is, propositions of the kind described in our first chapter, they are handed over to Probability. We find, for example, that three infants out of ten die in their first four years. It belongs to Induction to say whether we are justified in generalizing our observation into the assertion, All infants die in that proportion. When such a proposition is obtained, whatever may be the value to be assigned to it, we recognize in it a series of a familiar kind, and it is at once claimed by Probability.

In this latter case the division into two parts, the inductive and the ratiocinative, seems decidedly more than one of convenience; it is indeed imperatively necessary for clearness of thought and cogency of treatment. It is true that in almost every example that can be selected we shall find both of the above elements existing together and combining to determine the degree of our conviction, but when we come to examine them closely it appears to me that the grounds of their cogency, the kind of conviction they produce, and consequently the rules which they give rise to, are so entirely distinct that they cannot possibly be harmonized into a single consistent system.

The opinion therefore according to which certain Inductive formulæ are regarded as composing a portion of Probability, and which finds utterance in the Rule of Succession criticised in our last chapter, cannot, I think, be maintained. It would be more correct to say, as stated above, that Induction is quite distinct from Probability, yet co-operates in almost all its inferences. By Induction we determine, for example, whether, and how far, we can safely generalize the proposition that four men in ten live to be fifty-six; supposing such a proposition to be safely generalized, we hand it over to Probability to say what sort of inferences can be deduced from it.

§ 7. So much then for the opinion which tends to regard pure Induction as a subdivision of Probability. By the majority of philosophical and logical writers a widely different view has of course been entertained. They are mostly disposed to distinguish these sciences very sharply from, not to say to contrast them with, one another; the one being accepted as philosophical or logical, and the other rejected as mathematical. This may without offence be termed the popular prejudice against Probability.

A somewhat different view, however, must be noticed here, which, by a sort of reaction against the latter, seems even to go beyond the former; and which occasionally finds expression in the statement that all inductive reasoning of every kind is merely a matter of Probability. Two examples of this may be given.

Beginning with the older authority, there is an often quoted saying by Butler at the commencement of his *Analogy*, that 'probability is the very guide of life'; a saying which seems frequently to be understood to signify that the rules or principles of Probability are thus all-prevalent when we are drawing conclusions in practical life. Judging by the drift of the context, indeed, this seems a fair interpretation of his meaning, in so far of course as there could be said to be any such thing as a science of Probability in those days. Prof. Jevons, in his *Principles of Science* (p. 197), has expressed a somewhat similar view, of course in a way more consistent with the principles of modern science, physical and mathematical. He says, " I am convinced that it is impossible to expound the methods of induction in a sound manner, without resting them on the theory of Probability. Perfect knowledge alone can give certainty, and in nature perfect knowledge would be infinite knowledge, which is clearly beyond our capacities. We have, therefore, to content ourselves with partial knowledge,— knowledge mingled with ignorance, producing doubt[1]."

[1] See also Dugald Stewart (Ed. by Hamilton; VII. pp. 115—119).

§ 8.   There are two senses in which this disposition to
merge the two sciences into one may be understood.   Using
the word Probability in its vague popular signification,
nothing more may be intended than to call attention to the
fact, that in every case alike our conclusions are nothing
more than 'probable,' that is, that they are not, and cannot
be, absolutely certain.   This must be fully admitted, for of
course no one acquainted with the complexity of physical
and other evidence would seriously maintain that absolute
ideal certainty can be attained in any branch of applied
logic.   Hypothetical certainty, in abstract science, may be
possible, but not absolute certainty in the domain of the
concrete.   This has been already noticed in a former chapter,
where, however, it was pointed out that whatever justification may exist, on the subjective view of logic, for regarding
this common prevalence of absence of certainty as warranting
us in fusing the sciences into one, no such justification is
admitted when we take the objective view.

§ 9.   What may be meant, however, is that the *grounds*
of this absence of certainty are always of the same general
character.   This argument, if admitted, would have real
force, and must therefore be briefly noticed.   We have seen
abundantly that when we say of a conclusion within the
strict province of Probability, that it is not certain, all that
we mean is that in some proportion of cases only will such
conclusion be right, in the other cases it will be wrong.
Now when we say, in reference to any inductive conclusion,
that we feel uncertain about its absolute cogency, are we
conscious of the same interpretation ?   It seems to me that
we are not.   It is indeed quite possible that on ultimate
analysis it might be proved that experience of failure in
the past employment of our methods of investigation was
the main cause of our present want of perfect confidence in

them. But this, as we have repeatedly insisted, does not belong to the province of logical, but to that of Psychological enquiry. It is surely not the case that we are, as a rule, consciously guided by such occasional or repeated instances of past failure. In so far as they are at all influential, they seem to do their work by infusing a vague want of confidence which cannot be referred to any statistical grounds for its justification, at least not in a quantitative way. Part of our want of confidence is derived sympathetically from those who have investigated the matter more nearly at first hand. Here again, analysis might detect that a given proportion of past failures lay at the root of the distrust, but it does not show at the surface. Moreover, one reason why we cannot feel perfectly certain about our inductions is, that the *memory* has to be appealed to for some of our data; and will any one assert that the only reason why we do not place absolute reliance on our memory of events long past is that we have been deceived in that way before?

In any other sense, therefore, than as a needful protest against attaching too great demonstrative force to the conclusions of Inductive Logic, it seems decidedly misleading to speak of its reasonings as resting upon Probability.

§ 10. We may now see clearly the reasons for the limits within which causation[1] is necessarily required, but beyond which it is not needed. To be able to generalize a formula so as to extend it from the observed to the unobserved, it is clearly essential that there should be a certain permanence in the order of nature; this permanence is one form of what is implied in the term causation. If the

---

[1] Required that is for purposes of logical inference within the limits of Probability; it is not intended to imply any doubts as to its actual universal prevalence, or its all-importance for scientific purposes. The subject is more fully discussed in a future chapter.

circumstances under which men live and die remaining the same, we did not feel warranted in inferring that four men out of ten would continue to live to fifty, because in the case of those whom we had observed this proportion had hitherto done so, it is clear that we should be admitting that the same antecedents need not be followed by the same consequents. This uniformity being what the Law of Causation asserts, the truth of the law is clearly necessary to enable us to obtain our generalizations: in other words, it is necessary for the Inductive part of the process. But it seems to be equally clear that causation is not necessary for that part of the process which belongs to Probability. Provided only that the truth of our generalizations is secured to us, in the way just mentioned, what does it matter to us whether or not the individual members are subject to causation? For it is not in reality about these individuals that we make inferences. As this last point has been already fully treated in Chapter VI., any further allusion to it need not be made here.

§ 11. The above description, or rather indication, of the process of obtaining these generalizations must suffice for the present. Let us now turn and consider the means by which we are practically to make use of them when they are obtained. The point which we had reached in the course of the investigations entered into in the sixth and seventh chapters was this:—Given a series of a certain kind, we could draw inferences about the members which composed it; inferences, that is, of a peculiar kind, the value and meaning of which were fully discussed in their proper place.

We must now shift our point of view a little; instead of starting, as in the former chapters, with a determinate series supposed to be given to us, let us assume that the individual only is given, and that the work is imposed upon us of finding out the appropriate series. How are we to set about the

task ?   In the former case our data were of this kind:—
Eight out of ten men, aged fifty, will live eleven years more,
and we ascertained in what sense, and with what certainty,
we could infer that, say, John Smith, aged fifty, would live
to sixty-one.

§ 12.   Let us then suppose, instead, that John Smith
presents himself, how should we in this case set about obtaining a series for him ?   In other words, how should we
collect the appropriate statistics ?   It should be borne in
mind that when we are attempting to make real inferences
about things as yet unknown, it is in this form that the
problem will practically present itself.

At first sight the answer to this question may seem to be
obtained by a very simple process, viz. by counting how
many men of the age of John Smith, respectively do and do
not live for eleven years.   In reality however the process is
far from being so simple as it appears.   For it must be remembered that each individual thing has not one distinct
and appropriate class or group, to which, and to which alone,
it properly belongs.   We may indeed be practically in the
habit of considering it under such a single aspect, and it may
therefore seem to us more familiar when it occupies a place
in one series rather than in another; but such a practice is
merely customary on our part, not obligatory.   It is obvious
that every individual thing or event has an indefinite
number of properties or attributes observable in it, and
might therefore be considered as belonging to an indefinite
number of different classes of things.   By belonging to any
one class it of course becomes at the same time a member of
all the higher classes, the genera, of which that class was a
species.   But, moreover, by virtue of each accidental attribute which it possesses, it becomes a member of a class
intersecting, so to say, some of the other classes.   John Smith

is a consumptive man say, and a native of a northern climate.
Being a man he is of course included in the class of vertebrates, also in that of animals, as well as in any higher
such classes that there may be. The property of being consumptive refers him to another class, narrower than any of
the above; whilst that of being born in a northern climate
refers him to a new and distinct class, not conterminous with
any of the rest, for there are things born in the north which
are not men.

§ 13. When therefore John Smith presents himself to
our notice without, so to say, any particular label attached to
him informing us under which of his various aspects he is to
be viewed, the process of thus referring him to a class becomes to a great extent arbitrary. If he had been indicated
to us by a general name, that, of course, would have been
some clue; for the name having a determinate connotation
would specify at any rate a fixed group of attributes within
which our selection was to be confined. But names and
attributes being connected together, we are here supposed
to be just as much in ignorance what name he is to be
called by, as what group out of all his innumerable attributes
is to be taken account of; for to tell us one of these things
would be precisely the same in effect as to tell us the other.
In saying that it is thus arbitrary under which class he is
placed, we mean, of course, that there are no logical grounds
of decision; the selection must be determined by some extraneous considerations. Mere inspection of the individual
would simply show us that he could equally be referred
to an indefinite number of classes, but would in itself give
no inducement to prefer, for our special purpose, one of these
classes to another.

This variety of classes to which the individual may be
referred owing to his possession of a multiplicity of attri-

butes, has an important bearing on the process of inference which was indicated in the earlier sections of this chapter, and which we must now examine in more special reference to our particular subject.

§ 14. It will serve to bring out more clearly the nature of some of those peculiarities of the step which we are now about to take in the case of Probability, if we first examine the form which the corresponding step assumes in the case of ordinary Logic. Suppose then that we wished to ascertain whether a certain John Smith, a man of thirty, who is amongst other things a resident in India, and distinctly affected with cancer, will continue to survive there for twenty years longer. The terms in which the man is thus introduced to us refer him to different classes in the way already indicated. Corresponding to these classes there will be a number of propositions which have been obtained by previous observations and inductions, and which we may therefore assume to be available and ready at hand when we want to make use of them. Let us conceive them to be such as these following:—Some men live to fifty; some Indian residents live to fifty; no man suffering thus from cancer lives for five years. From the first and second of these premises nothing whatever can be inferred, for they are both[1] particular propositions, and therefore lead to no conclusion in this case. The third answers our enquiry decisively.

To the logical reader it will hardly be necessary to point out that the process here under consideration is that of finding middle terms which shall serve to connect the subject and predicate of our conclusion. This subject and predicate in the case in question, are the individual before

---

[1] As particular propositions they are both of course identical in form. The fact that the 'some' in the former corresponds to a larger proportion than in the latter, is a distinction alien to pure Logic.

us and his death within the stated period. Regarded by
themselves there is nothing in common between them, and
therefore no link by which they may be connected or disconnected with each other. The various classes above
referred to are a set of such middle terms, and the propositions belonging to them are a corresponding set of major
premises. By the help of any one of them we are enabled,
under suitable circumstances, to connect together the subject
and predicate of the conclusion, that is, to infer whether the
man will or will not live twenty years.

§ 15. Now in the performance of such a logical process
there are two considerations to which the reader's attention
must for a moment be directed. They are simple enough in
this case, but will need careful explanation in the corresponding case in Probability. In the first place, it is clear that
whenever we can make any inference at all, we can do so
with absolute certainty. Logic, within its own domain,
knows nothing of hesitation or doubt. If the middle term
is appropriate it serves to connect the extremes in such a
way as to preclude all uncertainty about the conclusion ;
if it is not, there is so far an end of the matter : no conclusion can be drawn, and we are therefore left where we were.
Assuming our premises to be correct, we either know our
conclusion for certain, or we know nothing whatever about
it. In the second place, it should be noticed that none of
the possible alternatives in the shape of such major premises
as those given above can ever contradict any of the others,
or be at all inconsistent with them. Regarded as isolated
propositions, there is of course nothing to secure such harmony ; they have very different predicates, and may seem
quite out of each other's reach for either support or opposition. But by means of the other premise they are in each
case brought into relation with one another, and the general

interests of truth and consistency prevent them therefore from contradicting one another. As isolated propositions it might have been the case that all men live to fifty, and that no Indian residents do so, but having recognised that some men are residents in India, we see at once that these premises are inconsistent, and therefore that one or other of them must be rejected. In all applied logic this necessity of avoiding self-contradiction is so obvious and imperious that no one would think it necessary to lay down the formal postulate that all such possible major premises are to be mutually consistent. To suppose that this postulate is not complied with, would be in effect to make two or more con tradictory assumptions about matters of fact.

§ 16. But now observe the difference when we attempt to take the corresponding step in Probability. For ordinary propositions, universal or particular, substitute statistical propositions of what we have been in the habit of calling the 'proportional' kind. In other words, instead of asking whether the man will live for twenty years, let us ask whether he will live for one year? We shall be unable to find any universal propositions which will cover the case, but we may without difficulty obtain an abundance of appropriate proportional ones. They will be of the following description:— Of men aged 30, 98 in 100 live another year; of residents in India a smaller proportion survive, let us for example say 90 in 100; of men suffering from cancer a smaller proportion still, let us say 20 in 100.

Now in both of the respects to which attention has just been drawn, propositions of this kind offer a marked contrast with those last considered. In the first place, they do not, like ordinary propositions, either assert unequivocally yes or no, or else refuse to open their lips; but they give instead a sort of qualified or hesitating answer concerning the individuals included in them. This is of course nothing more than the familiar characteristic of what may be called 'probability propositions.' But it leads up to, and indeed renders possible, the second and more important point; viz. that these various answers, though they cannot directly and formally contradict each other (this their nature as proportional propositions, will not as a rule permit), may yet, in a way which will now have to be pointed out, be found to be more or less in conflict with each other.

Hence it follows that in the attempt to draw a conclusion from premises of the kind in question, we may be placed in a position of some perplexity; but it is a perplexity which may present itself in two forms, a mild and an aggravated form. We will notice them in turn.

§ 17. The mild form occurs when the different classes to which the individual case may be appropriately referred are successively included one within another; for here our sets of statistics, though leading to different results, will not often be found to be very seriously at variance with one another. All that comes of it is that as we ascend in the scale by appealing to higher and higher genera, the statistics grow continually less appropriate to the particular case in point, and such information therefore as they afford becomes gradually less explicit and accurate.

The question that we originally wanted to determine, be it remembered, is whether John Smith will die within one year. But all knowledge of this fact being unattainable, owing to the absence of suitable inductions, we felt justified (with the explanation, and under the restrictions mentioned in Chap. VI.), in substituting, as the only available equivalent for such individual knowledge, the answer to the following statistical enquiry, What proportion of men in his circumstances die?

§ 18.   But then at once there begins to arise some doubt
and ambiguity as to what exactly is to be understood by his
circumstances.   We may know very well what these circumstances are in themselves, and yet be in perplexity as to
how many of them we ought to take into account when
endeavouring to estimate his fate.   We might conceivably,
for a beginning, choose to confine our attention to those
properties only which he has in common with all animals.
If so, and statistics on the subject were attainable, they
would presumably be of some such character as this, Ninety-
nine animals out of a hundred die within a year.   Unusual as
such a reference would be, we should, logically speaking, be
doing nothing more than taking a wider class than the one
we were accustomed to.   Similarly we might, if we pleased,
take our stand at the class of vertebrates, or at that of
mammalia, if zoologists were able to give us the requisite
information.   Of course we reject these wide classes and
prefer a narrower one.   If asked why we reject them, the
natural answer is that they are so general, and resemble the
particular case before us in so few points, that we should be
exceedingly likely to go astray in trusting to them.   Though
accuracy cannot be insured, we may at least avoid any needless exaggeration of the relative number and magnitude of
our errors.

§ 19.   The above answer is quite valid; but whilst cau-
tioning us against appealing to too wide a class, it seems to
suggest that we cannot go wrong in the opposite direction,
that is in taking too narrow a class.   And yet we do avoid
any such extremes.   John Smith is not only an Englishman;
he may also be a native of such a part of England, be living
in such a Presidency, and so on.   An indefinite number of
such additional characteristics might be brought out into
notice, many of which at any rate have some bearing upon

the question of vitality. Why do we reject any consideration
of these narrower classes? We do reject them, but it is for
what may be termed a practical rather than a theoretical
reason. As was explained in the first chapters, it is essential
that our series should contain a considerable number of terms
if they are to be of any service to us. Now many of the
attributes of any individual are so rare that to take them
into account would be at variance with the fundamental
assumption of our science, viz. that we are properly concerned
only with the averages of large numbers. The more special
and minute our statistics the better, provided only that we
can get enough of them, and so make up the requisite large
number of instances. This is, however, impossible in many
cases. We are therefore obliged to neglect one attribute
after another, and so to enlarge the contents of our class; at
the avowed risk of somewhat increased variety and unsuit-
ability in the members of it, for at each step of this kind we
diverge more and more from the sort of instances that we
really want. We continue to do so, until we no longer gain
more in quantity than we lose in quality. We finally take
our stand at the point where we first obtain statistics drawn
from a sufficiently large range of observation to secure the
requisite degree of stability and uniformity.

§ 20. In such an example as the one just mentioned,
where one of the successive classes—man—is a well-defined
natural kind or species, there is such a complete break in
each direction at this point, that every one is prompted to
take his stand here. On the one hand, no enquirer would
ever think of introducing any reference to the higher classes
with fewer attributes, such as animal or organized being:
and on the other hand, the inferior classes, created by our
taking notice of his employment or place of residence, &c.,
do not as a rule differ sufficiently in their characteristics

from the class *man* to make it worth our while to attend to them.

Now and then indeed these characteristics do rise into importance, and whenever this is the case we concentrate our attention upon the class to which they correspond, that is, the class which is marked off by their presence. Thus, for instance, the quality of consumptiveness separates any one off so widely from the majority of his fellow-men in all questions pertaining to mortality, that statistics about the lives of consumptive men differ materially from those which refer to men in general. And we see the result; if a consumptive man can effect an insurance at all, he must do it for a much higher premium, calculated upon his special circumstances. In other words, the attribute is sufficiently important to mark off a fresh class or series. So with insurance against accident. It is not indeed attempted to make a special rate of insurance for the members of each separate trade, but the differences of risk to which they are liable oblige us to take such facts to some degree into account. Hence, trades are roughly divided into two or three classes, such as the ordinary, the hazardous, and the extra-hazardous, each having to pay its own rate of premium.

§ 21. Where one or other of the classes thus corresponds to natural kinds, or involves distinctions of co-ordinate importance with those of natural kinds, the process is not difficult; there is almost always some one of these classes which is so universally recognised to be the appropriate one, that most persons are quite unaware of there being any necessity for a process of selection. Except in the cases where a man has a sickly constitution, or follows a dangerous employment, we seldom have occasion to collect statistics for him from any class but that of men in general of his age in the country.

When, however, these successive classes are not ready marked out for us by nature, and thence arranged in easily distinguishable groups, the process is more obviously arbitrary. Suppose we were considering the chance of a man's house being burnt down, with what collection of attributes should we rest content in this instance ? Should we include all kinds of buildings, or only dwelling-houses, or confine ourselves to those where there is much wood, or those which have stoves ? All these attributes, and a multitude of others may be present, and, if so, they are all circumstances which help to modify our judgment. We must be guided here by the statistics which we happen to be able to obtain in sufficient numbers. Here again, rough distinctions of this kind are practically drawn in Insurance Offices, by dividing risks into ordinary, hazardous, and extra-hazardous. We examine our case, refer it to one or other of these classes, and then form our judgment upon its prospects by the statistics appropriate to its class.

§ 22. So much for what may be called the mild form in which the ambiguity occurs; but there is an aggravated form in which it may show itself, and which at first sight seems to place us in far greater perplexity.

Suppose that the different classes mentioned above are not included successively one within the other. We may then be quite at a loss which of the statistical tables to employ. Let us assume, for example, that nine out of ten Englishmen are injured by residence in Madeira, but that nine out of ten consumptive persons are benefited by such a residence. These statistics, though fanciful, are conceivable and perfectly compatible. John Smith is a consumptive Englishman ; are we to recommend a visit to Madeira in his case or not ? In other words, what inferences are we to draw about the probability of his death ? Both of the statistical tables apply to his case, but they would lead us to directly contradictory conclusions. This does not mean, of course, contradictory precisely in the logical sense of that word, for one of these propositions does not assert that an event must happen and the other deny that it must; but contradictory in the sense that one would cause us in some considerable degree to believe what the other would cause us in some considerable degree to disbelieve. This refers, of course, to the individual events; the statistics are by supposition in no degree contradictory. Without further data, therefore, we can come to no decision.

§ 23. Practically, of course, if we were forced to a decision with only these data before us, we should make our choice by the consideration that the state of a man's lungs has probably more to do with his health than the place of his birth has; that is, we should conclude that the duration of life of consumptive Englishmen corresponds much more closely with that of consumptive persons in general than with that of their healthy countrymen. But this is, of course, to import empirical considerations into the question. The data, as they are given to us, and if we confine ourselves to them, leave us in absolute uncertainty upon the point. It may be that the consumptive Englishmen almost all die when transported into the other climate; it may be that they almost all recover. If they die, this is in obvious accordance with the first set of statistics; it will be found in accordance with the second set through the fact of the foreign consumptives profiting by the change of climate in more than what might be termed their due proportion. A similar explanation will apply to the other alternative, viz. to the supposition that the consumptive Englishmen mostly recover. The problem is, therefore, left absolutely indeterminate, for we cannot here appeal to any general rule so simple and so obviously applicable as that which, in a former case, recommended us always to prefer the more special statistics, when sufficiently extensive, to those which are wider and more general. We have no means here of knowing whether one set is more special than the other.

And in this no difficulty can be found, so long as we confine ourselves to a just view of the subject. Let me again recall to the reader's mind what our present position is; we have substituted for knowledge of the individual (finding that unattainable) a knowledge of what occurs in the average of similar cases. This step had to be taken the moment the problem was handed over to Probability. But the conception of similarity in the cases introduces us to a perplexity; we manage indeed to evade it in many instances, but here it is inevitably forced upon our notice. There are here two aspects of this similarity, and they introduce us to two distinct averages. Two assertions are made as to what happens in the long run, and both of these assertions, by supposition, are verified. Of their truth there need be no doubt, for both were supposed to be obtained from experience.

§ 24. It may perhaps be supposed that such an example as this is a *reductio ad absurdum* of the principle upon which Life and other Insurances are founded. But a moment's consideration will show that this is quite a mistake, and that the principle of insurance is just as applicable to examples of this kind as to any other. An office need find no difficulty in the case supposed. They *might* (for a reason to be mentioned presently, they probably *would* not) insure the individual without inconsistency at a rate determined by either average. They might say to him, "You are an Englishman. Out of the multitude of English who come to us nine in ten die if they go to Madeira. We will insure you at a rate assigned by these statistics, knowing that in the long run all will come right so far as we are concerned. You are also consumptive, it is true, and we do not know what proportion of the English are consumptive, nor what proportion of English consumptives die in Madeira. But this does not really matter for our purpose. The formula, nine in ten die, is in reality calculated by taking into account these unknown proportions; for, though we do not know them in themselves, statistics tell us all that we care to know about their results. In other words, whatever unknown elements may exist, must, in regard to all the effects which they can produce, have been already taken into account, so that our ignorance about them cannot in the least degree invalidate such conclusions as we are able to draw. And this is sufficient for our purpose." But precisely the same language might be held to him if he presented himself as a consumptive man; that is to say, the office could safely carry on its proceedings upon either alternative.

This would, of course, be a very imperfect state for the matter to be left in. The only rational plan would be to isolate the case of consumptive Englishmen, so as to make a separate calculation for their circumstances. This calculation would then at once supersede all other tables so far as they were concerned; for though, *in the end*, it could not arrogate to itself any superiority over the others, it would in the mean time be marked by fewer and slighter aberrations from the truth.

§ 25. The real reason why the Insurance office could not long work on the above terms is of a very different kind from that which some readers might contemplate, and belongs to a class of considerations which have been much neglected in the attempts to construct sciences of the different branches of human conduct. It is nothing else than

that annoying contingency to which prophets since the time
of Jonah have been subject, of uttering *suicidal* prophecies;
of publishing conclusions which are perfectly certain when
every condition and cause but one have been taken into
account, that one being the effect of the prophecy itself
upon those to whom it refers.

In our example above, the office (in so far as the particular cases in Madeira are concerned) would get on very well
until the consumptive Englishmen in question found out
what much better terms they could make by announcing
themselves as consumptives, and paying the premium appropriate to that class, instead of announcing themselves as
Englishmen. But if they did this they would of course be
disturbing the statistics. The tables were based upon the
assumption that a certain fixed proportion (it does not
matter what proportion) of the English lives would continue
to be consumptive lives, which, under the supposed circumstances, would probably soon cease to be true. When it is
said that nine Englishmen out of ten die in Madeira, it is
meant that of those who come to the office, as the phrase is,
at random, or in their fair proportions, nine-tenths die. The
consumptives are supposed to go there just like red-haired
men, or poets, or any other special class. Or they might go
in any proportions greater or less than those of other classes,
so long as they adhered to the same proportion throughout.
The tables are then calculated on the continuance of this
state of things; the practical contradiction is in supposing
such a state of things to continue after the people had once
had a look at the tables. If we merely make the assumption that the publication of these tables made no such alteration in the conduct of those to whom it referred, no hitch of
this kind need occur.

§ 26. The assumptions here made, as has been said, are

not in any way contradictory, but they need some explanation. It will readily be seen that, taken together, they are inconsistent with the supposition that each of these classes is homogeneous, that is, that the statistical proportions which hold of the whole of either of them will also hold of any portion of them which we may take. There are certain individuals (viz. the consumptive Englishmen) who belong to each class, and of course the two different sets of statistics cannot both be true of them taken by themselves. They might coincide in their characteristics with either class, but not with both; probably in most practical cases they will coincide with neither, but be of a somewhat intermediate character. Now when it is said of any such heterogeneous body that, say, nine-tenths die, what is meant (or rather implied) is that the class might be broken up into smaller subdivisions of a more homogeneous character, in some of which, of course, more than nine-tenths die, whilst in others less, the differences depending upon their character, constitution, profession, &c.; the number of such divisions and the amount of their divergence from one another being perhaps very considerable.

Now when we speak of either class as a whole and say that nine-tenths die, the most natural and soundest meaning is that that would be the proportion if all without exception went abroad, or (what comes to the same thing) if each of these various subdivisions was represented in fair proportion to its numbers. Or it might only be meant that they go in some other proportion, depending upon their tastes, pursuits, and so on. But whatever meaning be adopted one condition is necessary, viz. that the proportion of each class that went at the time the statistics were drawn up must be adhered to throughout. When the class is homogeneous this is not needed, but when it is heterogeneous the statistics would be interfered with unless this condition were secured.

We are here supposed to have two sets of statistics, one for the English and one for the consumptives, so that the consumptive English are in a sense counted twice over. If their mortality is of an intermediate amount, therefore, they serve to keep down the mortality of one class and to keep up that of the other. If the statistics are supposed to be exhaustive, by referring to the whole of each class, it follows that actually the same individuals must be counted each time; but if representatives only of each class are taken, the same individuals need not be inserted in each set of tables.

§ 27. When therefore they come to insure (our remarks are still confined to our supposed Madeira case), we have some English consumptives counted as English, and paying the high rate; and others counted as consumptives and paying the low rate. Logically indeed we may suppose them all entered in each class, and paying therefore each rate. What we have said above is that any individual may be conceived to present himself for either of these classes. Conceive that some one else pays his premium for him, so that it is a matter of indifference to him personally at which rate he insures, and there is nothing to prevent some of the class (or for that matter all) going to one class, and others (or all again) going to the other class.

So long therefore as we make the logically possible though practically absurd supposition that some men will continue to pay a higher rate than they need, there is nothing to prevent the English consumptives (some or all) from insuring in each category and paying its appropriate premium. As soon as they gave any thought to the matter, of course they would, in the case supposed, all prefer to insure as consumptives. But their doing this would disturb each set of statistics. The English mortality in Madeira would instantly become heavier, so far as the Insurance company was concerned, by the loss of all their best lives; whilst the consumptive statistics (unless *all* the English consumptives had already been taken for insurance) would be in the same way deteriorated[1]. A slight readjustment therefore of each scale of insurance would then be needed; this is the disturbance mentioned just above. It must be clearly understood, however, that it is not our original statistics which have proved to be inconsistent, but simply that there were practical obstacles to carrying out a system of insurance upon them.

§ 28. Examples subject to the difficulty now under consideration will doubtless seem perplexing to the student unacquainted with the subject. They are difficult to reconcile with any other view of the science than that insisted on throughout this Essay, viz. that we are only concerned with averages. It will perhaps be urged that there are two different values of the man's life in these cases, and that they cannot both be true. Why not? The 'value' of his life is simply the number of years to which men in his circumstances do, on the average, attain; we have the man set before us under two different circumstances; what wonder, therefore, that these should offer different averages? In such an objection it is forgotten that we have had to substitute for the unattainable result about the individual, the really attainable result about a set of men as much like him as possible. The difficulty and apparent contradiction only arise when people will try to find some justification for their belief in the individual case. What can we possibly con-

---

[1] The reason is obvious. The healthiest English lives in Madeira (viz. the consumptive ones) have now ceased to be reckoned as English; whereas the worst consumptive lives there (viz. the English) are now increased in relative numbers.

clude, it may be asked, about this particular man John Smith's prospects when we are thus offered two different values for his life ? Nothing whatever, it must be replied ; nor could we in reality draw a conclusion, be it remembered, in the former case, when we were practically confined to one set of statistics. There also we had what we called the 'value' of his life, and since we only knew of one such value, we came to regard it as in some sense appropriate to him as an individual. Here, on the other hand, we have two values, belonging to different series, and as these values are really different it may be complained that they are discordant, but such a complaint can only be made when we do what we have no right to do, viz. assign a value to the individual which shall admit of individual justification.

§ 29. Is it then perfectly arbitrary what series or class of instances we select by which to judge ? By no means ; it has been stated repeatedly that in choosing a series, we must seek for one the members of which shall resemble our individual in as many of his attributes as possible, subject only to the restriction that it must be a sufficiently extensive series. What is meant is, that in the above case, where we have two series, we cannot fairly call them contradictory; the only valid charge is one of incompleteness or insufficiency for their purpose, a charge which applies in exactly the same sense, be it remembered, to all statistics which comprise genera unnecessarily wider than the species with which we are concerned. The only difference between the two different classes of cases is, that in the one instance we are on a path which we know will lead at the last, through many errors, towards the truth (in the sense in which truth can be attained here), and we took it for want of a better. In the other instance we have two such paths, perfectly different paths, either of which however will lead us towards the truth as before. Contradiction can only seem to arise when it is attempted to justify each separate step on our paths, as well as their ultimate tendency.

Still it cannot be denied that these objections are a serious drawback to the completeness and validity of any anticipations which are merely founded upon statistical frequency, at any rate in an early stage of experience, when but few statistics have been collected. Such knowledge as Probability can give is not in any individual case of a high order, being subject to the characteristic infirmity of repeated error; but even when measured by its own standard it commences at a very low stage of proficiency. The errors are then relatively very numerous and large compared with what they may ultimately be reduced to.

§ 30. Here as elsewhere there is a continuous process of specialization going on. The needs of a gradually widening experience are perpetually calling upon us to subdivide classes which are found to be too heterogeneous. Sometimes the only complaint that has to be made is that the class to which we are obliged to refer is found to be somewhat too broad to suit our purpose, and that it might be subdivided with convenience. This is the case, as has been shown above, when an Insurance office finds that its increasing business makes it possible and desirable to separate off the men who follow some particular trades from the rest of their fellow-countrymen. Similarly in every other department in which statistics are made use of. This increased demand for specificness leads, in fact, as naturally in this direction, as does the progress of civilization to the subdivision of trades in any town or country. So in reference to the other kind of perplexity mentioned above. Nothing is more common in those sciences or practical arts, in which deduction is but little available, and where in consequence our knowledge is

for the most part of the empirical kind, than to meet with
suggestions which point more or less directly in contrary
directions. Whenever some new substance is discovered or
brought into more general use, those who have to deal with
it must be familiar with such a state of things. The medical
man who has to employ a new drug may often find himself confronted by the two distinct recommendations, that on
the one hand it should be employed for certain diseases, and
that on the other hand it should not be tried on certain constitutions. A man with such a constitution, but suffering
from such a disease, presents himself; which recommenda-
tion is the doctor to follow? He feels at once obliged to
set to work to collect narrower and more special statistics,
in order to escape from such an ambiguity.

§ 31. In this and a multitude of analogous cases
afforded by the more practical arts it is not of course necessary that numerical data should be quoted and appealed
to; it is sufficient that the judgment is more or less consciously determined by them. All that is necessary to make
the examples appropriate is that we should admit that in
their case statistical data are our ultimate appeal in the
present state of knowledge. Of course if the empirical
laws can be resolved into their component causes we may
appeal to direct deduction, and in this case the employment of statistics, and consequently the use of the theory of
Probability, may be superseded.

In this direction therefore, as time proceeds, the advance
of statistical refinement by the incessant subdivision of classes
to meet the developing wants of man is plain enough. But
if we glance backwards to a more primitive stage, we shall
soon see in what a very imperfect state the operation commences. At this early stage, however, Probability and Induction are so closely connected together as to be very apt to

be merged into one, or at any rate to have their functions confounded.

§ 32. Since the generalization of our statistics is found to belong to Induction, this process of generalization may be regarded as prior to, or at least independent of, Probability. We have, moreover, already discussed (in Chapter VI.) the step corresponding to what are termed immediate inferences, and (in Chapter VII.) that corresponding to syllogistic inferences. Our present position therefore is that in which we may consider ourselves in possession of any number of generalizations, but wish to employ them so as to make inferences about a given individual; just as in one department of common logic we are engaged in finding middle terms to establish the desired conclusion. In this latter case the process is found to be extremely simple, no accumulation of different middle terms being able to lead to any real ambiguity or contradiction. In Probability, however, the case is different. Here, if we attempt to draw inferences about the individual case before us, as often is attempted—in the Rule of Succession for example—we shall encounter the full force of this ambiguity and contradiction. Treat the question, however, fairly, and all difficulty disappears. Our inference really is not about the individuals as individuals, but about series or successions of them. We wished to know whether John Smith will die within the year; this, however, cannot be known. But John Smith, by the possession of many attributes, belongs to many different series. The multiplicity of middle terms, therefore, is what ought to be expected. We *can* know whether a succession of men, residents in India, consumptives, &c. die within a year. We may make our selection, therefore, amongst these, and in the long run the belief and consequent conduct of ourselves and other persons (as described in Chapter VI.) will become capable of justification. With regard to choosing one of these series rather than another, we have two opposing principles of guidance. On the one hand, the more special the series the better; for, though not more right in the end, we shall thus be more nearly right all along. But, on the other hand, if we try to make the series too special, we shall generally meet the practical objection arising from insufficient statistics.

CHAPTER X.

§ 1. THE remarks in the previous chapter will have served to clear the way for an enquiry which probably excites more popular interest than any other within the range of our subject, viz. the determination whether such and such events are to be attributed to Chance on the one hand, or to Causation or Design on the other. As the principal difficulty seems to arise from the ambiguity with which the problem is generally conceived and stated, owing to the extreme generality of the conceptions involved, it becomes necessary to distinguish clearly between the several distinct issues which are apt to be involved.

I. There is, to begin with, a very old objection, founded on the assumption which our science is supposed to make of the existence of *Chance*. The objection against chance is of course many centuries older than the Theory of Probability ; and as it seems a nearly obsolete objection at the present day we need not pause long for its consideration. If we spelt the word with a capital C, and maintained that it was representative of some distinct creative or administrative agency, we should presumably be guilty of some form of Manicheism. But the only rational meaning of the objection would appear to be that the principles of the science compel us to assume that events (some events, only, that is) happen without causes, and are thereby removed from the customary control of the Deity. As repeatedly pointed out already this is altogether a mistake. The science of Probability makes no assumption whatever about the way in which events are brought about, whether by causation or without it. All that we undertake to do is to establish and explain a body of rules which are applicable to classes of cases in which we do not or cannot make inferences about the individuals. The objection therefore must be somewhat differently stated, and appears finally to reduce itself to this;—that the assumptions upon which the science of Probability rests, are not inconsistent with a disbelief in causation within certain limits; causation being of course understood simply in the sense of regular sequence. So stated the objection seems perfectly valid, or rather the facts on which it is based must be admitted; though what connection there would be between such lack of causation and absence of Divine superintendence I quite fail to see.

As this Theological objection died away the men of physical science, and those who sympathized with them, began to enforce the same protest; and similar cautions are still to be found from time to time in modern treatises. Hume, for instance, in his short essay on *Probability*, commences with the remark, " though there be no such thing as chance in the world, our ignorance of the real cause of any event has the same influence on the understanding, &c." De Morgan indeed goes so far as to declare that "the foundations of the theory of Probability have ceased to exist in the mind that has formed the conception," "that anything ever did happen or will happen without some particular reason why it should have been precisely what it was and not anything else[1]." Similar remarks might be quoted from Laplace and others.

§ 2. In the particular form of the controversy above referred to, and which is mostly found in the region of the natural and physical sciences, the contention that chance and causation are irreconcileable occupies rather a defensive position ; the main fact insisted on being that, whenever in these subjects we may happen to be ignorant of the details we have no warrant for assuming as a consequence that the details are uncaused. But this supposed irreconcileability is sometimes urged in a much more aggressive spirit in reference to social enquiries. Here the attempt is often made to prove causation in the details, from the known and admitted regularity in the averages. A considerable amount of controversy was excited some years ago upon this topic, in great part originated by the vigorous and outspoken support of the necessitarian side by Buckle in his *History of Civilization.*

It should be remarked that in these cases the attempt is sometimes made as it were to startle the reader into acquiescence by the singularity of the examples chosen. Instances are selected which, though they possess no greater logical value, are, if one may so express it, emotionally more effective. Every reader of Buckle's History, for instance, will remember the stress which he laid upon the observed fact, that the number of suicides in London remains about the same, year by year ; and he may remember also the sort of panic with which the promulgation of this fact was accompanied in many quarters. So too the way in which Laplace notices that the number of undirected letters annually sent to the Post Office remains about the same, and the comments of Dugald Stewart upon this particular uniformity, seem to imply that they regarded

---

[1] *Essay on Probabilities*, p. 114.

this instance as more remarkable than many analogous ones taken from other quarters.

That there is a certain foundation of truth in the reasonings in support of which the above examples are advanced, cannot be denied, but their authors appear to me very much to overrate the sort of opposition that exists between the theory of Chances and the doctrine of Causation. As regards first that wider conception of order or regularity which we have termed uniformity, anything which might be called objective chance would certainly be at variance with this in one respect. In Probability ultimate regularity is always postulated; in tossing a die, if not merely the individual throws were uncertain in their results, but even the average also, owing to the nature of the die, or the number of the marks upon it, being arbitrarily interfered with, of course no kind of science would attempt to take any account of it.

§ 3. So much must undoubtedly be granted; but must the same admission be made as regards the succession of the individual events? Can causation, in the sense of invariable succession (for we are here shifting on to this narrower ground), be denied, not indeed without suspicion of scientific heterodoxy, but at any rate without throwing uncertainty upon the foundations of Probability? De Morgan, as we have seen, strongly maintains that this cannot be so. I find myself unable to agree with him here, but this disagreement springs not so much from differences of detail, as from those of the point of view in which we regard the science. He always appears to incline to the opinion that the individual judgment in probability is to admit of justification; that when we say, for instance, that the odds in favour of some event are three to two, that we can explain and justify our statement without any necessary reference to a series or class of such events. It is not easy to see how this can be done in any case, but the obstacles would doubtless be greater even than they are, if knowledge of the individual event were not merely unattained, but, owing to the absence of any causal connection, essentially unattainable. On the theory adopted in this work we simply postulate ignorance of the details, but it is not regarded as of any importance on what sort of grounds this ignorance is based. It may be that knowledge is out of the question from the nature of the case, the causative link, so to say, being missing. It may be that such links are known to exist, but that either we cannot ascertain them, or should find it troublesome to do so. It is the fact of this ignorance that makes us appeal to the theory of Probability, the grounds of it are of no importance.

§ 4. On the view here adopted we are concerned only with averages, or with the single event as deduced from an average and conceived to form one of a series. We start with the assumption, grounded on experience, that there is uniformity in this average, and, so long as this is secured to us, we can afford to be perfectly indifferent to the fate, as regards causation, of the individuals which compose the average. The question then assumes the following form :— Is this assumption, of average regularity in the aggregate, inconsistent with the admission of what may be termed causeless irregularity in the details ? It does not seem to me that it would be at all easy to prove that this is so. As a matter of fact the two beliefs have constantly co-existed in the same minds. This may not count for much, but it suggests that if there be a contradiction between them it is by no means palpable and obvious. Millions, for instance, have believed in the general uniformity of the seasons taken one with another, who certainly did not believe in, and would very likely have been ready distinctly to deny, the existence of necessary sequences in the various phenomena which compose what we call a season. So with cards and dice; almost every gambler must have recognized that judgment and foresight are of use in the long run, but writers on chance seem to think that gamblers need a good deal of reasoning to convince them that each separate throw is in its nature essentially predictable.

§ 5. In its application to moral and social subjects, what gives this controversy its main interest is its real or supposed bearing upon the vexed question of the freedom of the will; for in this region Causation, and Fatalism or Necessitarianism, are regarded as one and the same thing.

Here, as in the last case, that wide and somewhat vague kind of regularity that we have called Uniformity, must be admitted as a notorious fact. Statistics have put it out of the power of any reasonably informed person to feel any hesitation upon this point. Some idea has already been gained, in the earlier chapters, of the nature and amount of the evidence which might be furnished of this fact, and any quantity more might be supplied from the works of professed writers upon the subject. If, therefore, Free-will be so interpreted as to imply such essential irregularity as defies prediction both in the average, and also in the single case, then the negation of free-will follows, not as a remote logical consequence, but as an obvious inference from indisputable facts of experience.

Few persons, however, would go so far as to interpret it in this sense. All that troubles them is the fear that somehow this general regularity may be found to carry with it causation, certainly in the sense of regular invariable sequence, and probably also with the further association of compulsion. Rejecting the latter association as utterly unphilosophical, I cannot even see that the former consequence can be admitted as really proved, though it doubtless gains some confirmation from this source.

§ 6. The nature of the argument against free-will, drawn from statistics, at least in the form in which it is very commonly expressed, seems to me exceedingly defective. The antecedents and consequents, in the case of our volitions, must clearly be supposed to be very nearly *immediately* in succession, if anything approaching to causation is to be established : whereas in statistical enquiries the data are often widely separate, if indeed they do not apply merely to single groups of actions or results.   For instance, in the case of the misdirected letters, what it is attempted to prove is that each writer was so much the 'victim of circumstances' (to use a common but misleading expression) that he could not have done otherwise than he did under his circumstances. But really no accumulation of figures to prove that the number of such letters remains the same year by year, can have much bearing upon this doctrine, even though they were accompanied by corresponding figures which should connect the forgetfulness thus indicated with some other characteristics in the writers.   So with the number of suicides.   If 250 people do, or lately did, annually put an end to themselves in London, the fact, as it thus stands by itself, may be one of importance to the philanthropist and statesman, but it needs bringing into much closer relation with psychological elements if it is to convince us that the actions of men are always instances of inflexible order.   In fact, instead of having secured our *A* and *B* here in closest intimacy of succession to one another,—to employ the symbolic notation commonly used in works on Inductive Logic to illustrate the causal connection,—we find them separated by a considerable interval ; often indeed we merely have an *A* or a *B* by itself.

§ 7. Again, another deficiency in such reasoning seems
to be the laying undue weight upon the mere regularity or
persistency of the statistics. These may lead to very important results, but they are not exactly what is wanted
for the purpose of proving anything against the freedom
of the will; it is not indeed easy to see what connection
this has with such facts as that the annual number of thefts
or of suicides remains at pretty nearly the same figure.
Statistical uniformity seems to me to establish nothing else,
at least directly, in the case of human actions, than it does
in that of physical characteristics. Take but one instance,
that of the misdirected letters. We were already aware
that the height, weight, chest measurement, and so on, of
a large number of persons preserved a tolerably regular
average amidst innumerable deflections, and we were prepared by analogy to anticipate the same regularity in their
mental characteristics. All that we gain, by counting the
numbers of letters which are posted without addresses, is
a certain amount of direct evidence that this is the case.
Just as observations of the former kind had already shown
that statistics of the strength and stature of the human
body grouped themselves about a mean, so do those of the
latter that a similar state of things prevails in respect of the
readiness and general trustworthiness of the memory. The
evidence is not so direct and conclusive in the latter case,
for the memory is not singled out and subjected to measurement by itself, but is taken in combination with innumerable
other influencing circumstances. Still there can be little
doubt that the statistics tell on the whole in this direction,
and that by duly varying and extending them they may
obtain considerable probative force.

The fact is that Probability has nothing more to do with
Natural Theology, either in its favour or against it, than the

general principles of Logic or Induction have. It is simply a body of rules for drawing inferences about classes of events which are distinguished by a certain quality. The believer in a Deity will, by the study of nature, be led to form an opinion about His works, and so to a certain extent about His attributes. But it is surely unreasonable to propose that he should abandon his belief because the sequence of events,—not, observe, their general tendency towards happiness or misery, good or evil,—is brought about in a way different from what he had expected; whether it be by displaying order where he had expected irregularity, or by involving the machinery of secondary causes where he had expected immediate agency.

§ 8. It is both amusing and instructive to consider what very different feelings might have been excited in our minds by this co-existence of, what may be called, ignorance of individuals and knowledge of aggregates, if they had presented themselves to our observation in a reverse order. Being utterly unable to make assured predictions about a single life, or the conduct of individuals, people are sometimes startled, and occasionally even dismayed, at the unexpected discovery that such predictions can be confidently made when we are speaking of large numbers. And so some are prompted to exclaim, This is denying Providence! it is utter Fatalism! But let us assume, for a moment, that our familiarity with the subject had been experienced, in the first instance, in reference to the aggregates instead of the individual lives. It is difficult, perhaps, to carry out such a supposition completely; though we may readily conceive something approaching to it in the case of an ignorant clerk in a Life Assurance Office, who had never thought of life, except as having such a 'value' at such an age, and who had hardly estimated it except in the form of averages. Might we not suppose him, in some moment of reflectiveness, being astonished and dismayed at the sudden realization of the utter uncertainty in which the single life is involved ? And might not his exclamation in turn be, Why this is denying Providence ! It is utter chaos and chance ! A belief in a Creator and Administrator of the world is not confined to any particular assumption about the nature of the immediate sequence of events, but those who have been accustomed hitherto to regard the events under one of the aspects above referred to, will often for a time feel at a loss how to connect them with the other.

§ 9. So far we have been touching on a very general question ; viz. the relation of the fundamental postulates of Probability to the conception of Order or Uniformity in the world, physical or moral. The difficulties which thence arise are mainly theological, metaphysical or psychological. What we must now consider are problems of a more detailed or logical character. They are prominently these two ; (1) the distinction between chance arrangement and *causal* arrangement in physical phenomena ; and (2) the distinction between chance arrangement and *designed* arrangement where we are supposed to be contemplating rational agency as acting on one side at least.

II. The first of these questions raises the antithesis between chance and causation, not as a general characteristic pervading all phenomena, but in reference to some specified occurrence :—Is this a case of chance or not ? The most strenuous supporters of the universal prevalence of causation and order admit that the question is a relevant one, and they must therefore be supposed to have some rule for testing the answers to it.

Suppose, for instance, a man is seized with a fit in a house where he has gone to dine, and dies there ; and some

one remarks that that was the very house in which he was
born. We begin to wonder if this was an odd coincidence
and nothing more. But if our informant goes on to tell us
that the house was an old family one, and was occupied by
the brother of the deceased, we should feel at once that
these facts put the matter in a rather different light. Or
again, as Cournot suggests, if we hear that two brothers
have been killed in battle on the same day, it makes a great
difference in our estimation of the case whether they were
killed fighting in the same engagement or whether one fell
in the north of France and the other in the south. The
latter we should at once class with mere coincidences, whereas
the former might admit of explanation.

§ 10. The problem, as thus conceived, seems to be one
rather of Inductive Logic than of Probability, because there
is not the slightest attempt to calculate chances. But it
deserves some notice here. Of course no accurate thinker
who was under the sway of modern physical notions would
for a moment doubt that each of the two elements in question
had its own ' cause ' behind it, from which (assuming perfect
knowledge) it might have been confidently inferred. No
more would he doubt, I apprehend, that if we could take a
sufficiently minute and comprehensive view, and penetrate
sufficiently far back into the past, we should reach a stage at
which (again assuming perfect knowledge) the coexistence of
the two events could equally have been foreseen. The
employment of the word *casual* therefore does not imply any
rejection of a cause ; but it does nevertheless correspond to a
distinction of some practical importance. We call a coincidence casual, I apprehend, when we mean to imply that no
knowledge of one of the two elements, which we can suppose
to be practically attainable, would enable us to expect the
other. We know of no generalization which covers them

both, except of course such as are taken for granted to be inoperative. In such an application it seems that the word 'casual' is not used in antithesis to 'causal' or to 'designed', but rather to that broader conception of order or regularity to which I should apply the term Uniformity. The casual coincidence is one which we cannot bring under any special generalization; certain, probable, or even plausible.

A slightly different way of expressing this distinction is to regard these 'mere coincidences' as being simply cases in point of *independent* events, in the sense in which independence was described in a former chapter. We saw that any two events, *A* and *B*, were so described when each happens with precisely the same relative statistical frequency whether the other happens or not. This state of things seems to hold good of the successions of heads and tails in tossing coins, as in that of male and female births in a town, or that of the digits in many mathematical tables. Thus we suppose that when men are picked up in the street and taken into a house to die, there will not be in the long run any preferential selection for or against the house in which they were born. And all that we necessarily mean to claim when we deny of such an occurrence, in any particular case, that it is a mere coincidence, is that that particular case must be taken out of the common list and transferred to one in which there *is* some such preferential selection.

§ 11. III. The next problem is a somewhat more intricate one, and will therefore require rather careful subdivision. It involves the antithesis between Chance and Design. That is, we are not now (as in the preceding case) considering objects in their physical aspect alone, and taking account only of the relative frequency of their coexistence or sequence; but we are considering the agency by which they are produced, and we are enquiring whether that agency trusted to what we call chance, or whether it employed what we call design.

The reader must clearly understand that we are not now discussing the mere question of fact whether a certain assigned arrangement *is* what we call a chance one. This, as was fully pointed out in the fourth chapter, can be settled by mere inspection, provided the materials are extensive enough. What we are now proposing to do is to carry on the enquiry from the point at which we then had to leave it off, by solving the question, Given a certain arrangement, is it more likely that this was *produced* by design, or by some of the methods commonly called chance methods? The distinction will be obvious if we revert to the succession of figures which constitute the ratio π. As I have said, this arrangement, regarded as a mere succession of digits, appears to fulfil perfectly the characteristics of a chance arrangement. If we were to omit the first four or five digits, which are familiar to most of us, we might safely defy any one to whom it was shown to say that it was not got at by simply drawing figures from a bag. He might look at it for his whole life without detecting that it was anything but the result of such a chance selection. And rightly so, because regarded as a mere arrangement it *is* a chance one: it fulfils all the requirements of such an arrangement[1]. The question

---

[1] Doubts have been expressed about the truly random character of the digits in this case (v. De Morgan, *Budget of Paradoxes*, p. 291), and Jevons has gone so far as to ask (*Principles of Science*, p. 529), "Why should the value of π, when expressed to a great number of figures, contain the digit 7 much less frequently than any other digit!" I do not quite understand what this means. If such a question were asked in relation to any unusual divergence from the à *priori* chance in a case of throwing dice, say, we should probably substitute for it the following, as being more appropriate to our science:—Assign the degree of improbability of the event in question; i.e. its statistical rarity. And we should then proceed to judge, in the way indicated in the

we are now proceeding to discuss is this: Given any such arrangement how are we to determine the process by which it was arrived at?

We are supposed to have some event before us which might have been produced in either of two alternative ways, i.e. by chance or by some kind of deliberate design; and we are asked to determine the odds in favour of one or other of these alternatives. It is therefore a problem in Inverse Probability and is liable to all the difficulties to which problems of this class are apt to be exposed.

text, whether this improbability gave rise to any grounds of suspicion.

The calculation is simple. The actual number of 7's, in the 708 digits, is 53: whilst the fair average would be 71. The question is, What is the chance of such a departure from the average in 708 turns? By the usual methods of calculation (v. Galloway on *Probability*) the chances against an excess or defect of 18 are about 44 : 1, in respect of any specified digit. But of course what we want to decide are the chances against *some one of the ten* showing this divergence. This I estimate as being approximately determined by the fraction $(\frac{44}{45})^{10}$, viz. ·8. This represents odds of only about 4 : 1 against such an occurrence, which is nothing remarkable. As a matter of fact several digits in the two other magnitudes which Mr Shanks had calculated to the same length, viz. $\text{Tan}^{-1}\frac{1}{5}$ and $\text{Tan}^{-1}\frac{1}{239}$, show the same divergencies (v. *Proc. Roy. Soc.* xxi. 319).

I may call attention here to a point which should have been noticed in the chapter on Randomness. We must be cautious when we decide upon the random character by mere inspection. It is very instructive here to compare the digits in π with those within the 'period' of a circulating decimal of very long period. That of $1 \div 7699$, which yields the full period of 7698 figures, was calculated some years ago by two Cambridge graduates (Mr Lunn and Mr Suffield), and privately printed. If we confine our examination to a portion of the succession the random character seems plausible; i.e. the digits, and their various combinations, come out in nearly, but not exactly, equal numbers. So if we take batches of 10; the averages hover nicely about 45. But if we took the whole period which 'circulates,' we should find these characteristics overdone, and the random character would disappear. That is, instead of a merely ultimate approximation to equality we should have (as far as this is possible) an absolute attainment of it.

§ 12.   For the theoretic solution of such a question we require the two following data :—

(1)   The relative frequency of the two classes of agencies, viz. that which is to act in a chance way and that which is to act designedly.

(2)   The probability that each of these agencies, if it were the really operative one, would produce the event in question.

The latter of these data can generally be secured without any difficulty.   The determination of the various contingencies on the chance hypothesis ought not, if the example were a suitable one, to offer any other than arithmetical difficulties.   And as regards the design alternative, it is generally taken for granted that if this had been operative it would certainly have produced the result aimed at.   For instance, if ten pence are found on a table, all with head uppermost, and it be asked whether chance or design had been at work here ; we feel no difficulty up to a certain point.   Had the pence been tossed we should have got ten heads only once in 1024 throws ; but had they been placed designedly the result would have been achieved with certainty.

But the other postulate, viz. that of the relative prevalence of these two classes of agencies, opens up a far more serious class of difficulties.   Cases can be found no doubt, though they are not very frequent, in which this question can be answered approximately, and then there is no further trouble.   For instance, if in a school class-list I were to see the four names Brown, Jones, Robinson, Smith, standing in this order, it might occur to me to enquire whether this arrangement were alphabetical or one of merit.   In our enlarged sense of the terms this is equivalent to chance and design as the alternatives ; for, since the initial letter of a boy's name has no known connection with his attainments, the successive arrangement of these letters on any other than the alphabetical plan will display the random features, just as we found to be the case with the digits of an incommensurable magnitude. The odds are 23 to 1 against 4 names coming undesignedly in alphabetical order; they are equivalent to certainty in favour of their doing so if this order had been designed. As regards the relative frequency of the two kinds of orders in school examinations I do not know that statistics are at hand, though they could easily be procured if necessary, but it is pretty certain that the majority adopt the order of merit. Put for hypothesis the proportion as high as 9 to 1, and it would still be found more likely than not that in the case in question the order was really an alphabetical one.

§ 13. But in the vast majority of cases we have no such statistics at hand, and then we find ourselves exposed to very serious ambiguities. These may be divided into two distinct classes, the nature of which will best be seen by the discussion of examples.

In the first place we are especially liable to the drawback already described in a former chapter as rendering mere statistics so untrustworthy, which consists in the fact that the proportions are so apt to be disturbed almost from moment to moment by the possession of fresh hints or information. We saw for instance why it was that statistics of mortality were so very unserviceable in the midst of a disease or in the crisis of a battle. Suppose now that on coming into a room I see on the table ten coins lying face uppermost, and am asked what was the likelihood that the arrangement was brought about by design. Everything turns upon special knowledge of the circumstances of the case. Who had been in the room? Were they children, or coin-collectors, or persons who might have been supposed to have indulged in tossing for sport or for gambling purposes ? Were the coins new or old ones ? a distinction of this kind would be very pertinent when we were considering the existence of any motive for arranging them the same way uppermost. And so on ; we feel that our statistics are at the mercy of any momentary fragment of information.

§ 14. But there is another consideration besides this. Not only should we be thus influenced by what may be called external circumstances of a general kind, such as the character and position of the agents, we should also be influenced by what we supposed to be the conventional[1] estimate with which this or that particular chance arrangement was then regarded. Thus from time to time as new games of cards become popular new combinations acquire significance ; and therefore when the question of design takes the form of possible cheating a knowledge of the current estimate of such combinations becomes exceedingly important.

§ 15. The full significance of these difficulties will best be apprehended by the discussion of a case which is not fictitious or invented for the purpose, but which has actually given rise to serious dispute. Some years ago Prof. Piazzi Smyth published a work[2] upon the great pyramid of Ghizeh, the general object of which was to show that that building contained, in its magnitude, proportions and contents, a number of almost imperishable natural standards of length, volume, &c. Amongst other things it was determined that

[1] Of course this conventional estimate is nothing different in kind from that which may attach to *any* order or succession. Ten heads in succession is intrinsically or objectively indistinguishable in character from alternate heads and tails, or seven heads and three tails, &c. Its distinction only consists in its almost universal acceptance as remarkable.

[2] *Our Inheritance in the Great Pyramid*, Ed. III. 1877.

the value of π was accurately (the degree of accuracy is not, I think, assigned) indicated by the ratio of the sides to the height. The contention was that this result could not be accidental but must have been designed.

As regards the estimation of the value of the chance hypothesis the calculation is not quite so clear as in the case of dice or cards. We cannot indeed suppose that, for a given length of base, *any* height can be equally possible. We must limit ourselves to a certain range here; for if too high the building would be insecure, and if too low it would be ridiculous. Again, we must decide to how close an approximation the measurements are made. If they are guaranteed to the hundredth of an inch the coincidence would be of a quite different order from one where the guarantee extended only to an inch. Suppose that this has been decided, and that we have ascertained that out of 10,000 possible heights for a pyramid of given base just that one has been selected which would most nearly yield the ratio of the radius to the circumference of a circle.

The remaining consideration would be the relative frequency of the 'design' alternative,—what is called its *à priori* probability,—that is, the relative frequency with which such builders can be supposed to have aimed at that ratio; with the obvious implied assumption that if they did aim at it they would certainly secure it. Considering our extreme ignorance of the attainments of the builders it is obvious that no attempt at numerical appreciation is here possible. If indeed the 'design' was interpreted to mean conscious resolve to produce that ratio, instead of mere resolve to employ some method which happened to produce it, few persons would feel much hesitation. Not only do we feel tolerably certain that the builders did not know the value of π, except in the rude way in which all artificers must know it; but we can see no rational motive, if they did know it, which should induce them to perpetuate it in their building. If, however, to adopt an ingenious suggestion[1], we suppose that the builder may have proceeded in the following fashion, the matter assumes a different aspect. Suppose that having decided on the height of his pyramid he drew a circle with that as radius: that, laying down a cord along the line of this circle, he drew this cord out into a square, which square marked the base of the building. Hardly any simpler means could be devised in a comparatively rude age; and it is obvious that the circumference of the base, being equal to the length of the cord, would bear exactly the admitted ratio to the height. In other words, the exact attainment of a geometric value does not imply a knowledge of that ratio, but merely of some method which involves and displays it. A teredo can bore, as well as any of us, a hole which displays the geometric properties of a circle, but we do not credit it with corresponding knowledge.

As before said, all numerical appreciation of the likelihood of the design alternative is out of the question. But, *if* the precision is equal to what Mr Smyth claimed, I suppose that most persons (with the above suggestion before them) will think it somewhat more likely that the coincidence was not a chance one.

---

[1] Made in *Nature* (Jan. 24, 1878) by Mr J. G. Jackson. It must be remarked that Mr Smyth's alternative statement of his case leads up to that explanation :—"The vertical height of the great pyramid is the radius of a theoretical circle the length of whose curved circumference is exactly equal to the sum of the lengths of the four straight sides of the actual and practical square base." As regards the alternatives of chance and design, here, it must be remembered in justice to Mr Smyth's argument that the antithesis he admits to chance is not human, but divine design.

§ 16. There still remains a serious, and highly interesting speculative consideration. In the above argument we took it for granted, in calculating the chance alternative, that only *one* of the 10,000 possible values was favourable; that is, we took it for granted that the ratio π was the only one whose claims, so to say, were before the court. But it is clear that if we had obtained just double this ratio the result would have been of similar significance, for it would have been simply the ratio of the circumference to the diameter. In fact, Mr Smyth's selected ratio,—the height to twice the breadth of the base as compared with the diameter to the circumference,—is obviously only one of a plurality of ratios. Again; if the measured results had shown that the ratio of the height to one side of the base was $1 : \sqrt{2}$ (i.e. that of a side to a diagonal of a square) or $1 : \sqrt{3}$ (i.e. that of a side to a diagonal of a cube) would not such results equally show evidence of design? Proceeding in this way, we might suggest one known mathematical ratio after another until most of the 10,000 supposed possible values had been taken into account. We might then argue thus: since almost every possible height of the pyramid would correspond to *some* mathematical ratio, a builder, ignorant of them all alike, would be not at all unlikely to stumble upon one or other of them: why then attribute design to him in one case rather than another?

§ 17. The answer to this objection has been already hinted at. Everything turns upon the *conventional* estimate of one result as compared with another. Revert, for simplicity, to the coins. Ten heads is just as likely as alternate heads and tails, or five heads followed by five tails; or, in fact, as any one of the remaining 1023 possible cases. But universal convention has picked out a run of ten as being remarkable. Here, of course, the convention seems a very

natural and indeed inevitable one, but in other cases it is
wholly arbitrary. For instance, in cards, "queen of spades
and knave of diamonds" is exactly as uncommon as any
other such pair: moreover, till *bezique* was introduced it
offered presumably no superior interest over any other
specified pair. But during the time when that game was
very popular this combination was brought into the category
of coincidences in which interest was felt; and, given dishonesty amongst the players, its chance of being designed
stood at once on a much better footing[1].

Returning then to the pyramid, we see that in balancing
the claims of chance and design we must, in fairness to the
latter, reckon to its account several other values as well as
that of π, e.g. $\sqrt{2}$ and $\sqrt{3}$, and a few more such simple and
familiar ratios, as well as some of their multiples. But
though the number of such values which *might* be reckoned,
on the ground that they are actually known to us, is infinite,
yet the number that *ought* to be reckoned, on the ground
that they could have been familiar to the builders of a
pyramid, are very few. The order of probability for or against
the existence of design will not therefore be seriously altered
here by such considerations[2].

[1] See Cournot, *Essai sur les fonde-
ments de nos connaissances*. Vol. i.
p. 71.

[2] It deserves notice that considerations of this kind have found
their way into the Law Courts
though of course without any attempt at numerical valuation. Thus,
in the celebrated De Ros trial, in
so far as the evidence was indirect,
one main ground of suspicion seems
to have been that Lord De Ros,
when dealing at whist, obtained far
more court cards than chance could
be expected to assign him; and that
in consequence his average gains for
several years in succession were un-
usually large. The counsel for the
defence urged that still larger gains
had been secured by other players
without suspicion of unfairness,—
(I cannot find that it was explained
over how large an area of experience
these instances had been sought;
nor how far the magnitude of the
stakes, as distinguished from the

§ 18. Up to this point it will be observed that what we have been balancing against each other are two forms of agency,—of human agency, that is,—one acting through chance, and the other by direct design. In this case we know where we are, for we can thoroughly understand agency of this kind. The problem is indeed but seldom numerically soluble, and in most cases not soluble at all, but it is at any rate capable of being clearly stated. We know the kind of answer to be expected and the reasons which would serve to determine it, if they were attainable.

The next stage in the enquiry would be that of balancing ordinary human chance agency against,—I will not call it direct spiritualist agency, for that would be narrowing the hypothesis unnecessarily,—but against all other possible causes. Some of the investigations of the Society for Psychical Research will furnish an admirable illustration of what is intended by this statement. There is a full discussion of these applications in a recent essay by Mr F. Y. Edgeworth[1]; but as his account of the matter is connected with other calculations and diagrams I can only quote it in part. But I am in substantial agreement with him.

"It is recorded that 1833 guesses were made by a 'percipient' as to the suit of cards which the 'agent' had fixed upon. The number of successful guesses was 510, considerably above 458, the number which, as being the quarter of 1833, would, on the supposition of pure chance, be more likely than any other number. Now, by the Law of Error, we are able approximately to determine the probability of

number of successes, accounted for that of the actual gains),—and that large allowance must be made for skill where the actual gains were computed. (See the *Times*' report, Feb. 11, 1837.)

[1] *Metretike*. At the end of this volume will be found a useful list of a number of other publications by the same author on allied topics.

such an excess occurring by chance. It is equal to the extremity of the tail of a probability-curve such as [those we have already had occasion to examine].... The proportion of this extremity of the tail to the whole body is ·003 to 1. That fraction, then, is the probability of a chance shot striking that extremity of the tail; the probability that, if the guessing were governed by pure chance, a number of successful guesses equal or greater than 510 would occur": odds, that is, of about 332 to 1 against such occurrence.

§ 19. Mr Edgeworth holds, as strongly as I do, that for purposes of calculation, in any strict sense of the word, we ought to have some determination of the data on the non-chance side of the hypothesis. We ought to know its relative frequency of occurrence, and the relative frequency with which it attains its aims. I am also in agreement with him that "what that other cause may be,—whether some trick, or unconscious illusion, or *thought-transference* of the sort which is vindicated by the investigators—it is for common-sense and ordinary Logic to consider."

I am in agreement therefore with those who think that though we cannot form a quantitative opinion we can in certain cases form a tolerably decisive one. Of course if we allow the last word to the supporters of the chance hypothesis we can never reach proof, for it will always be open to them to revise and re-fix the antecedent probability of the counter hypothesis. What we may fairly require is that those who deny the chance explanation should assign some sort of minimum value to the probability of occurrence on the other supposition, and we can then try to surmount this by increasing the rarity of the actually produced phenomenon on the chance hypothesis. If, for instance, they declare that in their estimation the odds against any other than the chance agency being at work are greater than 332 to 1, we must try to secure a yet uncommoner occurrence than that in question. If the supporters of thought-transference have the courage of their convictions,—as they most assuredly have,—they would not shrink from accepting this test. I am inclined to think that even at present, on such evidence as that above, the probability that the results were got at by ordinary guessing is very small.

§ 20. The problems discussed in the preceding sections are at least intelligible even if they are not always resolvable. But before finishing this chapter we must take notice of some speculations upon this part of the subject which do not seem to keep quite within the limits of what is intelligible. Take for instance the question discussed by Arbuthnott (in a paper in the *Phil. Transactions*, Vol. XXVII.) under the title " An Argument for Divine Providence, taken from the constant Regularity observed in the birth of both sexes." Had his argument been of the ordinary teleological kind ; that is, had he simply maintained that the existent ratio of approximate equality, with a six per cent. surplusage of males, was a beneficent one, there would have been nothing here to object against. But what he contemplated was just such a balance of alternate hypotheses between chance and design as we are here considering. His conclusion in his own words is, " it is art, not chance, that governs."

It is difficult to render such an argument precise without rendering it simply ridiculous. Strictly understood it can surely bear only one of two interpretations. On the one hand we may be personifying Chance : regarding it as an agent which must be reckoned with as being quite capable of having produced man, or at any rate having arranged the proportion of the sexes. And then the decision must be drawn, as between this agent and the Creator, which of the two produced the existent arrangement. If so, and Chance be defined as any agent which produces a chance or random arrangement, I am afraid there can be little doubt that it was this agent that was at work in the case in question. The arrangement of male and female births presents, so far as we can see, one of the most perfect examples of chance : there is ultimate uniformity emerging out of individual irregularity : all the 'runs' or successions of each alternative are duly represented : the fact of, say, five sons having been already born in a family does not seem to have any certain effect in diminishing the likelihood of the next being a son, and so on. Such a nearly perfect instance of 'independent events' is comparatively very rare in physical phenomena. It is all that we can claim from a chance arrangement[1]. The only other interpretation I can see is to suggest that there was but one agent who might, like any one of us, have either tossed up or designed, and we have to ascertain which course he probably adopted in the case in question. Here too, if we are to judge of his mode of action by the tests we should apply to any work of our own, it would certainly look very much as if he had adopted some scheme of tossing.

§ 21.   The simple fact is that any rational attempt to

---

[1] That is, if we look simply to statistical results, as Arbuthnott did, and as we should do if we were examining the tosses of a penny. If the remarkable theory of Dr Düsing (*Die Regulierung des Geschlechtsverhältnisses...* Jena, 1884) be confirmed, the matter would assume a somewhat different aspect. He attempts to show, both on physiological grounds, and by analysis of statistics referring to men and animals, that there is a decidedly *compensatory* process at work. That is, if for any cause either sex attains a preponderance, agencies are at once set in motion which tend to redress the balance. This is a modification and improvement of the older theory, that the relative age of the parents has something to do with the sex of the offspring.

Quetelet (*Letters*, p. 61) has attempted to *prove* a proposition about the succession of male and female births by certain experiments supposed to be tried upon an urn with black and white balls in it. But this is going too far. (See the note at the end of this chapter.)

decide between chance and design as agencies must be confined to the case of finite intelligences. One of the important determining elements here, as we have seen, is the state of knowledge of the agent, and the conventional estimate entertained about this or that particular arrangement; and these can be appreciated only when we are dealing with beings like ourselves.

For instance, to return to that much debated question about the arrangement of the stars, there can hardly be any doubt that what Mitchell,—who started the discussion,—had in view was the decision between Chance and Design. He says (*Trans. Roy. Soc.* 1767) "The argument I intend to make use of...is of that kind which infers either design or some general law from a general analogy and from the greatness of the odds against things having been in the present situation if it was not owing to some such cause." And he concludes that had the stars "been scattered by mere chance as it might happen" there would be "odds of near 500,000 to 1 that no six stars out of that number [1500], scattered at random in the whole heavens, would be within so small a distance from each other as the Pleiades are." Under any such interpretation the controversy seems to me to be idle. I do not for a moment dispute that there is some force in the ordinary teleological argument which seeks to trace signs of goodness and wisdom in the general tendency of things. But what do we possibly understand about the nature of creation, or the designs of the Creator, which should enable us to decide about the likelihood of his putting the stars in one shape rather than in another, or which should allow any significance to "mere chance" as contrasted with his supposed all-pervading agency?

§ 22. Reduced to intelligible terms the two following questions seem to me to emerge from the controversy :—

(I) The stars being distributed through space, some of them would of course be nearly in a straight line behind others when looked at from our planet. Supposing that they were tolerably uniformly distributed, we could calculate about how many of them would thus be seen in apparent close proximity to one another. The question is then put, Are there more of them near to each other, two and two, than such calculation would account for? The answer is that there are many more. So far as I can see the only direct inference that can be drawn from this is that they are *not* uniformly distributed, but have a tendency to go in pairs. This, however, is a perfectly sound and reasonable application of the theory. Any further conclusions, such as that these pairs of stars will form systems, as it were, to themselves, revolving about one another, and for all practical purposes unaffected by the rest of the sidereal system, are of course derived from astronomical considerations[1]. Probability confines itself to the simple answer that the distribution is not uniform; it cannot pretend to say whether, and by what physical process, these binary systems of stars have been 'caused'[2].

§ 23 (II). The second question is this, Does the distribution of the stars, after allowing for the case of the binary

---

[1] It is precisely analogous to the conclusion that the *flowers* of the daisies (as distinguished from the *plants*, v. p. 109) are not distributed at random, but have a tendency to go in groups of two or more. Mere observation shows this: and then, from our knowledge of the growth of plants we may infer that these little groups spring from the same root.

[2] In this discussion, writers often speak of the probability of a "*physical connection*" between these double stars. The phrase seems misleading, for on the usual hypothesis of universal gravitation *all* stars are physically connected, by gravitation. It is therefore better, as above, to make it simply a question of relative proximity, and to leave it to astronomy to infer what follows from unusual proximity.

stars just mentioned, resemble that which would be produced by human agency sprinkling things 'at random'?
(We are speaking, of course, of their distribution as it appears to us, on the visible heavens, for this is nearly all that
we can observe; but if they extend beyond the telescopic
range in every direction, this would lead to practically much
the same discussion as if we considered their actual arrangement in space.) We have fully discussed, in a former chapter, the meaning of 'randomness.' Applying it to the case
before us, the question becomes this, Is the distribution
tolerably uniform on the whole, but with innumerable individual deflections? That is, when we compare large areas,
are the ratios of the number of stars in each equal area
approximately equal, whilst, as we compare smaller and
smaller areas, do the relative numbers become more and
more irregular? With certain exceptions, such as that of
the Milky Way and other nebular clusters, this seems to be
pretty much the case, at any rate as regards the bulk of the
stars[1].

[1] Professor Forbes in the paper
in the Philosophical Magazine already referred to (Ch. VII. § 18) gave
several diagrams to show what were
the actual arrangements of a random
distribution. He scattered peas over
a chess-board, and then counted the
number which rested on each square.
His figures seem to show that the
general appearance of the stars is
much the same as that produced by
such a plan of scattering.

Some recent investigations by
Mr R. A. Proctor seem to show,
however, that there are at least two
exceptions to this tolerably uniform
distribution. (1) He has ascertained

that the stars are decidedly more
thickly aggregated in the Milky Way
than elsewhere. So far as this is to
be relied on the argument is the
same as in the case of the double
stars; it tends to prove that the
proximity of the stars in the Milky
Way is not merely apparent, but
actual. (2) He has ascertained that
there are two large areas, in the
North and South hemispheres, in
which the stars are much more
thickly aggregated than elsewhere.
Here, it seems to me, Probability
proves nothing: we are simply denying that the distribution is uniform.
What may follow in the way of in-

All further questions: the decision, for instance, for or against any form of the Nebular Hypothesis: or, admitting this, the decision whether such and such parts of the visible heavens have sprung from the same nebula, must be left to Astronomy to adjudicate.

NOTE ON THE PROPORTIONS OF THE SEXES.

The following remarks were rather too long for convenient insertion on p. 259, and are therefore appended here.

The 'random' character of male and female births has generally been rested almost entirely on statistics of place and time. But what is more wanted, surely, is the proportion displayed when we compare a number of *families*. This seems so obvious that I cannot but suppose that the investigation must have been already made somewhere, though I have not found any trace of it in the most likely quarters. Thus Prof. Lexis (*Massenerscheinungen*) when supporting his view that the proportion between the sexes at birth is almost the only instance known to him, in natural phenomena, of true normal dispersion about a mean, rests his conclusions on the ordinary statistics of the registers of different countries.

It certainly needs proof that the same characteristics will hold good when the family is taken as the unit, especially as some theories (e.g. that of Sadler) would imply that 'runs' of boys or girls would be proportionally commoner than pure chance would assign. Lexis has shown that this is most markedly the case with *twins*: i.e., to use an obviously intelligible notation, (M for male, F for female), that M.M. and F.F. are very much commoner in proportion than M.F.

I have collected statistics including over 13,000 male and female births, arranged in families of four and upwards. They were taken from the pedigrees in the Herald's Visitations, and therefore represent as a rule a somewhat select class, viz. the families of the eldest sons of English country gentlemen in the sixteenth century. They are not sufficiently extensive yet for publication, but I give a summary of the results to indicate their tendency so far. The upper line of figures in each case gives the *observed* results: i.e.

ferences as to the physical process of causation by which the stars have been disposed is a question for the Astronomer. See Mr Proctor's *Essays on Astronomy*, p. 297. Also a series of Essays in *The Universe and the coming Transits.*

in the case of a family of four, the numbers which had four male, three male and one female, two male and two female, and so on. The lower line gives the *calculated* results; i.e. the corresponding numbers which would have been obtained had batches of M.s and F.s been drawn from a bag in which they were mixed in the ratio assigned by the total observed numbers for those families.

512 families of 4 ;	m^4	m^3f	m^2f^2	mf^3	f^4	
yielding	$81 + 148 + 161 + 98 + 24$					(observed.)
1188 M. : 860 F.	$57 + 168 + 184 + 88 + 15$					(calculated.)

512 families of 5 ;	m^5	m^4f	m^3f^2	m^2f^3	mf^4	f^5	
yielding	$50 + 82 + 161 + 143 + 61 + 15$						(obs.)
1402 M. : 1158 F.	$25 + 103 + 172 + 143 + 59 + 10$						(calc.)

512 families of 6 ;	m^6	m^5f	m^4f^2	m^3f^3	m^2f^4	mf^5	f^6	
yielding	$30 + 48 + 115 + 146 + 126 + 40 + 7$							(obs.)
1612 M. : 1460 F.	$10 + 56 + 133 + 159 + 108 + 41 + 5$							(calc.)

The numbers for the larger families are as yet too small to be worth giving, but they show the same tendency. It will be seen that in every case the observed central values are less than the calculated; and that the observed extreme values are much greater than the calculated. The results seem to suggest (so far) that a family cannot be likened to a chance drawing of the requisite number from *one* bag. A better analogy would be to suppose two bags, one with M.s in excess and the other with F.s in less excess, and that some persons draw from one and some from the other. But fuller statistics are needed.

It will be observed that the total excess of male births is large. This *may* arise from undue omission of females; but I have carefully confined myself to the two or three last generations, in each pedigree, for greater security.

CHAPTER XI.

ON CERTAIN CONSEQUENCES OF THE OBJECTIVE TREAT-MENT OF A SCIENCE OF INFERENCE[1].

§ 1. STUDENTS of Logic are familiar with that broad distinction between the two methods of treatment to which the names of Material and Conceptualist may be applied. The distinction was one which had been gradually growing up under other names before it was emphasized, and treated as a distinction within the field of Logic proper, by the publication of Mill's well known work. No one, for instance, can read Whewell's treatises on Induction, or Herschel's Discourse, without seeing that they are treating of much the same subject matter, and regarding it in much the same way, as that which Mill discussed under the name of Logic, though they were not disposed to give it that name. That is, these writers throughout took it for granted that what they had to do was to systematise the facts of nature in their objective form, and under their widest possible treatment, and to expound the principal modes of inference and the principal practical aids in the investigation of these

---

[1] In the previous edition a large part of this chapter was devoted to the general consideration of the distinction between a Material and a Conceptualist view of Logic. I have omitted most of this here, as also a large part of a chapter devoted to the detailed discussion of the Law of Causation, as I hope before very long to express my opinions on these subjects more fully, and more appropriately, in a treatise on the general principles of Inductive Logic.

modes of inference, which reason could suggest and which
experience could justify. What Mill did was to bring these
methods into close relation with such portions of the old
scholastic Logic as he felt able to retain, to work them out
into much fuller detail, to systematize them by giving them
a certain philosophical and psychological foundation,—and
to entitle the result *Logic*.

The practical treatment of a science will seldom correspond closely to the ideal which its supporters propose to
themselves, and still seldomer to that which its antagonists
insist upon demanding from the supporters. If we were to
take our account of the distinction between the two views of
Logic expounded respectively by Hamilton and by Mill,
from Mill and Hamilton respectively, we should certainly
not find it easy to bring them under one common definition.
By such a test, the material Logic would be regarded as
nothing more than a somewhat arbitrary selection from the
domain of Physical Science in general, and the conceptualist
Logic nothing more than a somewhat arbitrary selection from
the domain of Psychology. The former would omit all consideration of the laws of thought and the latter all consideration of the truth or falsehood of our conclusions.

Of course, in practice, such extremes as these are soon
seen to be avoidable, and in spite of all controversial exagge-
rations the expounders of the opposite views do contrive to
retain a large area of speculation in common. I do not propose here to examine in detail the restrictions by which this
accommodation is brought about, or the very real and important distinctions of method, aim, tests, and limits which
in spite of all approach to agreement are still found to subsist.
To attempt this would be to open up rather too wide an
enquiry to be suitable in a treatise on one subdivision only
of the general science of Inference.

§ 2.   One subdivision of this enquiry is however really forced upon our notice. It does become important to consider the restrictions to which the ultra-material account of the province of Logic has to be subjected, because we shall thus have our attention drawn to an aspect of the subject which, slight and fleeting as it is within the region of Induction becomes very prominent and comparatively permanent in that of Probability. According to this ultra-material view, Inductive Logic would generally be considered to have nothing to do with anything but objective facts: its duty is to start from facts and to confine itself to such methods as will yield nothing but facts.   What is doubtful it either establishes or it lets alone for the present, what is unattainable it rejects, and in this way it proceeds to build up by slow accretion a vast fabric of certain knowledge.

But of course all this is supposed to be done by human minds, and therefore if we enquire whether notions or concepts.—call them what we will,—have no place in such a scheme it must necessarily be admitted that they *have* some place.   The facts which form our starting point must be grasped by an intelligent being before inference can be built upon them; and the 'facts' which form the conclusion have often, at any rate for some time, no place anywhere else than in the mind of man.   But no one can read Mill's treatise, for instance, without noticing how slight is his reference to this aspect of the question. He remarks, in almost contemptuous indifference, that the man who digs must of course have a notion of the ground he digs and of the spade he puts into it, but he evidently considers that these 'notions' need not much more occupy the attention of the speculative logician, in so far as his mere inferences are concerned, than they occupy that of the husbandman.

§ 3.   It must be admitted that there is some warrant

for this omission of all reference to the subjective side of
inference so long as we are dealing with Inductive Logic.
The inductive *discoverer* is of course in a very different
position. If he is worthy of the name his mind at every
moment will be teeming with notions which he would be as
far as any one from calling facts : he is busy making them
such to the best of his power. But the logician who follows
in his steps, and whose business it is to explain and justify
what his leader has discovered, is rather apt to overlook this
mental or uncertain stage. What he mostly deals in are the
'complete inductions' and 'well-grounded generalizations'
and so forth, or the exploded errors which contradict them:
the prisoners and the corpses respectively, which the real
discoverer leaves on the field behind him whilst he presses
on to complete his victory. The whole method of science,—
expository as contrasted with militant,—is to emphasize the
distinction between fact and non-fact, and to treat of little
else but these two. In other words a treatise on Inductive
Logic *can* be written without any occasion being found to
define what is meant by a notion or concept, or even to employ
such terms.

§ 4. And yet, when we come to look more closely, signs
may be detected even within the field of Inductive Logic,
of an occasional breaking down of the sharp distinction in
question; we may meet now and then with entities (to use
the widest term attainable) in reference to which it would
be hard to say that they are either facts or conceptions.
For instance, Inductive Logic has often occasion to make use
of Hypotheses : to which of the above two classes are these
to be referred ? They do not seem in strictness to belong to
either ; nor are they, as will presently be pointed out, by any
means a solitary instance of the kind.

It is true that within the province of Inductive Logic

these hypotheses do not give much trouble on this score. However vague may be the form in which they first present themselves to the philosopher's mind, they have not much business to come before us in our capacity of logicians until they are well on their way, so to say, towards becoming facts: until they are beginning to harden into that firm tangible shape in which they will eventually appear. We generally have some such recommendations given to us as that our hypotheses shall be well-grounded and reasonable. This seems only another way of telling us that however freely the philosopher may make his guesses in the privacy of his own study, he had better not bring them out into public until they can with fair propriety be termed facts, even though the name be given with some qualification, as by terming them 'probable facts.' The reason, therefore, why we do not take much account of this intermediate state in the hypothesis, when we are dealing with the inductive processes, is that here at any rate it plays only a temporary part; its appearance in that guise is but very fugitive. If the hypothesis be a sound one, it will soon take its place as an admitted fact; if not, it will soon be rejected altogether. Its state as a hypothesis is not a normal one, and therefore we have not much occasion to scrutinize its characteristics. In so saying, it must of course be understood that we are speaking as inductive logicians; the philosopher in his workshop ought, as already remarked, to be familiar enough with the hypothesis in every stage of its existence from its origin; but the logician's duty is different, dealing as he does with proof rather than with the processes of original investigation and discovery.

We might indeed even go further, and say that in many cases the hypothesis does not present itself to the reader, that is to the recipient of the knowledge, until it has ceased

to deserve that name at all. It may be first suggested to
him along with the proof which establishes it, he not having
had occasion to think of it before. It thus comes at a single
step out of the obscurity of the unknown into the full possession of its rights as a fact, skipping practically the intermediate or hypothetical stage altogether. The original investigator himself may have long pondered over it, and kept
it present to his mind, in this its dubious stage, but finally
have given it to the world with that amount of evidence
which raises it at once in the minds of others to the level of
commonly accepted facts.

Still this doubtful stage exists in every hypothesis,
though for logical purposes, and to most minds, it exists
in a very fugitive way only. When attention has been
directed to it, it may be also detected elsewhere in Logic.
Take the case, for instance, of the reference of names.
Mill gives the examples of the sun, and a battle, as distinguished from the ideas of them which we, or children,
may entertain. Here the distinction is plain and obvious
enough. But if, on the other hand, we take the case of
things whose existence is doubtful or disputed, the difficulty
above mentioned begins to show itself. The case of merely
extinct things, or such as have not yet come into existence,
offers indeed no trouble, since of course actually *present*
existence is not necessary to constitute a fact. The usual
distinction may even be retained also in the case of mythical
existences. Centaur and Griffin have as universally recognised a significance amongst the poets, painters, and heralds
as lion and leopard have. Hence we may claim, even here,
that our conceptions shall be 'truthful,' 'consistent with
fact,' and so on, by which we mean that they are to be in
accordance with universal convention upon such subjects.
Necessary and universal accordance is sometimes claimed

to be all that is meant by 'objective,' and since universal
accordance is attainable in the case of the notoriously fictitious, our fundamental distinction between fact and conception, and our determination that our terms shall refer to
what is objective rather than to what is subjective, may with
some degree of strain be still conceived to be tenable even here.

§ 5. But when we come to the case of disputed phenomena the difficulty re-emerges. A supposed planet or
new mineral, a doubtful fact in history, a disputed theological
doctrine, are but a few examples out of many that might be
offered. What some persons strenuously assert, others as
strenuously deny, and whatever hope there may be of speedy
agreement in the case of physical phenomena, experience
shows that there is not much prospect of this in the case of
those which are moral and historical, to say nothing of theological. So long as those who are in agreement confine their
intercourse to themselves, their 'facts' are accepted as such,
but as soon as they come to communicate with others all
distinction between fact and conception is lost at once, the
'facts' of one party being mere groundless 'conceptions' to
their opponents. There is therefore, I think, in these cases
a real difficulty in carrying out distinctly and consistently
the account which the Materialist logician offers as to the
reference of names. It need hardly be pointed out that
what thus applies to names or terms applies equally to
propositions in which particular or general statements are
made involving names.

§ 6. But when we step into Probability, and treat this
from the same material or Phenomenal point of view, we can
no longer neglect the question which is thus presented to us.
The difficulty cannot here be rejected, as referring to what is
merely temporary or occasional. The intermediate condition
between conjecture and fact, so far from being temporary

or occasional only, is here normal. It is just the condition which is specially characteristic of Probability. Hence it follows that however decidedly we may reject the Conceptualist theory we cannot altogether reject the use of Conceptualist language. If we can prove that a given man will die next year, or attain sufficiently near to proof to leave us practically certain on the point, we may speak of his death as a (future) fact. But if we merely contemplate his death as probable? This is the sort of inference, or substitute for inference, with which Probability is specially concerned. We may, if we so please, speak of 'probable facts,' but if we examine the meaning of the words we may find them not merely obscure, but self-contradictory. Doubtless there are facts here, in the fullest sense of the term, namely the statistics upon which our opinion is ultimately based, for these are known and admitted by all who have looked into the matter. The same language may also be applied to that extension of these statistics by induction which is involved in the assertion that similar statistics will be found to prevail elsewhere, for these also may rightfully claim universal acceptance. But these statements, as was abundantly shown in the earlier chapters, stand on a very different footing from a statement concerning the individual event; the establishment and discussion of the former belong by rights to Induction, and only the latter to Probability.

§ 7. It is true that for want of appropriate terms to express such things we are often induced, indeed compelled, to apply the same name of 'facts' to such individual contingencies. We should not, for instance, hesitate to speak of the fact of the man dying being probable, possible, unlikely, or whatever it might be. But I cannot help regarding such expressions as a strictly incorrect usage arising out of a deficiency of appropriate technical terms. It is doubtless certain that one or other of the two alternatives must happen, but this alternative certainty is not the subject of our contemplation; what we have before us is the *single* alternative, which is notoriously uncertain. It is this, and this only, which is at present under notice, and whose occurrence has to be estimated. We have surely no right to dignify this with the name of a fact, under any qualifications, when the opposite alternative has claims, not perhaps actually equal to, but at any rate not much inferior to its own. Such language, as already remarked, may be quite right in Inductive logic, where we are only concerned with conjectures of such a high degree of likelihood that their non-occurrence need not be taken into practical account, and which are moreover regarded as merely temporary. But in Probability the conjecture may have any degree of likelihood about it; it may be just as likely as the other alternative, nay it may be much less likely. In these latter cases, for instance, if the chances are very much against the man's death, it is surely an abuse of language to speak of the 'fact' of his dying, even though we qualify it by declaring it to be highly improbable. The subject-matter essential to Probability being the uncertain, we can never with propriety employ upon it language which in its original and correct application is only appropriate to what is actually or approximately certain.

§ 8. It should be remembered also that this state of things, thus characteristic of Probability, is *permanent* there. So long as they remain under the treatment of that science our conjectures, or whatever we like to call them, never develop into facts. I calculate, for instance, the chance that a die will give ace, or that a man will live beyond a certain age. Such an approximation to knowledge as is thus acquired is as much as we can ever afterwards hope to get, unless we resort to other methods of enquiry. We do not, as in Induction, feel ourselves on the brink of some experimental or other proof which at any moment may raise it into certainty. It is nothing but a conjecture of a certain degree of strength, and such it will ever remain, so long as Probability is left to deal with it. If anything more is ever to be made out of it we must appeal to direct experience, or to some kind of inductive proof. As we have so often said, individual facts can never be determined here, but merely ultimate tendencies and averages of many events. I may, indeed, by a second appeal to Probability improve the character of my conjecture, through being able to refer it to a narrower and better class of statistics; but its essential nature remains throughout what it was.

It appears to me therefore that the account of the Materialist view of logic indicated at the commencement of this chapter, though substantially sound, needs some slight reconsideration and restatement. It answers admirably so far as ordinary Induction is concerned, but needs some revision if it is to be equally applicable to that wider view of the nature and processes of acquiring knowledge wherein the science of logic is considered to involve Probability also as well as Induction.

§ 9. Briefly then it is this. We regard the scientific thinker, whether he be the original investigator who discovers, or the logician who analyses and describes the proofs that may be offered, as surrounded by a world of objective phenomena extending indefinitely both ways in time, and in every direction in space. Most of them are, and always will remain, unknown. If we speak of them as facts we mean that they are potential objects of human knowledge, that under appropriate circumstances men could come to determinate and final agreement about them. The scientific or

material logician has to superintend the process of converting
as much as possible of these unknown phenomena into what
are known, of aggregating them, as we have said above, about
the nucleus of certain data which experience and observation
had to start with.   In so doing his principal resources are
the Methods of Induction, of which something has been
said in a former chapter; another resource is found in the
Theory of Probability, and another in Deduction.

Now, however such language may be objected to as
savouring of Conceptualism, I can see no better compendious
way of describing these processes than by saying that we are
engaged in getting at conceptions of these external phenomena, and as far as possible converting these conceptions
into facts.   What is the natural history of 'facts' if we trace
them back to their origin ?   They first come into being as
mere guesses or conjectures, as contemplated possibilities
whose correspondence with reality is either altogether dis-
believed or regarded as entirely doubtful.   In this stage, of
course, their contrast with facts is sharp enough.   *How* they
arise it does not belong to Logic but to Psychology to say.
Logic indeed has little or nothing to do with them whilst
they are in this form.   Everyone is busy all his life in entertaining such guesses upon various subjects, the superiority of
the philosopher over the common man being mainly found in
the quality of his guesses, and in the skill and persistence
with which he sifts and examines them.   In the next stage
they mostly go by the name of theories or hypotheses, when
they are comprehensive in their scope, or are in any way on
a scale of grandeur and importance : when however they are
of a trivial kind, or refer to details, we really have no distinctive or appropriate name for them, and must be content
therefore to call them 'conceptions.'   Through this stage
they flit with great rapidity in Inductive Logic; often the

logician keeps them back until their evidence is so strong
that they come before the world at once in the full dignity
of facts. Hence, as already remarked, this stage of their
career is not much dwelt upon in Logic. But the whole
business of Probability is to discuss and estimate them at
this point. Consequently, so far as this science is concerned,
the explanation of the Material logician as to the reference
of names and propositions has to be modified.

§ 10. The best way therefore of describing our position
in Probability is as follows :—We are *entertaining a conception* of some event, past, present, or future. From the nature
of the case this conception is all that can be actually entertained by the mind. In its present condition it would be
incorrect to call it a fact, though we would willingly, if we
could, convert it into such by making certain of it one way
or the other. But so long as our conclusions are to be
effected by considerations of Probability only, we cannot do
this. The utmost we can do is to *estimate* or *evaluate* it.
The whole function of Probability is to give rules for so
doing. By means of reference to statistics or by direct
deduction, as the case may be, we are enabled to say how
much this conception is to be believed, that is in what proportion out of the total number of cases we shall be right
in so doing. Our position, therefore, in these cases seems
distinctly that of entertaining a conception, and the process
of inference is that of ascertaining to what extent we are
justified in adding this conception to the already received
body of truth and fact.

So long, then, as we are confined to Probability these
conceptions remain such. But if we turn to Induction we
see that they are meant to go a step further. Their final
stage is not reached until they have ripened into facts, and
so taken their place amongst uncontested truths. This is

their final destination in Logic, and our task is not accomplished until they have reached it.

§ 11.   Such language as this in which we speak of our position in Probability as being that of entertaining a conception, and being occupied in determining what degree of belief is to be assigned to it, may savour of Conceptualism, but is in spirit perfectly different from it.   Our ultimate reference is always to facts.   We start from them as our data, and reach them again eventually in our results whenever it is possible.   In Probability, of course, we cannot do this in the individual result, but even then (as shown in Ch. VI.) we always *justify* our conclusions by appeal to facts, viz. to what happens in the long run.

The discussion which has been thus given to this part of the subject may seem somewhat tedious, but it was so obviously forced upon us when considering the distinction between the two main views of Logic, that it was impossible to pass it over without fear of misapprehension and confusion.   Moreover, as will be seen in the course of the next chapter, several important conclusions could not have been properly explained and justified without first taking pains to make this part of our ground perfectly plain and satisfactory.

CHAPTER XII.

CONSEQUENCES OF THE FOREGOING DISTINCTIONS.

§ 1. We are now in a position to explain and justify some important conclusions which, if not direct consequences of the distinctions laid down in the last chapter, will at any rate be more readily appreciated and accepted after that exposition.

In the first place, it will be seen that in Probability *time* has nothing to do with the question; in other words, it does not matter whether the event, whose probability we are discussing, be past, present, or future. The problem before us, in its simplest form, is this :—Statistics (extended by Induction, and practically often gained by Deduction) inform us that a certain event has happened, does happen, or will happen, in a certain way in a certain proportion of cases. We form a conception of that event, and regard it as possible ; but we want to do more; we want to know *how much* we ought to expect it (under the explanations given in a former chapter about quantity of belief). There is therefore a sort of relative futurity about the event, inasmuch as our knowledge of the fact, and therefore our justification or otherwise of the correctness of our surmise, almost necessarily comes after the surmise was formed; but the futurity is only relative. The evidence by which the question is to be settled may not be forthcoming yet, or we may have it by us but only consult it afterwards. It is from the fact of the futurity being, as above described, only relative, that I have preferred to speak of the conception of the event rather than of the anticipation of it. The latter term, which in some respects would have seemed more intelligible and appropriate, is open to the objection, that it does rather, in popular estimation, convey the notion of an absolute as opposed to a relative futurity.

§ 2. For example; a die is thrown. Once in six times it gives ace; if therefore we assume, without examination, that the throw is ace, we shall be right once in six times. In so doing we may, according to the usual plan, go *forwards* in time; that is, form our opinion about the throw beforehand, when no one can tell what it will be. Or we might go *backwards;* that is, form an opinion about dice that had been cast on some occasion in time past, and then correct our opinion by the testimony of some one who had been a witness of the throws. In either case the mental operation is precisely the same; an opinion formed merely on statistical grounds is afterwards corrected by specific evidence. The opinion may have been formed upon a past, present, or future event; the evidence which corrects it afterwards may be our own eyesight, or the testimony of others, or any kind of inference; by the evidence is merely meant such subsequent examination of the case as is assumed to set the matter at rest. It is quite possible, of course, that this specific evidence should never be forthcoming; the conception in that case remains as a conception, and never obtains that degree of conviction which qualifies it to be regarded as a 'fact.' This is clearly the case with all past throws of dice the results of which do not happen to have been recorded.

In discussing games of chance there are obvious advantages in confining ourselves to what is really, as well as relatively, future, for in that case direct information concerning the contemplated result being impossible, all persons are on precisely the same footing of comparative ignorance, and must form their opinion entirely from the known or inferred frequency of occurrence of the event in question.   On the other hand, if the event be passed, there is almost always evidence of some kind and of some value, however slight, to inform us what the event really was; if this evidence is not actually at hand, we can generally, by waiting a little, obtain something that shall be at least of some use to us in forming our opinion.   Practically therefore we generally confine ourselves, in anticipations of this kind, to what is really future, and so in popular estimation futurity becomes indissolubly associated with probability.

§ 3.   There is however an error closely connected with the above view of the subject, or at least an inaccuracy of expression which is constantly liable to lead to error, which has found wide acceptance, and has been sanctioned by writers of the greatest authority.   For instance, both Butler, in his *Analogy*, and Mill, have drawn attention, under one form of expression or another, to the distinction between improbability before the event and improbability after the event, which they consider to be perfectly different things. That this phraseology indicates a distinction of importance cannot be denied, but it seems to me that the language in which it is often expressed requires to be amended.

Butler's remarks on this subject occur in his *Analogy*, in the chapter on miracles.   Admitting that there is a strong presumption against miracles (his equivalent for the ordinary expression, an 'improbability before the event') he strives to obtain assent for them by showing that other events, which also have a strong presumption against them, are received on what is in reality very slight evidence.   He says, "There is a very strong presumption against common speculative truths, and against the most ordinary facts, before the proof of them; which yet is overcome by almost any proof. There is a presumption of millions to one against the story of Cæsar, or of any other man. For, suppose a number of common facts so and so circumstanced, of which one had no kind of proof, should happen to come into one's thoughts, every one would without any possible doubt conclude them to be false. And the like may be said of a single common fact."

§ 4. These remarks have been a good deal criticized, and they certainly seem to me misleading and obscure in their reference. If one may judge by the context. and by another passage in which the same argument is afterwards referred to[1], it would certainly appear that Butler drew no distinction between miraculous accounts, and other accounts which, to use any of the various expressions in common use, are unlikely or improbable or have a presumption against them; and concluded that since some of the latter were instantly accepted upon somewhat mediocre testimony, it was altogether irrational to reject the former when similarly or better supported[2]. This subject will come again under our notice, and demand fuller discussion, in the chapter on the Credibility of extraordinary stories. It will suffice here to

---

[1] "Is it not self-evident that internal improbabilities of all kinds weaken external proof? Doubtless, but to what practical purpose can this be alleged here, when it has been proved before, that real internal improbabilities, which rise even to moral certainty, are overcome by the most ordinary testimony." Part II. ch. III.

[2] "Miracles must not be compared to common natural events; or to events which, though uncommon, are similar to what we daily experience; but to the extraordinary phenomena of nature. And then the comparison will be between the presumption against miracles, and the presumption against such uncommon appearances, suppose as comets,"...... Part II. ch. II.

remark that, however satisfactory such a view of the matter might be to some theologians, no antagonist of miracles would for a moment accept it. He would naturally object that, instead of the miraculous element being (as Butler considers) "a small additional presumption" against the narrative, it involved the events in a totally distinct class of incredibility; that it multiplied, rather than merely added to, the difficulties and objections in the way of accepting the account.

Mill's remarks (*Logic*, Bk. III. ch. XXV. § 4) are of a different character. Discussing the grounds of disbelief he speaks of people making the mistake of "overlooking the distinction between (what may be called) improbability before the fact, and improbability after it, two different properties, the latter of which is always a ground of disbelief, the former not always." He instances the throwing of a die. It is improbable beforehand that it should turn up ace, and yet afterwards, "there is no reason for disbelieving it if any credible witness asserts it." So again, "the chances are greatly against A. B.'s dying, yet if any one tells us that he died yesterday we believe it."

§ 5. That there is some difficulty about such problems as these must be admitted. The fact that so many people find them a source of perplexity, and that such various explanations are offered to solve the perplexity, are a sufficient proof of this[1]. The considerations of the last chapter,

---

[1] For instance, Sir J. F. Stephen explains it by drawing a distinction between chances and probabilities, which he says that Butler has confused together; "the objection that very ordinary proof will overcome a presumption of millions to one is based upon a confusion between pro- babilities and chances. The proba- bility of an event is its capability of being proved. Its chance is the numerical proportion between the number of possible cases—supposed to be equally favourable—favourable to its occurrence; and the number of possible cases unfavourable to its

however, over-technical and even scholastic as some of the
language in which it was expressed may have seemed to the
reader, will I hope guide us to a more satisfactory way of
regarding the matter.

When we speak of an improbable event, it must be
remembered that, objectively considered, an event can only
be more or less *rare;* the extreme degree of rarity being of
course that in which the event does not occur at all. Now,
as was shown in the last chapter, our position, when forming
judgments of the time in question, is that of entertaining
a conception or conjecture (call it what we will), and assigning a certain weight of trustworthiness to it. The real
distinction, therefore, between the two classes of examples
respectively, which are adduced both by Butler and by Mill,
consists in the way in which those conceptions are obtained ;
they being obtained in one case by the process of guessing,
and in the other by that of giving heed to the reports of
witnesses.

§ 6. Take Butler's instance first. In the 'presumption
before the proof' we have represented to us a man thinking
of the story of Cæsar, that is, making a guess about certain
historical events without any definite grounds for it, and
then speculating as to what value is to be attached to the
probability of its truth. Such a guess is of course, as he
says, concluded to be false. But what does he understand
by the 'presumption after the proof'? That a story not
adopted at random, but actually suggested and supported by
witnesses, should be true. The latter might be accepted,
whilst the former would undoubtedly be rejected ; but all
that this proves, or rather illustrates, is that the testimony

occurrence" (*General view of the Cri-*
minal Law of England, p. 255).
Donkin, again (*Phil. Magazine,* June,
1851), employs the terms improbability and incredibility to mark the
same distinction.

of almost any witness is in most cases vastly better than a mere guess[1]. We may in both cases alike speak of 'the event' if we will; in fact, as was admitted in the last chapter, common language will not readily lend itself to any other way of speaking. But it should be clearly understood that, phrase it how we will, what is really present to the man's mind, and what is to have its probable value assigned to it, is the conception of an event, in the sense in which that expression has already been explained. And surely no two conceptions can have a much more important distinction put between them than that which is involved in supposing one to rest on a mere guess, and the other on the report of a witness. Precisely the same remarks apply to the example given by Mill. Before A. B.'s death our opinion upon the subject was nothing but a guess of our own founded upon life statistics; after his death it was founded upon the evidence of some one who presumably had tolerable opportunities of knowing what the facts really were.

§ 7. That the distinction before us has no essential connection whatever with time is indeed obvious on a moment's consideration. Conceive for a moment that some one had opportunities of knowing whether A. B. would die or not. If he told us that A. B. would die to-morrow, we should in that case be just as ready to believe him as when he tells us that A. B. *has* died. If we continued to feel any doubt about the statement (supposing always that we had full

---

[1] In the extreme case of the witness himself merely guessing, or being as untrustworthy as if he merely guessed, the two stories will of course stand on precisely the same footing. This case will be noticed again in Chapter xvii. It may be remarked that there are several subtleties here which cannot be adequately noticed without some previous investigation into the question of the credibility of witnesses.

confidence about his veracity in matters into which he had
duly enquired), it would be because we thought that in his
case, as in ours, it was equivalent to a guess, and nothing
more. So with the event when past, the fact of its being
past makes no difference whatever; until the credible witness informs us of what he knows to have occurred, we
should doubt it if it happened to come into our minds, just
as much as if it were future.

The distinction, therefore, between probability before the
event and probability after the event seems to resolve itself
simply into this;—before the event we often have no better
means of information than to appeal to statistics in some
form or other, and so to guess amongst the various possible
alternatives; after the event the guess may most commonly
be improved or superseded by appeal to specific evidence,
in the shape of testimony or observation. Hence, naturally,
our estimate in the latter case is commonly of much more
value. But if these characteristics were anyhow inverted;
if, that is, we were to confine ourselves to guessing about the
past, and if we could find any additional evidence about the
future, the respective values of the different estimates would
also be inverted. The difference between these values has
no necessary connection with time, but depends entirely
upon the different grounds upon which our conception or
conjecture about the event in question rests.

§ 8. The following imaginary example will serve to
bring out the point indicated above. Conceive a people with
very short memories, and who preserved no kind of record to
perpetuate their hold upon the events which happened
amongst them[1]. The whole region of the past would then be

---

[1] According to Dante, something
resembling this prevailed amongst
the occupants of the *Inferno*. The

cardinals and others whom he there
meets are able to *give* information
about many events which were yet

to them what much of the future is to us; viz. a region of
guesses and conjectures, one in reference to which they
could only judge upon general considerations of probability,
rather than by direct and specific evidence. But conceive
also that they had amongst them a race of prophets who
could succeed in foretelling the future with as near an
approach to accuracy and trustworthiness as our various
histories, and biographies, and recollections, can attain in
respect to the past. The present and usual functions of
direct evidence or testimony, and of probability, would then
be simply inverted; and so in consequence would the present accidental characteristics of improbability before and
after the event. It would then be the latter which would
by comparison be regarded as 'not always a ground of disbelief,' whereas in the case of the former we should then
have it maintained that it always was so.

§ 9. The origin of the mistake just discussed is worth
enquiring into. I take it to be as follows. It is often the
case, as above remarked, when we are speculating about
a future event, and almost always the case when that future
event is taken from a game of chance, that all persons are in
precisely the same condition of ignorance in respect to it.
The limit of available information is confined to statistics,
and amounts to the knowledge that the unknown event
must assume some one of various alternative forms. The
conjecture, therefore, of any one man about it is as valuable
as that of any other. But in regard to the past the case is
very different. Here we are not in the habit of relying
upon statistical information. Hence the conjectures of different men are of extremely different values; in the case of
many they amount to what we call positive knowledge.

to happen upon earth, but they had   actually had happened.
to *ask* it for many events which

This puts a broad distinction, in popular estimation, between what may be called the objective certainty of the past and of the future, a distinction, however, which from the standing-point of a science of inference ought to have no existence.

In consequence of this, when we apply to the past and the future respectively the somewhat ambiguous expression 'the chance of the event,' it commonly comes to bear very different significations. Applied to the future it bears its proper meaning, namely, the value to be assigned to a conjecture upon statistical grounds. It does so, because in this case hardly any one has more to judge by than such conjectures. But applied to the past it shifts its meaning, owing to the fact that whereas some men have conjectures only, others have positive knowledge. By the chance of the event is now often meant, not the value to be assigned to a conjecture founded on statistics, but to such a conjecture derived from and enforced by any body else's conjecture, that is by his knowledge and his testimony.

§ 10. There is a class of cases in apparent opposition to some of the statements in this chapter, but which will be found, when examined closely, decidedly to confirm them. I am walking, say, in a remote part of the country, and suddenly meet with a friend. At this I am naturally surprised. Yet if the view be correct that we cannot properly speak about events in themselves being probable or improbable, but only say this of our conjectures about them, how do we explain this? We had formed no conjecture beforehand, for we were not thinking about anything of the kind, but yet few would fail to feel surprise at such an incident.

The reply might fairly be made that we *had* formed such anticipations tacitly. On any such occasion every one unconsciously divides things into those which are known to him and those which are not. During a considerable previous period a countless number of persons had met us, and all fallen into the list of the unknown to us. There was nothing to remind us of having formed the anticipation or distinction at all, until it was suddenly called out into vivid consciousness by the exceptional event. The words which we should instinctively use in our surprise seem to show this:—'Who would have thought of seeing you here?' viz. Who would have given any weight to the latent thought if it had been called out into consciousness beforehand? We put our words into the past tense, showing that we have had the distinction lurking in our minds all the time. We always have a multitude of such ready-made classes of events in our minds, and when a thing happens to fall into one of those classes which are very small we cannot help noticing the fact.

Or suppose I am one of a regiment into which a shot flies, and it strikes me, and me only. At this I am surprised, and why? Our common language will guide us to the reason. 'How strange that it should just have hit *me* of all men!' We are thinking of the very natural two-fold division of mankind into, ourselves, and everybody else; our surprise is again, as it were, retrospective, and in reference to this division. No anticipation was distinctly formed, because we did not think beforehand of the event, but the event, when it has happened, is at once assigned to its appropriate class.

§ 11. This view is confirmed by the following considerations. Tell the story to a friend, and he will be a little surprised, but less so than we were, *his* division in this particular case being,—his friends (of whom we are but one), and the rest of mankind. It is not a necessary division, but it is the one which will be most likely suggested to him.

Tell it again to a perfect stranger, and his division being

different (viz. we falling into the majority) we shall fail to make him perceive that there is anything at all remarkable in the event.

It is not of course attempted in these remarks to justify our surprise in every case in which it exists. Different persons might be differently affected in the cases supposed, and the examples are therefore given mainly for illustration. Still on principles already discussed (Ch. VI. § 32) we might expect to find something like a general justification of the amount of surprise.

§ 12. The answer commonly given in these cases is confined to attempting to show that the surprise should not arise, rather than to explaining how it does arise. It takes the following form,—' You have no right to be surprised, for nothing remarkable has really occurred. If this particular thing had not happened something equally improbable must. If the shot had not hit you or your friend, it must have hit some one else who was *à priori* as unlikely to be hit.'

For one thing this answer does not explain the fact that almost every one *is* surprised in such cases, and surprised somewhat in the different proportions mentioned above. Moreover it has the inherent unsatisfactoriness of admitting that something improbable has really happened, but getting over the difficulty by saying that all the other alternatives were equally improbable. A natural inference from this is that there is a class of things, in themselves really improbable, which can yet be established upon very slight evidence. Butler accepted this inference, and worked it out to the strange conclusion given above. Mill attempts to avoid it by the consideration of the very different values to be assigned to improbability before and after the event. Some further discussion of this point will be found in the chapter on Fallacies, and in that on the Credibility of Extraordinary Stories.

§ 13.   In connection with the subject at present under discussion we will now take notice of a distinction which we shall often find insisted on in works on Probability, but to which apparently needless importance has been attached. It is frequently said that probability is *relative*, in the sense that it has a different value to different persons according to their respective information upon the subject in question.   For example, two persons, *A* and *B*, are going to draw a ball from a bag containing 4 balls : *A* knows that the balls are black and white, but does not know more ; *B* knows that three are black and one white.   It would be said that the probability of a white ball to *A* is ½, and to *B* ¼.

When however we regard the subject from the material standing point, there really does not seem to me much more in this than the principle, equally true in every other science, that our inferences will vary according to the data we assume.   We might on logical grounds with almost equal propriety speak of the area of a field or the height of a mountain being relative, and therefore having one value to one person and another to another.   The real meaning of the example cited above is this : *A* supposes that he is choosing white at random out of a series which in the long run would give white and black equally often ; *B* supposes that he is choosing white out of a series which in the long run would give three black to one white.   By the application, therefore, of a precisely similar rule they draw different conclusions ; but so they would under the same circumstances in any other science.   If two men are measuring the height of a mountain, and one supposes his base to be 1000 feet, whilst the other takes it to be 1001, they would of course form different opinions about the height. The science of mensuration is not supposed to have anything to do with the truth of the data, but assumes them to have been correctly taken ; why should not this be equally the case with Probability, making of course due allowance for the peculiar character of the data with which it is concerned ?

§ 14. This view of the relativeness of probability is connected, as it appears to me, with the subjective view of the science, and is indeed characteristic of it. It seems a fair illustration of the weak side of that view, that it should lead us to lay any stress on such an expression. As was fully explained in the last chapter, in proportion as we work out the Conceptualist principle we are led away from the fundamental question of the material logic, viz. Is our belief actually correct, or not ? and, if the former, to what extent and degree is it correct ? We are directed rather to ask, What belief does any one as a matter of fact hold ? And, since the belief thus entertained naturally varies according to the circumstances and other sources of information of the person in question, its relativeness comes to be admitted as inevitable, or at least it is not to be wondered at if such should be the case.

On our view of Probability, therefore, its 'relativeness' in any given case is a misleading expression, and it will be found much preferable to speak of the effect produced by variations in the nature and amount of the data which we have before us. Now it must be admitted that there are frequently cases in our science in which such variations are peculiarly likely to be found. For instance, I am expecting a friend who is a passenger in an ocean steamer. There are a hundred passengers on board, and the crew also numbers a hundred. I read in the papers that one person was lost by falling overboard ; my anticipation that it was my friend who

was lost is but small, of course. On turning to another
paper, I see that the man who was lost was a passenger, not
one of the crew; my slight anxiety is at once doubled. But
another account adds that it was an Englishman, and on
that line at that season the English passengers are known
to be few; I at once begin to entertain decided fears. And
so on, every trifling bit of information instantly affecting my
expectations.

§ 15. Now since it is peculiarly characteristic of Probability, as distinguished from Induction, to be thus at the
mercy, so to say, of every little fact that may be floating
about when we are in the act of forming our opinion, what
can be the harm (it may be urged) of expressing this state
of things by terming our state of expectation *relative?*

There seem to me to be two objections. In the first place,
as just mentioned, we are induced to reject such an expression on grounds of consistency. It is inconsistent with the
general spirit and treatment of the subject hitherto adopted,
and tends to divorce Probability from Inductive logic instead
of regarding them as cognate sciences. We are aiming at
truth, as far as that goal can be reached by our road, and
therefore we dislike to regard our conclusions as relative in
any other sense than that in which truth itself may be said
to be relative.

In the second place, this condition of unstable assent,
this constant liability to have our judgment affected, to any
degree and at any moment, by the accession of new knowledge, though doubtless characteristic of Probability, does
not seem to me characteristic of it in its sounder and more
legitimate applications. It seems rather appropriate to a
precipitate judgment formed in accordance with the rules,
than a strict example of their natural employment. Such
precipitate judgments may occur in the case of ordinary de-

ductive conclusions. In the practical exigencies of life we
are constantly in the habit of forming a hasty opinion with
nearly full confidence, at any rate temporarily, upon the
strength of evidence which we must well know at the time
cannot be final. We wait a short time, and something else
turns up which induces us to alter our opinion, perhaps to
reverse it. Here our conclusions may have been perfectly
sound under the given circumstances, that is, they may be
such as every one else would have drawn who was bound to
make up his mind upon the data before us, and they are
unquestionably 'relative' judgments in the sense now under
discussion. And yet, I think, every one would shrink from
so terming them who wished systematically to carry out the
view that Logic was to be regarded as an organon of truth.

§ 16. In the examples of Probability which we have
hitherto employed, we have for the most part assumed that
there was a certain body of statistics set before us on which
our conclusion was to rest. It was assumed, on the one
hand, that no direct specific evidence could be got, so that
the judgment was really to be one of Probability, and to rest
on these statistics; in other words, that nothing better than
them was available for us. But it was equally assumed, on
the other hand, that these statistics were open to the observation of every one, so that we need not have to put up with
anything inferior to them in forming our opinion. In other
words, we have been assuming that here, as in the case of
most other sciences, those who have to draw a conclusion
start from the same footing of opportunity and information.
This, for instance, clearly is or ought to be the case when
we are concerned with games of chance; ignorance or misapprehension of the common data is never contemplated
there. So with the statistics of life, or other insurance: so
long as our judgment is to be accurate (after its fashion) or

justifiable, the common tables of mortality are all that any one has to go by.

§ 17. It is true that in the case of a man's prospect of death we should each qualify our judgment by what we knew or reasonably supposed as to his health, habits, profession, and so on, and should thus arrive at varying estimates. But no one could *justify* his own estimate without appealing explicitly or implicitly to the statistical grounds on which he had relied, and if these were not previously available to other persons, he must now set them before their notice. In other words, the judgments we entertain, here as elsewhere, are only relative so long as we rest them on grounds peculiar to ourselves. The process of justification, which I consider to be essential to logic, has a tendency to correct such individualities of judgment, and to set all observers on the same basis as regards their data.

It is better therefore to regard the conclusions of Probability as being absolute and objective, in the same sense as, though doubtless in a far less degree than, they are in Induction. Fully admitting that our conclusions will in many cases vary exceedingly from time to time by fresh accessions of knowledge, it is preferable to regard such fluctuations of assent as partaking of the nature of precipitate judgments, founded on special statistics, instead of depending only on those which are common to all observers. In calling such judgments precipitate it is not implied that there is any blame in entertaining them, but simply that, for one reason or another, we have been induced to form them without waiting for the possession of the full amount of evidence, statistical or otherwise, which might ultimately be looked for. This explanation will suit the facts equally well, and is more consistent with the general philosophical position maintained in this work.

CHAPTER XIII.

§ 1. THE reader who knows anything of the scholastic Logic will have perceived before now that we have been touching in a variety of places upon that most thorny and repulsive of districts in the logical territory;—modality. It will be advisable, however, to put together, somewhat more definitely, what has to be said upon the subject. I propose, therefore, to devote this chapter to a brief account of the principal varieties of treatment which the modals have received at the hands of professed logicians.

It must be remarked at the outset that the sense in which modality and modal propositions have been at various times understood, is by no means fixed and invariably the same. This diversity of view has arisen partly from corresponding differences in the view taken of the province and nature of logic, and partly from differences in the philosophical and scientific opinions entertained as to the constitution and order of nature. In later times, moreover, another very powerful agent in bringing about a change in the treatment of the subject must be recognized in the gradual and steady growth of the theory of Probability, as worked out by the mathematicians from their own point of view.

§ 2. In spite, however, of these differences of treatment, there has always been some community of subject-matter in the discussions upon this topic. There has almost always been some reference to quantity of belief; enough perhaps to justify De Morgan's[1] remark, that Probability was "the unknown God whom the schoolmen ignorantly worshipped when they so dealt with this species of enunciation, that it was said to be beyond human determination whether they most tortured the modals, or the modals them." But this reference to quantity of belief has sometimes been direct and immediate, sometimes indirect and arising out of the nature of the subject-matter of the proposition. The fact is, that that distinction between the purely subjective and purely objective views of logic, which I have endeavoured to bring out into prominence in the eleventh chapter, was not by any means clearly recognized in early times, nor indeed before the time of Kant, and the view to be taken of modality naturally shared in the consequent confusion. This will, I hope, be made clear in the course of the following chapter, which is intended to give a brief sketch of the principal different ways in which the modality of propositions has been treated in logic. As it is not proposed to give anything like a regular history of the subject, there will be no necessity to adhere to any strict sequence of time, or to discuss the opinions of any writers, except those who may be taken as representative of tolerably distinct views. The outcome of such investigation will be, I hope, to convince the reader (if, indeed, he had not come to that conviction before), that the logicians, after having had a long and fair trial, have failed to make anything satisfactory out of this subject of the modals by their methods of enquiry and treatment; and that it ought, therefore, to be banished entirely from that science, and relegated to Probability.

§ 3. From the earliest study of the syllogistic process it was seen that, complete as that process is within its own

[1] *Formal Logic*, p. 232.

domain, the domain, at any rate under its simplest treatment, is a very limited one. Propositions of the pure form,—All (or some) *A* is (or is not) *B*,—are found in practice to form but a small portion even of our categorical statements. We are perpetually meeting with others which express the relation of *B* to *A* with various degrees of necessity or probability; e.g. *A* must be *B*, *A* may be *B*; or the effect of such facts upon our judgment, e.g. I am perfectly certain that *A* is *B*, I think that *A* may be *B*; with many others of a more or less similar type. The question at once arises, How are such propositions to be treated? It does not seem to have occurred to the old logicians, as to some of their successors in modern times, simply to reject all consideration of this topic. Their faith in the truth and completeness of their system of inference was far too firm for them to suppose it possible that forms of proposition universally recognized as significant in popular speech, and forms of inference universally recognized there as valid, were to be omitted because they were inconvenient or complicated.

§ 4. One very simple plan suggests itself, and has indeed been repeatedly advocated, viz. just to transfer all that is characteristic of such propositions into that convenient receptacle for what is troublesome elsewhere, the predicate[1]. Has not another so-called modality been thus got rid of[2]?

---

[1] This appears to be the purport of some statements in a very confused passage in Whately's *Logic* (Bk. II., ch. IV. § 1). "A modal proposition may be stated as a pure one by attaching the mode to one of the terms, and the proposition will in all respects fall under the foregoing rules;...'It is probable that all knowledge is useful;' 'probably useful' is here the predicate." He draws apparently no such distinction as that between the true and false modality referred to in the next note. What is really surprising is that even Hamilton puts the two (the true and the false modality) upon the same footing. "In regard to these [the former] the case is precisely the same; the mode is merely a part of the predicate." *Logic*, I. 257.

[2] I allude of course to such ex-

and has it not been attempted by the same device to abolish
the distinctive characteristic of negative propositions, viz. by
shifting the negative particle into the predicate ? It must
be admitted that, up to a certain point, something may be
done in this way. Given the reasoning, ' Those who take
arsenic will probably die ; *A* has taken it, therefore he will
probably die ;' it is easy to convert this into an ordinary
syllogism of the pure type, by simply wording the major,
' Those who take arsenic are people-who-will-probably-die,'
when the conclusion follows in the same form, '*A* is one
who-will-probably-die.' But this device will only carry us
a very little way. Suppose that the minor premise also is
of the same modal description, e. g. '*A* has probably taken
arsenic,' and it will be seen that we cannot relegate the
modality here also to the predicate without being brought to
a stop by finding that there are four terms in the syllogism.

But even if there were not this particular objection, it
does not appear that anything is to be gained in the way of
intelligibility or method by such a device as the above. For

amples as '*A* killed *B* unjustly,' in
which the killing of *B* by *A* was
sometimes said to be asserted not
simply but with a modification.
(Hamilton's *Logic*, I. 256.) It is
obvious that the modification in
such cases is by rights merely a
part of the predicate, there being no
formal distinction between '*A* is the
killer of *B*' and '*A* is the unjust
killer of *B*.' Indeed some logicians
who were too conservative to reject
the generic name of modality in this
application adopted the common expedient of introducing a specific distinction which did away with its
meaning, terming the spurious kind

' material modality' and the genuine
kind ' formal modality'. The former
included all the cases in which the
modification belonged by right either
to the predicate or to the subject;
the latter was reserved for the cases
in which the modification affected
the real conjunction of the predicate
with the subject. (Keckermann,
Systema Logicæ, Lib. II. ch. 3.) It
was, I believe, a common scholastic
distinction.

For some account of the dispute
as to whether the negative particle
was to be considered to belong to
the copula or to the predicate, see
Hamilton's *Logic*, I. 253.

what is meant by a modal predicate, by the predicate 'probably mortal,' for instance, in the proposition 'All poisonings by arsenic are probably mortal'? If the analogy with ordinary pure propositions is to hold good, it must be a predicate referring to the *whole* of the subject, for the subject is distributed. But then we are at once launched into the difficulties discussed in a former chapter (Ch. VI. §§ 19—25), when we attempt to justify or verify the application of the predicate. We have to enquire (at least on the view adopted in this work) whether the application of the predicate 'probably mortal' to the *whole* of the subject, really means at bottom anything else than that the predicate 'mortal' is to be applied to a *portion* (more than half) of the members denoted by the subject. When the transference of the modality to the predicate raises such intricate questions as to the sense in which the predicate is to be interpreted, there is surely nothing gained by the step.

§ 5. A second, and more summary way of shelving all difficulties of the subject, so far at least as logic, or the writers upon logic, are concerned, is found by simply denying that modality has any connection whatever with logic. This is the course adopted by many modern writers, for instance, by Hamilton and Mansel, in reference to whom one cannot help remarking that an unduly large portion of their logical writings seems occupied with telling us what does *not* belong to logic. They justify their rejection on the ground that the mode belongs to the matter, and must be determined by a consideration of the matter, and therefore is extralogical. To a certain extent I agree with their grounds of rejection, for (as explained in Chapter VI.) it is not easy to see how the degree of modality of any proposition, whether premise or conclusion, can be justified without appeal to the matter. But then questions of justification, in any adequate sense of the term, belong to a range of considerations somewhat alien to Hamilton's and Mansel's way of regarding the science. The complete justification of our inferences is a matter which involves their truth or falsehood, a point with which these writers do not much concern themselves, being only occupied with the consistency of our reasonings, not with their conformity with fact. Were I speaking as a Hamiltonian I should say that modality *is* formal rather than material, for though we cannot justify the degree of our belief of a proposition without appeal to the matter, we can to a moderate degree of accuracy estimate it without any such appeal; and this would seem to be quite enough to warrant its being regarded as formal.

It must be admitted that Hamilton's account of the matter when he is recommending the rejection of the modals, is not by any means clear and consistent. He not only fails, as already remarked, to distinguish between the formal and the material (in other words, the true and the false) modality; but when treating of the former he fails to distinguish between the extremely diverse aspects of modality when viewed from the Aristotelian and the Kantian stand-points. Of the amount and significance of this difference we shall speak presently, but it may be just pointed out here that Hamilton begins (Vol. I. p. 257) by rejecting the modals on the ground that the distinctions between the necessary, the contingent, the possible, and the impossible, must be wholly rested on an appeal to the matter of the propositions, in which he is, I think, quite correct. But then a little further on (p. 260), in explaining 'the meaning of three terms which are used in relation to pure and modal propositions,' he gives the widely different Kantian, or threefold division into the apodeictic, the assertory, and the problematic. He does not take the precaution of pointing out to his hearers the very

different general views of logic from which these two accounts
of modality spring[1].

§ 6.   There is one kind of modal syllogism which it
would seem unreasonable to reject on the ground of its not
being formal, and which we may notice in passing.   The
premise 'Any *A* is probably *B*,' is equivalent to 'Most *A* are
B.'   Now it is obvious that from two such premises as 'Most
A are *B*,' 'Most *A* are *C*,' we can deduce the consequence,
'Some *C* are *B*.'   Since this holds good whatever may be
the nature of *A*, *B*, and *C*, it is, according to ordinary usage
of the term, a formal syllogism.   Mansel, however, refuses to
admit that any such syllogisms belong to formal logic.   His
reasons are given in a rather elaborate review[2] and criticism
of some of the logical works of De Morgan, to whom the
introduction of 'numerically definite syllogisms' is mainly
due.   Mansel does not take the particular example given
above, as he is discussing a somewhat more comprehensive
algebraic form.   He examines it in a special numerical
example[3]:—18 out of 21 *Y*s are *X*; 15 out of 21 *Y*s are *Z*;
the conclusion that 12 *Z*s are *X* is rejected from formal logic
on the ground that the arithmetical judgment involved is
synthetical, not analytical, and rests upon an intuition of
quantity.   We cannot enter upon any examination of these

[1] He has also given a short
discussion of the subject elsewhere
(*Discussions*, Ed. II. p. 702), in which
a somewhat different view is taken.
The modes are indeed here admitted
into logic, but only in so far as they
fall by subdivision under the relation
of genus and species, which is of
course tantamount to their entire
rejection; for they then differ in no
essential way from any other examples of that relation.

[2] *Letters, Lectures and Reviews*,
p. 61.   Elsewhere in the review (p.
45) he gives what appears to me a
somewhat different decision.

[3] It must be remembered that
this is not one of the proportional
propositions with which we have
been concerned in previous chapters :
it is meant that there are *exactly* 21
*Y*s, of which just 18 are *X*, not that
on the average 18 out of 21 may be
so regarded.

reasons here; but it may merely be remarked that his
criticism demands the acceptance of the Kantian doctrines
as to the nature of arithmetical judgments, and that it would
be better to base the rejection not on the ground that the
syllogism is not *formal*, but on the ground that it is not
analytical.

§ 7.   There is another and practical way of getting rid
of the perplexities of modal reasoning which must be noticed
here.   It is the resource of ordinary reasoners rather than the
decision of professed logicians[1], and, like the first method of
evasion already pointed out in this chapter, is of very partial
application.   It consists in treating the premises, during the
process of reasoning, as if they were pure, and then re-
introducing the modality into the conclusion, as a sort of
qualification of its full certainty.   When each of the premises is nearly certain, or when from any cause we are not
concerned with the extent of their departure from full certainty, this rough expedient will answer well enough.   It is,
I apprehend, the process which passes through the minds of
most persons in such cases, in so far as they reason consciously.
They would, presumably, in such an example as that previously given (§ 4), proceed as if the premises that 'those
who take arsenic will die,' and that 'the man in question
has taken it,' were quite true, instead of being only probably
true, and they would consequently draw the conclusion that
' he would die.'   But bearing in mind that the premises are
not certain, they would remember that the conclusion was
only to be held with a qualified assent.   This they would

---

[1] I consider however, as I have
said further on (p. 320), that the treatment in the older logics of Probable
syllogisms, and Dialectic syllogisms,
came to somewhat the same thing as
this, though they looked at the matter from a different point of view,
and expressed it in very different
language.

express quite correctly, if the mere nature and not the degree of that assent is taken into account, by saying that 'he is likely to die.' In this case the modality is rejected temporarily from the premises to be reintroduced into the conclusion.

It is obvious that such a process as this is of a very rough and imperfect kind. It does, in fact, omit from accurate consideration just the one point now under discussion. It takes no account of the varying shades of expression by which the degree of departure from perfect conviction is indicated, which is of course the very thing with which modality is intended to occupy itself. At best, therefore, it could only claim to be an extremely rude way of deciding questions, the accurate and scientific methods of treating which are demanded of us.

§ 8. In any employment of applied logic we have of course to go through such a process as that just mentioned. Outside of pure mathematics it can hardly ever be the case that the premises from which we reason are held with absolute conviction. Hence there must be a lapse from absolute conviction in the conclusion. But we reason on the hypothesis that the premises are true, and any trifling defection from certainty, of which we may be conscious, is mentally reserved as a qualification to the conclusion. But such considerations as these belong rather to ordinary applied logic; they amount to nothing more than a caution or hint to be borne in mind when the rules of the syllogism, or of induction, are applied in practice. When, however, we are treating of modality, the extent of the defection from full certainty is supposed to be sufficiently great for our language to indicate and appreciate it. What we then want is of course a scientific discussion of the principles in accordance with which this departure is to be measured and expressed, both in our premises and in our conclusion. Such a plan therefore for treating modality, as the one under discussion, is just as much a banishment of it from the field of real logical enquiry, as if we had determined avowedly to reject it from consideration.

§ 9. Before proceeding to a discussion of the various ways in which modality may be treated by those who admit it into logic, something must be said to clear up a possible source of confusion in this part of the subject. In the cases with which we have hitherto been mostly concerned, in the earlier chapters of this work, the characteristic of modality (for in this chapter we may with propriety use this logical term) has generally been found in singular and particular propositions. It presented itself when we had to judge of individual cases from a knowledge of the average, and was an expression of the fact that the proposition relating to these individuals referred to a portion only of the whole class from which the average was taken. Given that of men of fifty-five, three out of five will die in the course of twenty years, we have had to do with propositions of the vague form, 'It is probable that *AB* (of that age) will die,' or of the more precise form, 'It is three to two that *AB* will die,' within the specified time. Here the modal proposition naturally presents itself in the form of a singular or particular proposition.

§ 10. But when we turn to ordinary logic we may find *universal* propositions spoken of as modal. This must mostly be the case with those which are termed necessary or impossible, but it may also be the case with the probable. We may meet with the form 'All *X* is probably *Y.*' Adopting the same explanation here as has been throughout adopted in analogous cases, we must say that what is meant by the modality of such a proposition is the proportional number of times in which the universal proposition would be correctly made. And in this there is, so far, no difficulty. The only difference is that whereas the justification of the former, viz. the particular or individual kind of modal, was obtainable within the limits of the universal proposition which included it, the justification of the modality of a universal proposition has to be sought in a group or succession of other propositions. The proposition has to be referred to some group of similar ones and we have to consider the proportion of cases in which it will be true. But this distinction is not at all fundamental.

It is quite true that universal propositions from their nature are much less likely than individual ones to be justified, in practice, by such appeal. But, as has been already frequently pointed out, we are not concerned with the way in which our propositions are practically obtained, nor with the way in which men might find it most natural to test them; but with that ultimate justification to which we appeal in the last resort, and which has been abundantly shown to be of a statistical character. When, therefore, we say that 'it is probable that all X is Y,' what we mean is, that in more than half the cases we come across we should be right in so judging, and in less than half the cases we should be wrong.

§ 11. It is at this step that the possible ambiguity is encountered. When we talk of the chance that All X is Y, we contemplate or imply the complementary chance that it is not so. Now this latter alternative is not free from ambiguity. It might happen, for instance, in the cases of failure, that no X is Y, or it might happen that some X, only, is not Y; for both of these suppositions contradict the original proposition, and are therefore instances of its failure. In practice, no doubt, we should have various recognized rules and inductions to fall back upon in order to decide between these alternatives, though, of course, the appeal to them would be in strictness extralogical. But the mere existence of such an ambiguity, and the fact that it can only be cleared up by appeal to the subject-matter, are in themselves no real difficulty in the application of the conception of modality to universal propositions as well as to individual ones.

§ 12. Having noticed some of the ways in which the introduction of modality into logic has been evaded or rejected, we must now enter into a brief account of its treatment by those who have more or less deliberately admitted its claims to acceptance.

The first enquiry will be, What opinions have been held as to the nature of modality? that is, Is it primarily an affection of the matter of the proposition, and, if not, what is it exactly? In reference to this enquiry it appears to me, as already remarked, that amongst the earlier logicians no such clear and consistent distinction between the subjective and objective views of logic as is now commonly maintained, can be detected[1]. The result of this appears in their treatment of modality. This always had some reference to the subjective side of the proposition, viz. in this case to the nature or quantity of the belief with which it was entertained; but it is equally clear that this characteristic was not estimated at first hand, so to say, and in itself, but rather from a consideration of the matter determining what it should be. The commonly accepted scholastic or Aristotelian division, for instance, is into the necessary, the contingent, the possible, and the impossible. This is clearly a division according to

---

[1] The distinction is however by no means entirely neglected. Thus Smiglecius, when discussing the modal affections of certainty and necessity, says, " certitudo ad cognitionem spectat: necessitas vero est in re" (*Disputationes;* Disp. XIII., Quæst. XII.).

the matter almost entirely, for on the purely mental side the necessary and the impossible would be just the same; one implying full conviction of the truth of a proposition, and the other of that of its contradictory. So too, on the same side, it would not be easy to distinguish between the contingent and the possible. On the view in question, therefore, the modality of a proposition was determined by a reference to the nature of the subject-matter. In some propositions the nature of the subject-matter decided that the predicate was necessarily joined to the subject; in others that it was impossible that they should be joined; and so on.

§ 13. The artificial character of such a four-fold division will be too obvious to modern minds for it to be necessary to criticize it. A very slight study of nature and consequent appreciation of inductive evidence suffice to convince us that those uniformities upon which all connections of phenomena, whether called necessary or contingent, depend, demand extremely profound and extensive enquiry ; that they admit of no such simple division into clearly marked groups; and that, therefore, the pure logician had better not meddle with them[1].

The following extract from Grote's *Aristotle* (Vol. I. p. 192) will serve to show the origin of this four-fold division, its conformity with the science of the day, and consequently its utter want of conformity with that of our own time :—"The distinction of Problematical and Necessary Propositions corresponds, in the mind of Aristotle, to that capital and characteristic doctrine of his Ontology and Physics, already touched on in this chapter. He thought, as we have seen, that in the vast circumferential region of the Kosmos, from

[1] It may be remarked that Whately (*Logic*, Bk. II. ch. II. § 2) speaks of necessary, impossible and contingent matter, without any apparent suspicion that they belong entirely to an obsolete point of view.

the outer sidereal sphere down to the lunar sphere, celestial substance was a necessary existence and energy, sempiternal and uniform in its rotations and influence ; and that through its beneficent influence, pervading the concavity between the lunar sphere and the terrestrial centre (which included the four elements with their compounds) there prevailed a regularizing tendency called Nature; modified, however, and partly counteracted by independent and irregular forces called Spontaneity and Chance, essentially unknowable and unpredictable.　The irregular sequences thus named by Aristotle were the objective correlate of the Problematical Proposition in Logic.　In these sublunary sequences, as to future time, *may or may not,* was all that could be attained, even by the highest knowledge ; certainty, either of affirmation or negation, was out of the question.　On the other hand, the necessary and uniform energies of the celestial substance, formed the objective correlate of the Necessary Proposition in Logic ; this substance was not merely an existence, but an existence necessary and unchangeable...he considers the Problematical Proposition in Logic to be not purely subjective, as an expression of the speaker's ignorance, but something more, namely, to correlate with an objective essentially unknowable to all."

§ 14.　Even after this philosophy began to pass away, the divisions of modality originally founded upon it might have proved, as De Morgan has remarked[1], of considerable service in mediæval times.　As he says, people were much more frequently required to decide in one way or the other upon a single testimony, without there being a sufficiency of specific knowledge to test the statements made.　The old logician " did not know but that any day of the week might bring from Cathay or Tartary an account of men who ran on

[1] *Formal Logic,* p. 233.

four wheels of flesh and blood, or grew planted in the ground,
like Polydorus in the Æneid, as well evidenced as a great
many nearly as marvellous stories." Hence, in default of
better inductions, it might have been convenient to make
rough classifications of the facts which were and which were
not to be accepted on testimony (the necessary, the impossible, &c.), and to employ these provisional inductions (which
is all we should now regard them) as testing the stories
which reached him. Propositions belonging to the class of
the impossible might be regarded as having an antecedent
presumption against them so great as to prevail over almost
any testimony worth taking account of, and so on.

§ 15. But this old four-fold division of modals continued to be accepted and perpetuated by the logicians long
after all philosophical justification for it had passed away.
So far as I have been able to ascertain, scarcely any logician
of repute or popularity before Kant, was bold enough to
make any important change in the way of regarding them[1].
Even the Port-Royal Logic, founded as it is on Cartesianism,
repeats the traditional statements, though with extreme
brevity. This adherence to the old forms led, it need not be
remarked, to considerable inconsistency and confusion in
many cases. These forms were founded, as we have seen, on
an objective view of the province of logic, and this view was

---

[1] The subject was sometimes altogether omitted, as by Wolf. He
says a good deal however about probable propositions and syllogisms,
and, like Leibnitz before him, looked
forward to a "logica probabilium"
as something new and desirable. I
imagine that he had been influenced
by the writers on Chances, as of the
few who had already treated that
subject nearly all the most impor-

tant are referred to in one passage
(*Philosophia Rationalis sive Logica*,
§ 593).

Lambert stands quite apart. In
this respect, as in most others where
mathematical conceptions and symbols are involved, his logical attitude
is thoroughly unconventional. See,
for instance, his chapter 'Von dem
Wahrscheinlichen', in his *Neues
Organon*.

by no means rigidly carried out in many cases. In fact it
was beginning to be abandoned, to an extent and in directions which we have not opportunity here to discuss, before
the influence of Kant was felt. Many, for instance, added to
the list of the four, by including the true and the false;
occasionally also the probable, the supposed, and the certain
were added. This seems to show some tendency towards
abandoning the objective for the subjective view, or at least
indicates a hesitation between them.

§ 16. With Kant's view of modality almost every one is
familiar. He divides judgments, under this head, into the
apodeictic, the assertory, and the problematic. We shall have
to say something about the number and mutual relations of
these divisions presently; we are now only concerned with
the general view which they carry out. In this respect it will
be obvious at once what a complete change of position has
been reached. The 'necessary' and the 'impossible' demanded an appeal to the matter of a proposition in order to
recognize them; the 'apodeictic' and the 'assertory', on the
other hand, may be true of almost any matter, for they
demand nothing but an appeal to our consciousness in order
to distinguish between them. Moreover, the distinction
between the assertory and the problematic is so entirely
subjective and personal, that it may vary not only between
one person and another, but in the case of the same person
at different times. What one man knows to be true, another
may happen to be in doubt about. The apodeictic judgment
is one which we not only accept, but which we find ourselves
unable to reverse in thought; the assertory is simply accepted; the problematic is one about which we feel in
doubt.

This way of looking at the matter is the necessary outcome of the conceptualist or Kantian view of logic. It has

been followed by many logicians, not only by those who may be called followers of Kant, but by almost all who have felt his influence. Ueberweg, for instance, who is altogether at issue with Kant on some fundamental points, adopts it.

§ 17. The next question to be discussed is, How many subdivisions of modality are to be recognized? The Aristotelian or scholastic logicians, as we have seen, adopted a fourfold division. The exact relations of some of these to each other, especially the possible and the contingent, is an extremely obscure point, and one about which the commentators are by no means agreed. As, however, it seems tolerably clear that it was not consciously intended by the use of these four terms to exhibit a graduated scale of intensity of conviction, their correspondence with the province of modern probability is but slight, and the discussion of them, therefore, becomes rather a matter of special or antiquarian interest. De Morgan, indeed (*Formal Logic*, p. 232), says that the schoolmen understood by contingent more likely than not, and by possible less likely than not. I do not know on what authority this statement rests, but it credits them with a much nearer approach to the modern views of probability than one would have expected, and decidedly nearer than that of most of their successors[1]. The general conclusion at which I have arrived, after a reasonable amount of investigation, is that there were two prevalent views on the subject. Some (e.g. Burgersdyck, Bk. I. ch. 32) admitted that there were at bottom only two kinds of modality; the contingent and the possible being equipollent, as also the necessary and the impossible, provided the one asserts and the other denies. This is the view to which those would naturally be led who looked mainly to the nature of the subject-matter.

[1] I cannot find the slightest authority for the statement in the elaborate history of Logic by Prantl.

On the other hand, those who looked mainly at the form of
expression, would be led by the analogy of the four forms of
proposition, and the necessity that each of them should stand
in definite opposition to each other, to insist upon a distinction between the four modals[1]. They, therefore, endeavoured
to introduce a distinction by maintaining (e.g. Crackanthorpe,
Bk. III. ch. 11) that the contingent is that which now is but
may not be, and the possible that which now is not but may
be. A few appear to have made the distinction correspondent to that between the physically and the logically
possible.

§ 18. When we get to the Kantian division we have
reached much clearer ground. The meaning of each of these
terms is quite explicit, and it is also beyond doubt that they
have a more definite tendency in the direction of assigning a
graduated scale of conviction. So long as they are regarded
from a metaphysical rather than a logical standing point,
there is much to be said in their favour. If we use introspection merely, confining ourselves to a study of the judgments themselves, to the exclusion of the grounds on which
they rest, there certainly does seem a clear and well-marked
distinction between judgments which we cannot even conceive to be reversed in thought; those which we could
reverse, but which we accept as true; and those which we
merely entertain as possible.

Regarded, however, as a logical division, Kant's arrangement seems to me of very little service. For such logical
purposes indeed, as we are now concerned with, it really
seems to resolve itself into a *two*-fold division. The distinction between the apodeictic and the assertory will be

---

[1] " Hi quatuor modi magnam
censeri solent analogiam habere cum
quadruplici propositionum in quan-
titate et qualitate varietate" (Wallis's
Instit. Logic. Bk. II. ch. 8).

admitted, I presume, even by those who accept the metaphysical or psychological theory upon which it rests, to be a
difference which concerns, not the quantity of belief with
which the judgments are entertained, but rather the violence
which would have to be done to the mind by the attempt to
upset them. Each is fully believed, but the one can, and
the other cannot, be controverted. The belief with which an
assertory judgment is entertained is full belief, else it would
not differ from the problematic; and therefore in regard to
the quantity of belief, as distinguished from the quality or
character of it, there is no difference between it and the apodeictic. It is as though, to offer an illustration, the index
had been already moved to the top of the scale in the assertory judgment, and all that was done to convert this into
an apodeictic one, was to *clamp* it there. The only logical
difference which then remains is that between problematic
and assertory, the former comprehending all the judgments
as to the truth of which we have any degree of doubt, and
the latter those of which we have no doubt. The whole
range of the former, therefore, with which Probability is
appropriately occupied, is thrown undivided into a single
compartment. We can hardly speak of a ' division ' where
one class includes everything up to the boundary line, and
the other is confined to that boundary line. Practically,
therefore, on this view, modality, as the mathematical student of Probability would expect to find it, as completely
disappears as if it were intended to reject it.

§ 19. By less consistent and systematic thinkers, and
by those in whom ingenuity was an over prominent feature,
a variety of other arrangements have been accepted or proposed. There is, of course, some justification for such attempts
in the laudable desire to bring our logical forms into better
harmony with ordinary thought and language. In practice,

as was pointed out in an earlier chapter, every one recognizes a great variety of modal forms, such as 'likely,' 'very
likely,' 'almost certainly,' and so on almost without limit in
each direction. It was doubtless supposed that, by neglecting to make use of technical equivalents for some of these
forms, we should lose our logical control over certain possible
kinds of inference, and so far fall short even of the precision
of ordinary thought.

With regard to such additional forms, it appears to me
that all those which have been introduced by writers who
were uninfluenced by the Theory of Probability, have done
little else than create additional confusion, as such writers do
not attempt to marshal their terms in order, or to ascertain
their mutual relations. Omitting, of course, forms obviously
of material modality, we have already mentioned the true
and the false; the probable, the supposed, and the certain.
These subdivisions seem to have reached their climax at a
very early stage in Occam (Prantl, III. 380), who held that a
proposition might be modally affected by being 'vera, scita,
falsa, ignota, scripta, prolata, concepta, credita, opinata, du-
bitata.'

§ 20. Since the growth of the science of Probability,
logicians have had better opportunities of knowing what
they had to aim at; and, though it cannot be said that their
attempts have been really successful, these are at any rate a
decided improvement upon those of their predecessors. Dr
Thomson[1], for instance, gives a nine-fold division. He says
that, arranging the degrees of modality in an ascending
scale, we find that a judgment may be either possible,
doubtful, probable, morally certain for the thinker himself,
morally certain for a class or school, morally certain for all,
physically certain with a limit, physically certain without

----

[1] *Laws of Thought*, § 118.

limitation, and mathematically certain. Many other divisions might doubtless be mentioned, but, as every mathematician will recognize, the attempt to secure any general agreement in such a matter of arrangement is quite hopeless. It is here that the beneficial influence of the mathematical theory of Probability is to be gratefully acknowledged. As soon as this came to be studied it must have been perceived that in attempting to mark off clearly from one another certain gradations of belief, we should be seeking for breaches in a continuous magnitude. In the advance from a slight presumption to a strong presumption, and from that to moral certainty, we are making a gradual ascent, in the course of which there are no natural halting-places. The proof of this continuity need not be entered upon here, for the materials for it will have been gathered from almost every chapter of this work. The reader need merely be reminded that the grounds of our belief, in all cases which admit of number and measurement, are clearly seen to be of this description; and that therefore unless the belief itself is to be divorced from the grounds on which it rests, what thus holds as to their characteristics must hold also as to its own.

It follows, therefore, that modality in the old sense of the word, wherein an attempt was made to obtain certain natural divisions in the scale of conviction, must be finally abandoned. All that it endeavoured to do can now be done incomparably better by the theory of Probability, with its numerical scale which admits of indefinite subdivision. None of the old systems of division can be regarded as a really natural one; those which admit but few divisions being found to leave the whole range of the probable in one unbroken class, and those which adopt many divisions lapsing into unavoidable vagueness and uncertainty.

§ 21. Corresponding to the distinction between pure

and modal propositions, but even more complicated and unsatisfactory in its treatment, was that between pure and modal syllogisms. The thing discussed in the case of the latter was, of course, the effect produced upon the conclusion in respect of modality, by the modal affection of one or both premises. It is only when we reach such considerations as these that we are at all getting on to the ground appropriate to Probability; but it is obvious that very little could be done with such rude materials, and the inherent clumsiness and complication of the whole modal system come out very clearly here. It was in reference probably to this complication that some of the bitter sayings[1] of the schoolmen and others which have been recorded, were uttered.

Aristotle has given an intricate investigation of this subject, and his followers naturally were led along a similar track. It would be quite foreign to my purpose in the slight sketch in this chapter to attempt to give any account of these enquiries, even were I competent to do so; for, as has been pointed out, the connection between the Aristotelian modals and the modern view of the nature of Probability, though real, is exceedingly slight. It need only be remarked that what was complicated enough with four modals to be taken account of, grows intricate beyond all endurance when such as the ' probable' and the ' true' and the ' false' have also to be assigned a place in the list. The following examples[2] will show the kind of discussions with which the logi-

---

[1] "Haud scio magis ne doctrinam modalium scholastici exercuerint, quam ea illos vexarit. Certe usque adeo sudatum hic fuit, ut dicterio locus sit datus ; *De modalibus non gustabit asinus.*" Keckermann, *Syst. Log.* Bk. ii. ch. 3.

[2] *Smiglecii Disputationes*, Ingolstadt, 1618.

See also Prantl's *Geschichte der Logik* (under *Occam* and *Buridan*) for accounts of the excessive complication which the subtlety of those learned schoolmen evolved out of such suitable materials.

cians exercised themselves. 'Whether, with one premise certain, and the other probable, a certain conclusion may be inferred': 'Whether, from the impossible, the necessary can be inferred'; 'Whether, with one premise necessary and the other *de inesse*, the conclusion is necessary', and so on, endlessly.

§ 22. On the Kantian view of modality the discussion of such kinds of syllogisms becomes at once decidedly more simple (for here but three modes are recognized), and also somewhat more closely connected with strict Probability, (for the modes are more nearly of the nature of gradations of conviction). But, on the other hand, there is less justification for their introduction, as logicians might really be expected to know that what they are aiming to effect by their clumsy contrivances is the very thing which Probability can carry out to the highest desired degree of accuracy. The former methods are as coarse and inaccurate, compared with the latter, as were the roughest measurements of Babylonian night-watchers compared with the refined calculations of the modern astronomer. It is indeed only some of the general adherents of the Kantian Logic who enter upon any such considerations as these ; some, such as Hamilton and Mansel, entirely reject them, as we have seen. By those who do treat of the subject, such conclusions as the following are laid down; that when both premises are apodeictic the conclusion will be the same ; so when both are assertory or problematic. If one is apodeictic and the other assertory, the latter, or 'weaker,' is all that is to be admitted for the conclusion ; and so on. The English reader will find some account of these rules in Ueberweg's *Logic*[1].

§ 23. But although those modals, regarded as instruments of accurate thought, have been thus superseded by the

[1] Translation by T. M. Lindsay, p. 439.

precise arithmetical expressions of Probability, the question still remains whether what may be termed our popular modal expressions could not be improved and adapted to more accurate use. It is true that the attempt to separate them from one another by any fundamental distinctions is futile, for the magnitude of which they take cognizance is, as we have remarked, continuous; but considering the enormous importance of accurate terminology, and of recognizing numerical distinctions wherever possible, it would be a real advance if any agreement could be arrived at with regard to the use of modal expressions. We have already noticed (ch. II. § 16) some suggestions by Mr Galton as to the possibility of a natural system of classification, resting upon the regularity with which most kinds of magnitudes tend to group themselves about a mean. It might be proposed, for instance, that we should agree to apply the term 'good' to the first quarter, measuring from the best downwards; 'indifferent' to the middle half, and 'bad' to the last quarter. There seems no reason why a similarly improved terminology should not some day be introduced into the ordinary modal language of common life. It might be agreed, for instance, that 'very improbable' should as far as possible be confined to those events which had odds of (say) more than 99 to 1 against them; and so on, with other similar expressions. There would, no doubt, be difficulties in the way, for in all applications of classification we have to surmount the two-fold obstacles which lie in the way, firstly (to use Kant's expression) of the faculty of making rules, and secondly of that of subsumption under rules. That is to say, even if we had agreed upon our classes, there would still be much doubt and dispute, in the case of things which did not readily lend themselves to be counted or measured, as to whether the odds were more or less than the assigned quantity.

It is true that when we know the odds for or against an event, we can always state them explicitly without the necessity of first agreeing as to the usage of terms which shall imply them. But there would often be circumlocution and pedantry in so doing, and as long as modal terms are in practical use it would seem that there could be no harm, and might be great good, in arriving at some agreement as to the degree of probability which they should be generally understood to indicate. Bentham, as is well known, in despair of ever obtaining anything accurate out of the language of common life on this subject, was in favour of a direct appeal to the numerical standard. He proposed the employment, in judicial trials, of an instrument, graduated from 0 to 10, on which scale the witness was to be asked to indicate the degree of his belief of the facts to which he testified : similarly the judge might express the force with which he held his conclusion. The use of such a numerical scale, however, was to be optional only, not compulsory, as Bentham admitted that many persons might feel at a loss thus to measure the degree of their belief. (*Rationale of Judicial Evidence,* Bk. I., Ch. VI.)

§ 24. Throughout this chapter we have regarded the modals as the nearest counterpart to modern Probability which was afforded by the old systems of logic. The reason for so regarding them is, that they represented some slight attempt, rude as it was, to recognize and measure certain gradations in the degree of our conviction, and to examine the bearing of such considerations upon our logical inferences.

But although it is amongst the modals that the germs of the methods of Probability are thus to be sought; the true subject-matter of our science, that is, the classes of objects with which it is most appropriately concerned, are rather represented by another part of the scholastic logic. This

was the branch commonly called Dialectic, in the old sense
of that term.   Dialectic, according to Aristotle, seems to
have been a sort of sister art to Rhetoric.   It was concerned
with syllogisms differing in no way from demonstrative syllogisms, except that their premises were probable instead of
certain.   Premises of this kind he termed topics, and the
syllogisms which dealt with them enthymemes.   They were
said to start from 'signs and likelihoods' rather than from
axioms[1].

§ 25.   The terms in which such reasonings are commonly described sound very much like those applicable to
Probability, as we now understand it.   When we hear of
likelihood, and of probable syllogisms, our first impression
might be that the inferences involved would be of a similar
character[2].   This, however, would be erroneous.   In the

[1] "The εἰκὸς and σημεῖον themselves are propositions; the former
stating a *general probability*, the
latter a fact, which is known to be
an indication, more or less certain,
of the truth of some further statement, whether of a single fact, or
of a general belief.   The former is a
general proposition, nearly, though
not quite, universal; as, 'most men
who envy hate'; the latter is a
singular proposition, which however
is not regarded as a sign, except
relatively to some other proposition,
which it is supposed may be inferred
from it." (Mansel's Aldrich; Appen-
dix F, where an account will be
found of the Aristotelian enthy-
meme, and dialectic syllogism.   Also,
of course, in Grote's Aristotle, *Topics*,
and elsewhere.)

[2] "Nam in hoc etiam differt de-
monstratio, seu demonstrativa argu-
mentatio, à probabili, quia in illâ
tam conclusio quam præmissæ neces-
sariæ sunt; in probabili autem argu-
mentatione sicut conclusio ut probabilis infertur ita præmissæ ut pro-
babiles afferuntur" (Crackanthorpe,
Bk. v., Ch. 1); almost the words with
which De Morgan distinguishes between logic and probability in a
passage already cited (see Ch. vi. § 3).

Perhaps it was a development of
some such view as this that Leibnitz
looked forward to. "J'ai dit plus d'une
fois qu'il faudrait une nouvelle espèce
de Logique, qui traiteroit des degrés
de Probabilité, puisqu'Aristote dans
ses Topiques n'a rien moins fait que
cela" (*Nouveaux essais*, Lib. iv. ch.
xvi).   It is possible, indeed, that he
may have had in his mind more what
we now understand by the mathema-

first place the province of this Dialectic was much too wide, for it covered in addition the whole field of what we should now term Scientific or Material Induction. The distinctive characteristic of the dialectic premises was their want of certainty, and of such uncertain premises Probability (as I have frequently insisted) takes account of one class only, Induction concerning itself with another class. Again, not the slightest attempt was made to enter upon the enquiry, *How* uncertain are the premises ? It is only when this is attempted that we can be considered to enter upon the field of Probability, and it is because, after a rude fashion, the modals attempted to grapple with this problem, that we have regarded them as in any way occupied with our special subject-matter.

§ 26. Amongst the older logics with which I have made any acquaintance, that of Crackanthorpe gives the fullest discussion upon this subject. He divides his treatment of the syllogism into two parts, occupied respectively with the 'demonstrative' and the 'probable' syllogism. To the latter a whole book is devoted. In this the nature and consequences of thirteen different 'loci'[1] are investigated, though it is not very clear in what sense they can every one of them be regarded as being 'probable.'

tical theory of Probability, but in the infancy of a science it is of course hard to say whether any particular subject is definitely contemplated or not. Leibnitz (as Todhunter has shown in his history) took the greatest interest in such chance problems as had yet been discussed.

[1] By *loci* were understood certain general classes of premises. They stood, in fact, to the major premise in somewhat the same relation that the Category or Predicament did to the term. Crackanthorpe says of them, " sed duci a *loco probabiliter arguendi*, hoc vere proprium est Argumentationis probabilis; et in hoc a Demonstratione differt, quia Demonstrator utitur solummodo quatuor Locis eisque necessariis.... Præter hos autem, ex quibus quoque probabiliter arguere licet, sunt multo plures Loci arguendi probabiliter; ut a Genere, a Specie, ab Adjuncto, ab Oppositis, et similia" (*Logica*, Lib. v., ch. II.).

It is doubtless true, that if the old logicians had been in possession of such premises as modern Probability is concerned with, and had adhered to their own way of treating them, they would have had to place them amongst such *loci*, and thus to make the consideration of them a part of their Dialectic. But inasmuch as there does not seem to have been the slightest attempt on their part to do more here than recognize the *fact* of the premises being probable ; that is, since it was not attempted to *measure* their probability and that of the conclusion, I cannot but regard this part of Logic as having only the very slightest relation to Probability as now conceived. It seems to me little more than one of the ways (described at the commencement of this chapter) by which the problem of Modality is not indeed rejected, but practically evaded.

§ 27. As Logic is not the only science which is directly and prominently occupied with questions about belief and evidence, so the difficulties which have arisen there have been by no means unknown elsewhere. In respect of the modals, this seems to have been manifestly the case in Jurisprudence. Some remarks, therefore, may be conveniently made here upon this application of the subject, though of course with the brevity suitable on the part of a layman who has to touch upon professional topics.

Recall for a moment what are the essentials of modality. These I understand to be the attempt to mark off from one another, without any resort to numerical notation, varying degrees of conviction or belief, and to determine the consequent effect of premises, thus affected, upon our conclusions. Moreover, as we cannot construct or retain a scale of any kind without employing a standard from and by which to measure it, the attainment and recognition of a standard of certainty, or of one of the other degrees of conviction, is

almost inseparably involved in the same enquiry. In this
sense of the term, modal difficulties have certainly shown
themselves in the department of Law. There have been
similar attempts here, encountered by similar difficulties, to
come to some definite agreement as to a scale of arrangement of the degrees of our assent. It is of course much
more practicable to secure such agreement in the case of a
special science, confined more or less to the experts, than in
subjects into which all classes of outsiders have almost equal
right of entry. The range of application under the former
circumstances is narrower, and the professional experts have
acquired habits and traditions by which the standards may
be retained in considerable integrity. It does not appear,
however, according to all accounts, as if any very striking
success had been attained in this direction by the lawyers.

§ 28.   The difficulty in its scientific, or strictly jurispru-
dential shape, seems to have shown itself principally in the
attempt to arrange legal evidence into classes in respect of
the degree of its cogency. This, I understand, was the case
in the Roman law, and in some of the continental systems of
jurisprudence which took their rise from the Roman law.
"The direct evidence of so many witnesses was *plena probatio*. Then came *minus plena probatio*, then *semiplenâ
major* and *semiplenâ minor;* and by adding together a
certain number of half-proofs—for instance, by the production of a tradesman's account-books, *plus* his supplementary oath—full proof might be made out. It was on
this principle that torture was employed to obtain a confession. The confession was evidence suppletory to the circumstances which were held to justify its employment[1]."

According to Bentham[2], the corresponding scale in the

---

[1] Stephen's *General View of the*   [2] *Rationale of Judicial Evidence;*
Criminal Law of England, p. 241.   Bk. i. ch. vi.

English school was:—Positive proof, Violent presumption, Probable presumption, Light or Rash presumption. Though admitted by Blackstone and others, I understand that these divisions are not at all generally accepted at the present day.

§ 29. In the above we are reminded rather of modal syllogisms. The principal practical form in which the difficulty underlying the simple modal propositions presents itself, is in the attempt to obtain some criterion of judicial certainty. By 'certainty' here we mean, of course, not what the metaphysicians term apodeictic[1], for that can seldom or never be secured in practical affairs, but such a degree of conviction, short of this, as every reasonable person will feel to be sufficient for all his wants. Here again, one would think, the quest must appear, to accurate thinkers, an utterly hopeless one; an effort to discover natural breaks in a continuous magnitude. There cannot indeed be the least doubt that, amongst limited classes of keen and practised intellects, a standard of certainty, as of everything else, might be retained and handed down with considerable accuracy: this is possible in matters of taste and opinion where personal peculiarities of judgment are far more liable to cause disagreement and confusion. But then such a consensus is almost entirely an affair of tact and custom; whereas what is wanted in the case in question is some criterion to which the comparatively uninitiated may be able to appeal. The standard, therefore, must not merely be retained by recollection, but be generally recognizable by its characteristics. If such a criterion could

---

[1] Though this is claimed by some Kantian logicians;—Nie darf an einem angeblichen Verbrecher die gesetzliche Strafe vollzogen werden, bevor er nicht selbst das Verbrechen eingestanden. Denn wenn auch alle Zeugnisse und die übrigen Anzeigen wider ihn wären, so bleibt doch das Gegentheil immer möglich" (Krug, *Denklehre*, § 131).

be secured, its importance could hardly be overrated. But so far as one may judge from the speeches of counsel, the charges of judges, and the verdicts of juries, nothing really deserving the name is ever attained.

§ 30. The nearest approach, perhaps, to a recognized standard is to be found in the frequent assurance that juries are not bound to convict only in case they have *no* doubt of the guilt of the accused; for the absolute exclusion of all doubt, the utter impossibility of suggesting any counter hypothesis which this assumes, is unattainable in human affairs. But, it is frequently said, they are to convict if they have no 'reasonable doubt,' no such doubt, that is, as would be 'a hindrance to acting in the important affairs of life.' As a caution against seeking after unattainable certainty, such advice may be very useful; but it need hardly be remarked that the certainty upon which we act in the important affairs of life is no fixed standard, but varies exceedingly according to the nature of those affairs. The greater the reward at stake, the greater the risk we are prepared to run, and conversely. Hardly any degree of certainty can exist, upon the security of which we should not be prepared to act under appropriate circumstances[1].

Some writers indeed altogether deny that any standard, in the common sense of the word, either is, or ought to be, aimed at in legal proceedings. For instance, Sir J. F.

[1] As Mr C. J. Monro puts it: "Suppose that a man is suspected of murdering his daughter. Evidence which would not convict him before an ordinary jury might make a grand jury find a true bill; evidence which would not do this might make a coroner's jury bring in a verdict against him; evidence which would not do this would very often prevent a Chancery judge from appointing the man guardian to a ward of the court; evidence which would not affect the judge's mind might make a father think twice on his death-bed before he appointed the man guardian to *his* daughter."

Stephen, in his work on English Criminal Law[1], after noticing and rejecting such standards as that last indicated, comes to the conclusion that the only standard recognized by our law is that which induces juries to convict :— "What is judicial proof? That which being permitted by law to be given in evidence, induces twelve men, chosen according to the Jury Act, to say that, having heard it, their minds are satisfied of the truth of the proposition which it affirms. They may be prejudiced, they may be timid, they may be rash, they may be ignorant; but the oath, the number, and the property qualification, are intended, as far as possible, to neutralize these disadvantages, and answer precisely to the conditions imposed upon standards of value or length." (p. 263.)

To admit this is much about the same thing as to abandon such a standard as unattainable. Evidence which induces a jury to convict may doubtless be a standard to me and others of what we ought to consider 'reasonably certain,' provided of course that the various juries are tolerably uniform in their conclusions. But it clearly cannot be proposed as a standard to the juries themselves; if their decisions are to be consistent and uniform, they want some external indication to guide them. When a man is asking, *How* certain ought I to feel? to give such an answer as the above is, surely, merely telling him that he is to be as certain as

---

[1] The portions of this work which treat of the nature of proof in general, and of judicial proof in particular, are well worth reading by every logical student. It appears to me, however, that the author goes much too far in the direction of regarding proof as subjective, that is as what *does* satisfy people, rather than as what *should* satisfy them. He compares the legislative standard of certainty with that of value; this latter is declared to be a certain weight of gold, irrespective of the rarity or commonness of that metal. So with certainty; if people grow more credulous the intrinsic value of the standard will vary.

he is. If, indeed, juries composed a close profession, they might, as was said above, retain a traditional standard. But being, as they are, a selection from the ordinary lay public, their own decisions in the past can hardly be held up to them as a direction what they are to do in future.

§ 31. It would appear therefore that we may fairly say that the English law, at any rate, definitely rejects the main assumption upon which the logical doctrine of modality and its legal counterpart are based: the assumption, namely, that different grades of conviction can be marked off from one another with sufficient accuracy for us to be able to refer individual cases to their corresponding classes. And that with regard to the collateral question of fixing a standard of certainty, it will go no further than pronouncing, or implying, that we are to be content with nothing short of, but need not go beyond, 'reasonable certainty.'

This is a statement of the standard, with which the logician and scientific man can easily quarrel; and they may with much reason maintain that it has not the slightest claim to accuracy, even if it had one to strict intelligibility. If a man wishes to know whether his present degree of certainty *is* reasonable, whither is he to appeal? He can scarcely compare his mental state with that which is experienced in 'the important affairs of life,' for these, as already remarked, would indicate no fixed value. At the same time, one cannot suppose that such an expression is destitute of all signification. People would not continue to use language, especially in matters of paramount importance and interest, without meaning something by it. We are driven therefore to conclude that 'reasonable certainty' does in a rude sort of way represent a traditional standard to which it is attempted to adhere. As already remarked, this is perfectly practicable in the case of any class of professional

men, and therefore not altogether impossible in the case of
those who are often and closely brought into connection with
such a class. Though it is hard to believe that any such
expressions, when used for purposes of ordinary life, attain
at all near enough to any conventional standard to be worth
discussion; yet in the special case of a jury, acting under
the direct influence of a judge, it seems quite possible that
their deliberate assertion that they are 'fully convinced'
may reach somewhat more nearly to a tolerably fixed standard
than ordinary outsiders would at first think likely.

§ 32.   Are there then any means by which we could
ascertain what this standard is; in other words, by which we
could determine what is the real worth, in respect of accuracy, of this 'reasonable certainty' which the juries are supposed to secure? In the absence of authoritative declara-
tions upon the subject, the student of Logic and Probability
would naturally resort to two means, with a momentary
notice of which we will conclude this enquiry.

The first of these would aim at determining the standard
of judicial certainty indirectly, by simply determining the
statistical frequency with which the decisions (say) of a jury
were found to be correct. This may seem to be a hopeless
task; and so indeed it is, but not so much on any theoretic
insufficiency of the determining elements as on account of
the numerous arbitrary assumptions which attach to most
of the problems which deal with the probability of testimony
and judgments. It is not necessary for this purpose that we
should have an infallible superior court which revised the
decisions of the one under consideration[1]; it is sufficient if a

---

[1] The question will be more fully
discussed in a future chapter, but a
few words may be inserted here by
way of indication. Reduce the case
to the simplest possible elements by
supposing only two judges or courts,
of the same average correctness of
decision. Let this be indicated by

large number of ordinary representative cases are submitted to a court consisting even of exactly similar materials to the one whose decisions we wish to test. Provided always that we make the monstrous assumption that the judgments of men about matters which deeply affect them are 'independent' in the sense in which the tosses of pence are independent, then the statistics of mere agreement and disagreement will serve our purpose. We might be able to say, for instance, that a jury of a given number, deciding by a given majority, were right nine times out of ten in their verdict. Conclusions of this kind, in reference to the French courts, are what Poisson has attempted at the end of his great work on the Probability of Judgments, though I do not suppose that he attached much numerical accuracy to his results.

A scarcely more hopeful means would be found by a reference to certain cases of legal 'presumptions.' A 'conclusive presumption' is defined as follows:—" Conclusive, or as they are elsewhere termed imperative or absolute presumptions of law, are rules determining the quantity of evidence requisite for the support of any particular averment which is not permitted to be overcome by any proof that the fact is otherwise[1]." A large number of such presumptions will be found described in the text-books, but they seem to refer to matters far too vague, for the most part, to admit of any reduction to statistical frequency of occurrence. It is indeed maintained by some authorities that any assignment of degree of Probability is not their present object, but that they are simply meant to exclude the troublesome delays

x. Then the chance of their agreeing is $x^2+(1-x)^2$, for they agree if both are right or both wrong. If the statistical frequency of this agreement is known,—that is, the frequency with which the first judgment is confirmed by the second, we have the means of determining x.

[1] Taylor on Evidence: the latter part of the extract does not seem very clear.

that would ensue if everything were considered open to
doubt and question. Moreover, even if they did assign a
degree of certainty this would rather be an indication of
what legislators or judges thought reasonable than of what
was so considered by the juries themselves.

There are indeed presumptions as to the time after which
a man, if not heard of, is supposed to be dead (capable of
disproof, of course, by his reappearance). If this time varied
with the age of the man in question, we should at once have
some such standard as we desire, for a reference to the Life
tables would fix his probable duration of life, and so determine indirectly the measure of probability which satisfied
the law. But this is not the case; the period chosen is
entirely irrespective of age. The nearest case in point (and
that does not amount to much) which I have been able to
ascertain is that of the age after which it has been pre-
sumed that a woman was incapable of bearing children.
This was the age of 53. A certain approach to a statistical
assignment of the chances in this case is to be found in
Quetelet's *Physique Sociale* (Vol. I. p. 184, note). According
to the authorities which he there quotes it would seem that
in about one birth in 5500 the mother was of the age of 50
or upwards. This does not quite assign the degree of what
may be called the à priori chance against the occurrence of a
birth at that age, because the fact of having commenced a
family at an early age represents some diminution of the
probability of continuing it into later life. But it serves to
give some indication of what may be called the odds against
such an event.

It need not be remarked that any such clues as these to
the measure of judicial certainty are far too slight to be of
any real value. They only deserve passing notice as a possible logical solution of the problem in question, or rather as

an indication of the mode in which, in theory, such a solution
would have to be sought, were the English law, on these
subjects, a perfectly consistent scheme of scientific evidence.
This is the mode in which one would, under those circumstances, attempt to extract from its proceedings an admission
of the exact measure of that standard of certainty which it
adopted, but which it declined openly to enunciate.

CHAPTER XIV.

FALLACIES.

§ 1. In works on Logic a chapter is generally devoted to the discussion of Fallacies, that is, to the description and classification of the different ways in which the rules of Logic may be transgressed. The analogy of Probability to Logic is sufficiently close to make it advisable to adopt the same plan here. In describing his own opinions an author is, of course, perpetually obliged to describe and criticise those of others which he considers erroneous. But some of the most widely spread errors find no supporters worth mentioning, and exist only in vague popular misapprehension. It will be found the best arrangement, therefore, at the risk of occasional repetition, to collect a few of the errors that occur most frequently, and as far as possible to trace them to their sources; but it will hardly be worth the trouble to attempt any regular system of arrangement and classification. We shall mainly confine ourselves, in accordance with the special province of this work, to problems which involve questions of logical interest, or to those which refer to the application of Probability to moral and social science. We shall avoid the discussion of isolated problems in games of chance and skill except when some error of principle seems to be involved in them.

§ 2. (I.) One of the most fertile sources of error and confusion upon the subject has been already several times alluded to, and in part discussed in a previous chapter. This consists in choosing the class to which to refer an event, and therefore judging of the rarity of the event and the consequent improbability of foretelling it, *after it has happened,* and then transferring the impressions we experience to a supposed contemplation of the event beforehand. The process in itself is perfectly legitimate (however unnecessary it may be), since time does not in strictness enter at all into questions of Probability. No error therefore need arise in this way, if we were careful as to the class which we thus selected; but such carefulness is often neglected.

An illustration may afford help here. A man once pointed to a small target chalked upon a door, the target having a bullet hole through the centre of it, and surprised some spectators by declaring that he had fired that shot from an old fowling-piece at a distance of a hundred yards. His statement was true enough, but he suppressed a rather important fact. The shot had really been aimed in a general way at the barn-door, and had hit it; the target was afterwards chalked round the spot where the bullet struck. A deception analogous to this is, I think, often practised unconsciously in other matters. We judge of events on a similar principle, feeling and expressing surprise in an equally unreasonable way, and deciding as to their occurrence on grounds which are really merely a subsequent adjunct of our own. Butler's remarks about 'the story of Cæsar,' discussed already in the twelfth chapter, are of this character. He selects a series of events from history, and then imagines a person guessing them correctly who at the time had not the history before him. As I have already pointed out, it is one thing to be unlikely to guess an event rightly without specific evidence; it is another and very different thing to appreciate the truth of a story which is founded partly or entirely upon evidence. But it is a great mistake to transfer to one of these ways of viewing the matter the mental impressions which properly belong to the other. It is like drawing the target afterwards, and then being surprised to find that the shot lies in the centre of it.

§ 3. One aspect of this fallacy has been already discussed, but it will serve to clear up difficulties which are often felt upon the subject if we reexamine the question under a somewhat more general form.

In the class of examples under discussion we are generally presented with an individual which is not indeed definitely referred to a class, but in regard to which we have no great difficulty in choosing the appropriate class. Now suppose we were contemplating such an event as the throwing of sixes with a pair of dice four times running. Such a throw would be termed a very unlikely event, as the odds against its happening would be $36 \times 36 \times 36 \times 36 - 1$ to 1 or 1679615 to 1. The meaning of these phrases, as has been abundantly pointed out, is simply that the event in question occurs very rarely; that, stated with numerical accuracy, it occurs once in 1679616 times.

§ 4. But now let us make the assumption that the throw has actually occurred; let us put ourselves into the position of contemplating sixes four times running when it is known or reported that this throw has happened. The same phrase, namely that the event is a very unlikely one, will often be used in relation to it, but we shall find that this phrase may be employed to indicate, on one occasion or another, extremely different meanings.

(1) There is, firstly, the most correct meaning. The

event, it is true, has happened, and we know what it is, and therefore, we have not really any occasion to resort to the rules of Probability; but we can nevertheless conceive ourselves as being in the position of a person who does not know, and who has only Probability to appeal to. By calling the chances 1679615 to 1 against the throw we then mean to imply the fact, that inasmuch as such a throw occurs only once in 1679616 times, our guess, were we to guess, would be correct only once in the same number of times; provided, that is, that it is a fair guess, based simply on these statistical grounds.

§ 5. (2) But there is a second and very different conception sometimes introduced, especially when the event in question is supposed to be known, not as above by the evidence of our experience, but by the report of a witness. We may then mean by the 'chances against the event' (as was pointed out in Chapter XII.) not the proportional number of times we should be right in guessing the event, but the proportional number of times the witness will be right in reporting it. The bases of our inference are here shifted on to new ground. In the former case the statistics were the throws and their respective frequency, now they are the witnesses' statements and their respective truthfulness.

§ 6. (3) But there is yet another meaning sometimes intended to be conveyed when persons talk of the chances against such an event as the throw in question. They may mean—not, Here is an event, how often should I have guessed it?—nor, Here is a report, how often will it be correct?—but something different from either, namely, Here is an event, how often will it be found to be produced by some one particular kind of cause?

When, for example, a man hears of dice giving the same throw several times running, and speaks of this as very

extraordinary, we shall often find that he is not merely
thinking of the improbability of his guess being right, or of
the report being true, but, that along with this, he is introducing the question of the throw having been produced by
fair dice. There is, of course, no reason whatever why such
a question as this should not also be referred to Probability,
provided always that we could find the appropriate statistics
by which to judge. These statistics would be composed, not
of throws of the particular dice, nor of reports of the particular witness, but of the occasions on which such a throw as
the one in question respectively had, and had not, been
produced fairly. The objection to entering upon this view
of the question would be that no such statistics are obtainable, and that if they were, we should prefer to form our
opinion (on principles to be described in Chapter XVI.) from
the special circumstances of the case rather than from an
appeal to the average.

§ 7. The reader will easily be able to supply examples
in illustration of the distinctions just given; we will briefly
examine but one. I hide a banknote in a certain book in a
large library, and leave the room. A person tells me that,
after I went out, a stranger came in, walked straight up to
that particular book, and took it away with him. Many
people on hearing this account would reply, How extremely
improbable! On analysing the phrase, I think we shall
find that certainly two, and possibly all three, of the above
meanings might be involved in this exclamation. (1) What
may be meant is this,—Assuming that the report is true,
and the stranger innocent, a rare event has occurred. Many
books might have been thus taken without that particular
one being selected. I should not therefore have expected
the event, and when it has happened I am surprised. Now
a man has a perfect right to be surprised, but he has no

logical right (so long as we confine ourselves to this view) to make his surprise a ground for disbelieving the event. To do this is to fall into the fallacy described at the commencement of this chapter. The fact of my not having been likely to have guessed a thing beforehand is no reason in itself for doubting it when I am informed of it. (2) Or I may stop short of the events reported, and apply the rules of Probability to the report itself. If so, what I mean is that such a story as this now before me is of a kind very generally false, and that I cannot therefore attach much credit to it now. (3) Or I may accept the truth of the report, but doubt the fact of the stranger having taken the book at random. If so, what I mean is, that of men who take books in the way described, only a small proportion will be found to have taken them really at random; the majority will do so because they had by some means ascertained, or come to suspect, what there was inside the book.

Each of the above three meanings is a possible and a legitimate meaning. The only requisite is that we should be careful to ascertain which of them is present to the mind, so as to select the appropriate statistics. The first makes in itself the most legitimate use of Probability; the drawback being that at the time in question the functions of Probability are superseded by the event being otherwise known. The second or third, therefore, is the more likely meaning to be present to the mind, for in these cases Probability, if it could be practically made use of, would, at the time in question, be a means of drawing really important inferences. The drawbacks are the difficulty of finding such statistics, and the extreme disturbing influence upon these statistics of the circumstances of the special case.

§ 8. (II.) Closely connected with the tendency just mentioned is that which prompts us to confound a true

chance selection with one which is more or less picked.
When we are dealing with familiar objects in a concrete
way, especially when the greater rarity corresponds to superiority of quality, almost every one has learnt to recognize
the distinction. No one, for instance, on observing a fine
body of troops in a foreign town, but would be prompted to
ask whether they came from an average regiment or from
one that was picked. When however the distinction refers
to unfamiliar objects, and especially when only comparative
rarity seems to be involved, the fallacy may assume a rather
subtle and misleading form, and seems to deserve special
notice by the consideration of a few examples.

Sometimes the result is not so much an actual fallacy as
a slight misreckoning of the order of probability of the event
under consideration. For instance, in the Pyramid question,
we saw that it made some difference whether we considered
that π alone was to be taken into account or whether we
put this constant into a class with a small number of other
similar ones. In deciding, however, whether or not there is
anything remarkable in the actual falling short of the
representation of the number 7 in the evaluation of π
(v. p. 248) the whole question turns upon considerations of
this kind. The only enquiry raised is whether there is anything remarkable in this departure from the mean, and the
answer depends upon whether we suppose that we are referring to a predetermined digit, or to whatever digit of the
ten happens to be most above or below the average. Or,
take the case raised by Cournot (*Exposition de la Théorie
des Chances*, §§ 102, 114), that a certain deviation from the
mean in the case of Departmental returns of the proportion
between male and female births is significant and indicative
of a difference in kind, provided that we select at random a
single French Department; but that the same deviation may

be accidental if it is the maximum of the respective returns for several Departments[1]. The answer may be given one way or the other according as we bear this consideration in mind.

§ 9.   We are peculiarly liable to be misled in this way when we are endeavouring to determine the cause of some phenomenon, by mere statistics, in entire ignorance as to the direction in which the cause should be expected. In such cases an ingenious person who chooses to look about over a large field can never fail to hit upon an explanation which is plausible in the sense that it fits in with the hitherto observed facts.   With a tithe of the trouble which Mr Piazzi Smyth expended upon the measurement of the great pyramid, I think I would undertake to find plausible intimations of several of the important constants and standards which he discovered there, in the dimensions of the desk at which I am writing.   The oddest instance of this sort of conclusion is perhaps to be found in the researches of a writer who has discovered[2] that there is a connection of a striking kind between the respective successes of the Oxford and the Cambridge boat in the annual race, and the greater and less frequency of sun-spots.

Of course our usual practical resource in such cases is to make appeal to our previous knowledge of the subject in question, which enables us to reject as absurd a great number of hypotheses which can nevertheless make a fair show when they are allowed to rest upon a limited amount of adroitly selected instances.   But it must be remembered that if any theory chooses to appeal to statistics, to statistics it must be suffered to go for judgment.   Even the boat race theory

---

[1] Discussed by Mr F. Y. Edgeworth, in the *Phil. Mag.* for April, 1887.

[2] *Journal of the Statistical Soc.* (Vol. XLII. p. 328) Dare one suspect a joke?

could be established (if sound) on this ground alone. That is, if it really could be shown that experience in the long run confirmed the preponderance of successes on one side or the other according to the relative frequency of the sun-spots, we should have to accept the fact that the two classes of events were not really independent. One of the two, whichever it may be, must be suspected of causing or influencing the other; or both must be caused or influenced by some common circumstances.

§ 10. (III.) The fallacy described at the commencement of this chapter arose from determining to judge of an observed or reported event by the rules of Probability, but employing a wrong set of statistics in the process of judging. Another fallacy, closely connected with this, arises from the practice of taking some only of the characteristics of such an event, and arbitrarily confining to these the appeal to Probability. Suppose I toss up twelve pence, and find that eleven of them give heads. Many persons on witnessing such an occurrence would experience a feeling which they would express by the remark, How near that was to getting all heads! And if any thing very important were staked on the throw they would be much excited at the occurrence. But in what sense were we near to twelve? There is a not uncommon error, I apprehend, which consists in unconsciously regarding the eleven heads as a thing which is already somehow secured, so that one might as it were keep them, and then take our chance for securing the remaining one. The eleven are mentally set aside, looked upon as certain (for they have already happened), and we then introduce the notion of chance merely for the twelfth. But this twelfth, having also happened, has no better claim to such a distinction than any of the others. If we will introduce the notion of chance in the case of the one that gave tail we must do the same in

the case of all the others as well. In other words, if the
tosser be dissatisfied at the appearance of the one tail, and
wish to cancel it and try his luck again, he must toss up the
whole lot of pence again fairly together. In this case, of
course, so far from his having a better prospect for the next
throw he may think himself in very good luck if he makes
again as good a throw as the one he rejected. What he is
doing is confounding this case with that in which the throws
are really *successive.* If eleven heads have been tossed up in
turn, we are of course within an even chance of getting a
twelfth; but the circumstances are quite different in the
instance proposed.

§ 11. In the above example the error is transparent.
But in forming a judgment upon matters of greater complexity than dice and pence, especially in the case of what are
called 'narrow escapes,' a mistake of an analogous kind is, I
apprehend, far from uncommon. A person, for example, who
has just experienced a narrow escape will often be filled
with surprise and anxiety amounting almost to terror. The
event being past, these feelings are, at the time, in strictness
inappropriate. If, as is quite possible, they are merely instinctive, or the result of association, they do not fall within
the province of any kind of Logic. If, however, as seems
more likely, they partially arise from a supposed transference
of ourselves into that point of past time at which the event
was just about to happen, and the production by imagination of the feelings we should then expect to experience,
this process partakes of the nature of an inference, and can
be right or wrong. In other words, the alarm may be proportionate or disproportionate to the amount of danger that
might fairly have been reckoned upon in such a hypothetical
anticipation. If the supposed transfer were completely
carried out, there would be no fallacy; but it is often very

incompletely done, some of the component parts of the event being supposed to be determined or 'arranged' (to use a sporting phrase) in the form in which we now know that they actually have happened, and only the remaining ones being fairly contemplated as future chances.

A man, for example, is out with a friend, whose rifle goes off by accident, and the bullet passes through his hat. He trembles with anxiety at thinking what might have happened, and perhaps remarks, 'How very near I was to being killed!' Now we may safely assume that he means something more than that a shot passed very close to him. He has some vague idea that, as he would probably say, 'his chance of being killed then was very great.' His surprise and terror may be in great part physical and instinctive, arising simply from the knowledge that the shot had passed very near him. But his mental state may be analysed, and we shall then most likely find, at bottom, a fallacy of the kind described above. To speak or think of chance in connection with the incident, is to refer the particular incident to a class of incidents of a similar character, and then to consider the comparative frequency with which the contemplated result ensues. Now the series which we may suppose to be most naturally selected in this case is one composed of shooting excursions with his friend; up to this point the proceedings are assumed to be designed, beyond it only, in the subsequent event, was there accident. Once in a thousand times perhaps on such occasions the gun will go off accidentally; one in a thousand only of those discharges will be directed near his friend's head. If we will make the accident a matter of Probability, we ought by rights in this way (to adopt the language of the first example), to 'toss up again' fairly. But we do not do this; we seem to assume for certain that the shot goes within an inch of our heads, de-

tach that from the notion of chance at all, and then begin to
introduce this notion again for possible deflections from that
saving inch.

§ 12.   (IV.) We will now notice a fallacy connected with
the subjects of betting and gambling. Many or most of the
popular misapprehensions on this subject imply such utter
ignorance and confusion as to the foundations of the science
that it would be needless to discuss them here. The following however is of a far more plausible kind, and has been a
source of perplexity to persons of considerable acuteness.

The case, put into the simplest form, is as follows[1].
Suppose that a person *A* is playing against *B*, *B* being
either another individual or a group of individuals, say a
gambling bank. They begin by tossing for a shilling, and
A maintains that he is in possession of a device which will
insure his winning. If he does win on the first occasion he
has clearly gained his point so far. If he loses, he stakes
next time two shillings instead of one. The result of course
is that if he wins on the second occasion he replaces his
former loss, and is left with one shilling profit as well. So
he goes on, doubling his stake after every loss, with the
obvious result that on the first occasion of success he makes
good all his previous losses, and is left with a shilling over.
But such an occasion must come sooner or later, by the
assumptions of chance on which the game is founded. Hence
it follows that he can insure, sooner or later, being left a
final winner. Moreover he may win to any amount; firstly
from the obvious consideration that he might make his
initial stake as large as he pleased, a hundred pounds, for

[1] It appears to have been long
known to gamblers under the name
of the *Martingale*. There is a paper
by Babbage (*Trans. of Royal Soc. of*
Edinburgh, for 1823) which discusses
certain points connected with it, but
scarcely touches on the subject of the
sections which follow.

instance, instead of a shilling; and secondly, because what he has done once he may do again. He may put his shilling by, and have a second spell of play, long or short as the case may be, with the same termination to it. Accordingly by mere persistency he may accumulate any sum of money he pleases, in apparent defiance of all that is meant by luck.

§ 13. I have classed this opinion among fallacies, as the present is the most convenient opportunity of discussing it, though in strictness it should rather be termed a paradox, since the conclusion is perfectly sound. The only fallacy consists in regarding such a way of obtaining the result as mysterious. On the contrary, there is nothing more easy than to insure ultimate success under the given conditions. The point is worth enquiry, from the principles it involves, and because the answers commonly given do not quite meet the difficulty. It is sometimes urged, for instance, that no bank would or does allow the speculator to choose at will the amount of his stake, but puts a limit to the amount for which it will consent to play. This is quite true, but is of course no answer to the hypothetical enquiry before us, which assumes that such a state of things *is* allowed. Again, it has been urged that the possibility in question turns entirely upon the fact that credit must be supposed to be given, for otherwise the fortune of the player may not hold out until his turn of luck arrives:—that, in fact, sooner or later, if he goes on long enough, his fortune will not hold out long enough, and all his gains will be swept away. It is quite true that credit is a *condition* of success, but it is in no sense the cause. We may suppose both parties to agree at the outset that there shall be no payments until the game be ended, *A* having the right to decide when it shall be considered to be ended. It still remains true that whereas in ordinary gambling, i.e. with fixed or haphazard stakes, *A* could not ensure winning eventually to any extent, he can do so if he adopt such a scheme as the one in question. And this is the state of things which seems to call for explanation.

§ 14. What causes perplexity here is the supposed fact that in some mysterious way certainty has been conjured out of uncertainty; that in a game where the detailed events are utterly inscrutable, and where the average, by supposition, shows no preference for either side, one party is nevertheless succeeding somehow in steadily drawing the luck his own way. It looks as if it were a parallel case with that of a man who should succeed by some device in permanently securing more than half of the tosses with a penny which was nevertheless to be regarded as a perfectly fair one.

This is quite a mistake. The real fact is that *A* does not expose his gains to chance at all; all that he so exposes is the number of times he has to wait until he gains. Put such a case as this. I offer to give a man any sum of money he chooses to mention provided he will at once give it back again to me with one pound more. It does not need much acuteness to see that it is a matter of indifference to me whether he chooses to mention one pound, or ten, or a hundred. Now suppose that instead of leaving it to his choice which of these sums is to be selected each time, the two parties agree to leave it to chance. Let them, for instance, draw a number out of a bag each time, and let that be the sum which *A* gives to *B* under the prescribed conditions. The case is not altered. *A* still gains his pound each time, for the introduction of the element of chance has not in any way touched this. All that it does is to make this pound the result of an uncertain subtraction, sometimes 10 *minus* 9, sometimes 50 *minus* 49, and so on. It is these numbers only, not their difference, which he submits to luck, and this is of no consequence whatever.

To suggest to any individual or company that they should consent to go on playing upon such terms as these would be too barefaced a proposal. And yet the case in question is identical in principle, and almost identical in form, with this. To offer to give a man any sum he likes to name provided he gives you back again that same sum *plus* one, and to offer him any number of terms he pleases of the series 1, 2, 4, 8, 16, &c., provided you have the next term of the set, are equivalent. The only difference is that in the latter case the result is attained with somewhat more of arithmetical parade. Similarly equivalent are the processes in case we prefer to leave it to chance, instead of to choice, to decide what sum or what number of terms shall be fixed upon. This latter is what is really done in the case in question. A man who consents to go on doubling his stake every time he wins, is leaving nothing else to chance than the determination of the particular number of terms of such a geometrical series which shall be allowed to pass before he stops.

§ 15. It may be added that there is no special virtue in the particular series in question, viz. that in accordance with which the stake is doubled each time. All that is needed is that the last term of the series should more than balance all the preceding ones. Any other series which increased faster than this geometrical one, would answer the purpose as well or better. Nor is it necessary, again, that the game should be an even or 'fair' one. Chance, be it remembered, affects nothing here but the number of terms to which the series attains on each occasion, its final result being always arithmetically fixed. When a penny is tossed up it is only on one of every two occasions that the series runs to more than two terms, and so his fixed gains come in pretty regularly. But unless he was playing for a limited time only, it would not affect him if the series ran to two hundred terms; it would merely take him somewhat longer to win his stakes. A man might safely, for instance, continue to lay an *even* bet that he would get the single prize in a lottery of a thousand tickets, provided he thus doubled, or more than doubled, his stake each time, and unlimited credit was given.

§ 16. So regarded, the problem is simple enough, but there are two points in it to which attention may conveniently be directed.

In the first place, it serves very pointedly to remind us of the distinction between a series of events (in this case the tosses of the penny) which really are subjects of chance, and our conduct founded upon these events, which may or may not be so subject[1]. It is quite possible that this latter may be so contrived as to be in many respects a matter of absolute certainty,—a consideration, I presume, familiar enough to professional betting men. Why is the ordinary way of betting on the throws of a penny fair to both parties? Because a 'fair' series is 'fairly' treated. The heads and tails occur at random, but on an average equally often, and the stakes are either fixed or also arranged at random. If a man backs heads every time for the same amount, he will of course in the long run neither win nor lose. Neither will he if he varies the stake every time, provided he does not vary it in such a way as to make its amount dependent on the fact of his having won or lost the time before. But he may, if he pleases, and the other party consents, so arrange his stakes (as in the case in question) that Chance, if one might so express it, does not get a fair chance. Here the human elements of choice and design have been so brought to bear upon a series of events which, regarded by them-

---

[1] Attention will be further directed to this distinction in the chapter on Insurance and Gambling.

selves, exhibit nothing but the physical characteristics of
chance, that the latter elements disappear, and we get a
result which is arithmetically certain. Other analogous
instances might be suggested, but the one before us has the
merit of most ingeniously disguising the actual process.

§ 17.　The meaning of the remark just made will be
better seen by a comparison with the following case. It has
been attempted[1] to explain the preponderance of male births
over female by assuming that the chances of the two are
equal, but that the general desire to have a male heir tends
to induce many unions to persist until the occurrence of this
event, and no longer. It is supposed that in this way there
would be a slight preponderance of families which consisted
of one son only, or of two sons and one daughter, and so forth.

This is quite fallacious (as had been noticed by Laplace,
in his *Essai*); and there could not be a better instance
chosen than this to show just what we can do and what we
cannot do in the way of altering the luck in a real chance-
succession of events. To suppose that the number of actual
births could be influenced in the way in question is exactly
the same thing as to suppose that a number of gamblers
could increase the ratio of heads to tails, to something over
one-half, by each handing the coin to his neighbour as soon
as he had thrown a head: that they have only to leave off as
soon as head has appeared; an absurdity which we need not
pause to explain at this stage. The essential point about
the 'Martingale' is that, whereas the occurrence of the
events on which the stakes are laid is unaffected, the stakes
themselves can be so adjusted as to make the luck swing one
way.

---

[1] As by Prevost in the *Bibliothè-
que Universelle de Genève*, Oct. 1829.
The explanation is noted, and apparently accepted, by Quetelet (*Physique Sociale* I. 171).

§ 18. In the second place, this example brings before us
what has had to be so often mentioned already, namely, that
the series of Probability are in strictness supposed to be
interminable. If therefore we allow either party to call
upon us to stop, especially at a point which just happens to
suit him, we may get results decidedly opposed to the
integrity of the theory. In the case before us it is a necessary stipulation for *A* that he may be allowed to leave off
when he wishes, that is at one of the points at which the
throw is in his favour. Without this stipulation he may be
left a loser to any amount.

Introduce the supposition that one party may arbitrarily
call for a stoppage when it suits him and refuse to permit it
sooner, and almost any system of what would be otherwise fair
play may be converted into a very one-sided arrangement.
Indeed, in the case in question, *A* need not adopt this device
of doubling the stakes every time he loses. He may play
with a fixed stake, and nevertheless insure that *one* party
shall win any assigned sum, assuming that the game is even
and that he is permitted to play on credit.

§ 19. (V.) A common mistake is to assume that a very
unlikely thing will not happen at all. It is a mistake which,
when thus stated in words, is too obvious to be committed,
for the meaning of an unlikely thing is one that happens at
rare intervals; if it were not assumed that the event would
happen sometimes it would not be called unlikely, but impossible. This is an error which could scarcely occur except
in vague popular misapprehension, and is so abundantly re-
futed in works on Probability, that it need only be touched
upon briefly here. It follows of course, from our definition
of Probability, that to speak of a very rare combination of
events as one that is 'sure never to happen,' is to use language incorrectly. Such a phrase may pass current as a

loose popular exaggeration, but in strictness it involves a contradiction. The truth about such rare events cannot be better described than in the following quotation from De Morgan[1]:—

"It is said that no person ever *does* arrive at such extremely improbable cases as the one just cited [drawing the same ball five times running out of a bag containing twenty balls]. That a given individual should never throw an ace twelve times running on a single die, is by far the most likely; indeed, so remote are the chances of such an event in any twelve trials (more than 2,000,000,000 to 1 against it) that it is unlikely the experience of any given country, in any given century, should furnish it. But let us stop for a moment, and ask ourselves to what this argument applies. A person who rarely touches dice will hardly believe that doublets sometimes occur three times running; one who handles them frequently knows that such is sometimes the fact. Every very practised user of those implements has seen still rarer sequences. Now suppose that a society of persons had thrown the dice so often as to secure a run of six aces observed and recorded, the preceding argument would still be used against twelve. And if another society had practised long enough to see twelve aces following each other, they might still employ the same method of doubting as to a run of twenty-four; and so on, *ad infinitum.* The power of imagining cases which contain long combinations so much exceeds that of exhibiting and arranging them, that it is easy to assign a telegraph which should make a separate signal for every grain of sand in a globe as large as the visible universe, upon the hypothesis of the most space-penetrating astronomer. The fallacy of the preceding objection lies in supposing events in number beyond our experience, composed

[1] *Essay on Probabilities*, p. 126.

entirely of sequences such as fall within our experience. It makes the past necessarily contain the whole, as to the quality of its components; and judges by samples. Now the least cautious buyer of grain requires to examine a handful before he judges of a bushel, and a bushel before he judges of a load. But relatively to such enormous numbers of combinations as are frequently proposed, our experience does not deserve the title of a handful as compared with a bushel, or even of a single grain."

§ 20. The origin of this inveterate mistake is not difficult to be accounted for. It arises, no doubt, from the exigencies of our practical life. No man can bear in mind every contingency to which he may be exposed. If therefore we are ever to do anything at all in the world, a large number of the rarer contingencies must be left entirely out of account. And the necessity of this oblivion is strengthened by the shortness of our life. Mathematically speaking, it would be said to be certain that any one who lives long enough will be bitten by a mad dog, for the event is not an impossible, but only an improbable one, and must therefore come to pass in time. But this and an indefinite number of other disagreeable contingencies have on most occasions to be entirely ignored in practice, and thence they come almost necessarily to drop equally out of our thought and expectation. And when the event is one in itself of no importance, like a rare throw of the dice, a great effort of imagination may be required, on the part of persons not accustomed to abstract mathematical calculation, to enable them to realize the throw as being even possible.

Attempts have sometimes been made to estimate what extremity of unlikelihood ought to be considered as equivalent to this practical zero point of belief. In so far as such attempts are carried out by logicians, or by those who are unwilling to resort to mathematical valuation of chances, they must be regarded as merely a special form of the modal difficulties discussed in the last chapter, and need not therefore be reconsidered here; but a word or two may be added concerning the views of some who have looked at the matter from the mathematician's point of view.

The principal of these is perhaps Buffon. He has arrived at the estimate (*Arithmétique Morale* § VIII.) that this practical zero is equivalent to a chance of $\frac{1}{10,000}$. The grounds for selecting this fraction are found in the fact that, according to the tables of mortality accessible to him, it represents the chance of a man of 56 dying in the course of the next day. But since no man under common circumstances takes the chance into the slightest consideration, it follows that it is practically estimated as having no value.

It is obvious that this result is almost entirely arbitrary, and in fact his reasons cannot be regarded as anything more than a slender justification from experience for adopting a conveniently simple fraction; a justification however which would apparently have been equally available in the case of any other fractions lying within wide limits of the one selected[1].

§ 21. There is one particular form of this error, which, from the importance occasionally attached to it, deserves perhaps more special examination. As stated above, there can be no doubt that, however unlikely an event may be, if we (loosely speaking) vary the circumstances sufficiently, or

[1] This theoretical or absolute neglect of what is very rare must not be confused with the practical neglect sometimes recommended by astronomical and other observers. A criterion, known as Chauvenet's, for indicating the limits of such rejection will be found described in Mr Merriman's *Least Squares* (p. 166). But this rests on the understanding that a smaller balance of error would thus result in the long run. The very rare event is deliberately rejected, not overlooked.

if, in other words, we keep on trying long enough, we shall meet with such an event at last. If we toss up a pair of dice a few times we shall get doublets; if we try longer with three we shall get triplets, and so on. However unusual the event may be, even were it sixes a thousand times running, it will come some time or other if we have only patience and vitality enough. Now apply this result to the letters of the alphabet. Suppose that one letter at a time is drawn from a bag which contains them all, and is then replaced. If the letters were written down one after another as they occurred, it would commonly be expected that they would be found to make mere nonsense, and would never arrange themselves into the words of any language known to men. No more they would in general, but it is a commonly accepted result of the theory, and one which we may assume the reader to be ready to admit without further discussion, that, if the process were continued long enough, words making sense would appear; nay more, that any book we chose to mention,—Milton's *Paradise Lost* or the plays of Shakespeare, for example,—would be produced in this way at last. It would take more days than we have space in this volume to represent in figures, to make tolerably certain of obtaining the former of these works by thus drawing letters out of a bag, but the desired result would be obtained at length[1].

[1] The process of calculation may be readily indicated. There are, say, about 350,000 letters in the work in question. Since any of the 26 letters of the alphabet may be drawn each time, the possible number of combinations would be $26^{350,000}$; a number which, as may easily be inferred from a table of logarithms, would demand for its expression nearly 500,000 figures. Only one of these combinations is favourable, if we reject variations of spelling. Hence unity divided by this number would represent the chance of getting the desired result by successive random selection of the required number of 350,000 letters.

If this chance is thought too small, and any one asks how often the above random selection must be repeated in order to give him odds of 2

Now many people have not unnaturally thought it derogatory to genius to suggest that its productions could have also been obtained by chance, whilst others have gone on to argue, If this be the case, might not the world itself in this manner have been produced by chance?

§ 22. We will begin with the comparatively simple, determinate, and intelligible problem of the possible production of the works of a great human genius by chance. With regard to this possibility, it may be a consolation to some timid minds to be reminded that the power of producing the works of a Shakespeare, *in time*, is not confined to consummate genius and to mere chance. There is a third alternative, viz. that of purely mechanical procedure. Any one, down almost to an idiot, might do it, if he took sufficient time about the task. For suppose that the required number of letters were procured and arranged, not by chance, but designedly, and according to rules suggested by the theory of permutations: the letters of the alphabet and the number of them to be employed being finite, every order in which they could occur would come in its due turn, and therefore every thing which can be expressed in language would be arrived at some time or other.

There is really nothing that need shock any one in such a result. Its possibility arises from the following cause.

to 1 in favour of success, this also can be easily shown. If the chance of an event on each occasion is $\frac{1}{n}$, the chance of getting it once at least in n trials is $1 - \left(\frac{n-1}{n}\right)^n$; for we shall do this unless we fail n times running. When (as in the case in question) n is very large, this may be shown algebraically to be equivalent to odds of about 2 to 1. That is, when we have drawn the requisite quantity of letters a number of times equal to the inconceivably great number above represented, it is still only 2 to 1 that we shall have secured what we want:—and then we have to recognize it.

The number of letters, and therefore of words, at our disposal is limited; whatever therefore we may desire to express in language necessarily becomes subject to corresponding limitation. The possible variations of thought are literally infinite, so are those of spoken language (by intonation of the voice, &c.); but when we come to words there is a limitation, the nature of which is distinctly conceivable by the mind, though the restriction is one that in practice will never be appreciable, owing to the fact that the number of combinations which may be produced is so enormous as to surpass all power of the imagination to realize[1]. The answer therefore is plain, and it is one that will apply to many other cases as well, that to put a finite limit upon the number of ways in which a thing can be done, is to determine that any one who is able and willing to try long enough shall succeed in doing it. If a great genius condescends to perform it under these circumstances, he must submit to the possibility of having his claims rivalled or disputed by the chance-man and idiot. If Shakespeare were limited to the use of eight or nine assigned words, the time within which the latter agents might claim equality with him would not be very great. As it is, having had the range of the English language at his disposal, his reputation is not in danger of being assailed by any such methods.

§ 23. The case of the possible production of the world by chance leads us into an altogether different region of discussion. We are not here dealing with figures the nature and use of which are within the fair powers of the understanding, however the imagination may break down in attempting to realize the smallest fraction of their full signi-

---

[1] The longest life which could reasonably be attributed to any language would of course dwindle into utter insignificance in the face of such periods of time as are being here arithmetically contemplated.

ficance. The understanding itself is wandering out of its
proper province, for the conditions of the problem cannot be
assigned. When we draw letters out of a bag we know very
well what we are doing; but what is really meant by producing a world by chance ? By analogy of the former case,
we may assume that some kind of agent is presupposed;—
perhaps therefore the following supposition is less absurd
than any other. Imagine some being, not a Creator but a
sort of Demiurgus, who has had a quantity of materials put
into his hands, and he assigns them their collocations and
their laws of action, blindly and at haphazard: what are the
odds that such a world as we actually experience should have
been brought about in this way ?

If it were worth while seriously to set about answering
such a question, and if some one would furnish us with the
number of the letters of such an alphabet, and the length of
the work to be written with them, we could proceed to indicate the result. But so much as this may surely be affirmed
about it;—that, far from merely finding the length of this
small volume insufficient for containing the figures in which
the adverse odds would be given, all the paper which the
world has hitherto produced would be used up before we had
got far on our way in writing them down.

§ 24. The most seductive form in which the difficulty
about the occurrence of very rare events generally presents
itself is probably this. 'You admit (some persons will be
disposed to say) that such an event may sometimes happen;
nay, that it does sometimes happen in the infinite course of
time. How then am I to know that *this* occasion is not one
of these possible occurrences ?' To this, one answer only can
be given,—the same which must always be given where
statistics and probability are concerned,—'The present *may*
be such an occasion, but it is inconceivably unlikely that it

should be one. Amongst countless billions of times in which you, and such as you, urge this, one person only will be justified; and it is not likely that you are that one, or that this is that occasion.'

§ 25. There is another form of this practical inability to distinguish between one high number and another in the estimation of chances, which deserves passing notice from its importance in arguments about heredity. People will often urge an objection to the doctrine that qualities, mental and bodily, are transmitted from the parents to the offspring, on the ground that there are a multitude of instances to the contrary, in fact a great majority of such instances. To raise this objection implies an utter want of appreciation of the very great odds which possibly may exist, and which the argument in support of heredity implies *do* exist against any given person being distinguished for intellectual or other eminence. This is doubtless partly a matter of definition, depending upon the degree of rarity which we consider to be implied by eminence ; but taking any reasonable sense of the term, we shall readily see that a very great proportion of failures may still leave an enormous preponderance of evidence in favour of the heredity doctrine. Take, for instance, that degree of eminence which is implied by being one of four thousand. This is a considerable distinction, though, since there are about two thousand such persons to be found amongst the total adult male population of Great Britain, it is far from implying any conspicuous genius. Now suppose that in examining the cases of a large number of the children of such persons, we had found that 199 out of 200 of them failed to reach the same distinction. Many persons would conclude that this was pretty conclusive evidence against any hereditary transmission. To be able to adduce only one favourable, as against 199 hostile instances, would

to them represent the entire break-down of any such theory.
The error, of course, is obvious enough, and one which, with
the figures thus before him, hardly any one could fail to
avoid. But if one may judge from common conversation
and other such sources of information, it is found in practice
exceedingly difficult adequately to retain the conviction that
even though only one in 200 instances were favourable,
this would represent odds of about 20 to 1 in favour of the
theory. If hereditary transmission did not prevail, only one
in 4000 sons would thus rival their fathers; but we find
actually, let us say (we are of course taking imaginary proportions here), that one in 200 does. Hence, if the statistics
are large enough to be satisfactory, there has been some
influence at work which has improved the chances of mere
coincidence in the ratio of 20 to 1. We are in fact so little
able to realise the meaning of very large numbers,—that is,
to retain the *ratios* in the mind, where large numbers are
concerned,—that unless we repeatedly check ourselves by
arithmetical considerations we are too apt to treat and estimate all beyond certain limits as equally vast and vague.

§ 26. (VI.) In discussing the nature of the connexion
between Probability and Induction, we examined the claims
of a rule commonly given for inferring the probability that
an event which had been repeatedly observed would recur
again. I endeavoured to show that all attempts to obtain
and prove such a rule were necessarily futile; if these reasons
were conclusive the employment of such a rule must of
course be regarded as fallacious. A few examples may conveniently be added here, tending to show how instead of
there being merely a single rule of succession we might better
divide the possible forms into three classes.

(1) In some cases when a thing has been observed to
happen several times it becomes in consequence *more* likely

that the thing should happen again. This agrees with the ordinary form of the rule, and is probably the case of most frequent occurrence. The necessary vagueness of expression when we talk of the 'happening of a thing' makes it quite impossible to tolerate the rule in this general form, but if we specialize it a little we shall find it assume a more familiar shape. If, for example, we have observed two or more properties to be frequently associated together in a succession of individuals, we shall conclude with some force that they will be found to be so connected in future. The strength of our conviction however will depend not merely on the number of observed coincidences, but on far more complicated considerations; for a discussion of which the reader must be referred to regular treatises on Inductive evidence. Or again, if we have observed one of two events succeed the other several times, the occurrence of the former will excite in most cases some degree of expectation of the latter. As before, however, the degree of our expectation is not to be assigned by any simple formula; it will depend in part upon the supposed intimacy with which the events are connected. To attempt to lay down definite rules upon the subject would lead to a discussion upon laws of causation, and the circumstances under which their existence may be inferred, and therefore any further consideration of the matter must be abandoned here.

§ 27. (2) Or, secondly, the past recurrence may in itself give no valid grounds for inference about the future; this is the case which most properly belongs to Probability[1].

---

[1] We are here assuming of course that the ultimate limit to which our average tends is known, either from knowledge of the causes or from previous extensive experience. We are assuming that *e.g.* the die is known to be a fair one; if this is not known but a possible bias has to be inferred from its observed performances, the case falls under the former head.

That it does so belong will be easily seen if we bear in mind the fundamental conception of the science. We are there introduced to a series,—for purposes of inference an indefinitely extended series,—of terms, about the details of which, information, except on certain points, is not given; our knowledge being confined to the statistical fact, that, say, one in ten of them has some attribute which we will call X. Suppose now that five of these terms in succession have been X, what hint does this give about the sixth being also an X? Clearly none at all; this past fact tells us nothing; the formula for our inference is still precisely what it was before, that one in ten being X it is one to nine that the next term is X. And however many terms in succession had been of one kind, precisely the same formula would still be given.

§ 28. The way in which events will justify the answer given by this formula is often misunderstood. For the benefit therefore of those unacquainted with some of the conceptions familiar to mathematicians, a few words of explanation may be added. Suppose then that we have had X twelve times in succession. This is clearly an anomalous state of things. To suppose anything like this continuing to occur would be obviously in opposition to the statistics, which assert that in the long run only one in ten is X. But how is this anomaly got over? In other words, how do we obviate the conclusion that X's must occur more frequently than once in ten times, after such a long succession of them as we have now had? Many people seem to believe that there must be a diminution of X's afterwards to counterbalance their past preponderance. This however would be quite a mistake; the proportion in which they occur in future must remain the same throughout; it cannot be altered if we are to adhere to our statistical formula. The fact is that the rectification of the exceptional disturbance in the proportion will be brought about simply by the continual influx of fresh terms in the series. These will in the long run neutralize the disturbance, not by any special adaptation, as it were, for the purpose, but by the mere weight of their overwhelming numbers. At every stage therefore, in the succession, whatever might have been the number and nature of the preceding terms, it will still be true to say that one in ten of the terms will be an X.

If we had to do only with a finite number of terms, however large that number might be, such a disturbance as we have spoken of would, it is true, need a special alteration in the subsequent proportions to neutralize its effects. But when we have to do with an infinite number of terms, this is not the case; the 'limit' of the series, which is what we then have to deal with, is unaffected by these temporary disturbances. In the continued progress of the series we shall find, as a matter of fact, more and more of such disturbances, and these of a more and more exceptional character. But whatever the point we may occupy at any time, if we look forward or backward into the indefinite extension of the series, we shall still see that the ultimate limit to the proportion in which its terms are arranged remains the same; and it is with this limit, as above mentioned, that we are concerned in the strict rules of Probability.

The most familiar example, perhaps, of this kind is that of tossing up a penny. Suppose we have had four heads in succession; people[1] have tolerably realized by now that 'head the fifth time' is still an even chance, as 'head' was each

---

[1] Except indeed the gamblers. According to a gambling acquaintance whom Houdin, the conjurer, describes himself as having met at Spa, "the oftener a particular combination has occurred the more certain it is that it will not be repeated at the next *coup:* this is the groundwork of all theories of probabilities and is termed the maturity of chances" (*Cardsharping exposed*, p. 85).

time before, and will be ever after. The preceding paragraph explains how it is that these occasional disturbances
in the average become neutralized in the long run.

§ 29. (3) There are other cases which, though rare,
are by no means unknown, in which such an inference as
that obtained from the Rule of Succession would be the direct reverse of the truth. The oftener a thing happens, it
may be, the more unlikely it is to happen again. This is the
case whenever we are drawing things from a limited source
(as balls from a bag without replacing them), or whenever
the act of repetition itself tends to prevent the succession
(as in giving false alarms).

I am quite ready to admit that we believe the results described in the last two classes on the strength of some such
general Inductive rule, or rather principle, as that involved
in the first. But it would be a great error to confound this
with an admission of the validity of the rule in each special
instance. We are speaking about the application of the rule
to individual cases, or classes of cases; this is quite a distinct thing, as was pointed out in a previous chapter, from
giving the grounds on which we rest the rule itself. If a
man were to lay it down as a universal rule, that the testimony of all persons was to be believed, and we adduced an
instance of a man having lied, it would not be considered
that he saved his rule by showing that we believed that it
was a lie on the word of other persons. But it is perfectly
consistent to give as a merely general, but not universal,
rule, that the testimony of men is credible ; then to separate
off a second class of men whose word is not to be trusted,
and finally, if any one wants to know our ground for the
second rule, to rest it upon the first. If we were speaking
of *necessary* laws, such a conflict as this would be as
hopeless as the old 'Cretan' puzzle in logic; but in in-

stances of Inductive and Analogical extension it is perfectly harmless.

§ 30. A familiar example will serve to bring out the three different possible conclusions mentioned above. We have observed it rain on ten successive days. *A* and *B* conclude respectively for and against rain on the eleventh day ; *C* maintains that the past rain affords no data whatever for an opinion. Which is right ? We really cannot determine *à priori*. An appeal must be made to direct observation, or means must be found for deciding on independent grounds to which class we are to refer the instance. If, for example, it were known that every country produces its own rain, we should choose the third rule, for it would be a case of drawing from a limited supply. If again we had reasons to believe that the rain for our country might be produced anywhere on the globe, we should probably conclude that the past rainfall threw no light whatever on the prospect of a continuance of wet weather, and therefore take the second. Or if, finally, we knew that rain came in long spells or seasons, as in the tropics, then the occurrence of ten wet days in succession would make us believe that we had entered on one of these seasons, and that therefore the next day would probably resemble the preceding ten.

Since then all these forms of such an Inductive rule are possible, and we have often no *à priori* grounds for preferring one to another, it would seem to be unreasonable to attempt to establish any universal formula of anticipation. All that we can do is to ascertain what are the circumstances under which one or other of these rules is, as a matter of fact, found to be applicable, and to make use of it under those circumstances.

§ 31. (VII.) In the cases discussed in (V.) the almost infinitely small chances with which we were concerned were

rightly neglected from all practical consideration, however
proper it might be, on speculative grounds, to keep our minds
open to their actual existence. But it has often occurred to
me that there is a common error in neglecting to take them into
account when they may, though individually small, make up
for their minuteness by their number. As the mathematician
would express it, they may occasionally be capable of being
integrated into a finite or even considerable magnitude.

For instance, we may be confronted with a difficulty out
of which there appears to be only one appreciably possible
mode of escape. The attempt is made to force us into
accepting this, however great the odds apparently are against
it, on the ground that improbable as it may seem, it is at
any rate vastly more probable than any of the others. I
can quite admit that, on practical grounds, we may often find
it reasonable to adopt this course ; for we can only *act* on
one supposition, and we naturally and rightly choose, out
of a quantity of improbabilities, the least improbable. But
when we are not forced to act, no such decisive preference is
demanded of us. It is then perfectly reasonable to refuse
assent to the proposed explanation ; even to say distinctly
that we do not believe it, and at the same time to decline,
at present, to accept any other explanation. We remain, in
fact, in a state of suspense of judgment, a state perfectly
right and reasonable so long as no action demanding a specific choice is forced upon us. One alternative may be
decidedly probable as compared with any other individually,
but decidedly improbable as compared with all others collectively. This in itself is intelligible enough ; what people
often fail to see is that there is no necessary contradiction
between saying and feeling this, and yet being prepared
vigorously to act, when action is forced upon us, as though
this alternative were really the true one.

§ 32.   To take a specific instance, this way of regarding
the matter has often occurred to me in disputes upon 'Spiritualist' manifestations.   Assent is urged upon us because,
it is said, no other possible solution can be suggested.   It
may be quite true that apparently overwhelming difficulties
may lie as against each separate alternative solution; but is
it always sufficiently realized how numerous such solutions
may be ?   No matter that each individually may be almost
incredible : they ought all to be massed together and thrown
into the scale against the proffered solution, when the only
question asked is, Are we to accept this solution ?   There is
no unfairness in such a course.   We are perfectly ready to
adopt the same plan against any other individual alternative, whenever any person takes to claiming this as *the*
solution of the difficulty.   We are looking at the matter
from a purely logical point of view, and are quite willing, so
far, to place every solution, spiritualist or otherwise, upon the
same footing.   The partisans of every alternative are in
somewhat the same position as the members of a deliberative
assembly, in which no one will support the motion of any
other member.   Every one can aid effectively in rejecting
every other motion, but no one can succeed in passing his
own.   Pressure of urgent necessity may possibly force them
out of this state of practical inaction, by, so to say, breaking
through the opposition at some point of least resistance; but
unless aided by some such pressure they are left in a state of
hopeless dead-lock.

§ 33.   Assuming that the spiritualistic solution admits
of, and is to receive, scientific treatment, this, it seems to
me, is the conclusion to which one might sometimes be led
in the face of the evidence offered.   We might have to say to
every individual explanation, It is incredible, I cannot accept
it ; and unless circumstances should (which it is hardly pos-

sible that they should) force us to a hasty decision,—a decision, remember, which need indicate no preference of the
judgment beyond what is just sufficient to turn the scale in its
favour as against any other single alternative,—we leave the
matter thus in abeyance. It will very likely be urged that
one of the explanations (assuming that all the possible ones
had been included) must be true ; this we readily admit.
It will probably also be urged that (on the often-quoted
principle of Butler) we ought forthwith to accept the one
which, as compared with the others, is the most plausible,
whatever its absolute worth may be. This seems distinctly
an error. To say that such and such an explanation is the
one we should accept, *if* circumstances compelled us to anticipate our decision, is quite compatible with its present
rejection. The only rational position surely is that of
admitting that the truth is somewhere amongst the various
alternatives, but confessing plainly that we have no such
preference for one over another as to permit our saying anything else than that we disbelieve each one of them.

§ 34. (VIII.) The very common fallacy of 'judging by
the event,' as it is generally termed, deserves passing notice
here, as it clearly belongs to Probability rather than to Logic ;
though its nature is so obvious to those who have grasped the
general principles of our science, that a very few words of
remark will suffice. In one sense every proposition must
consent to be judged by the event, since this is merely, in
other words, submitting it to the test of experience. But
there is the widest difference between the test appropriate
to a universal proposition and that appropriate to a merely
proportional or statistical one. The former is subverted by a
single exception ; the latter not merely admits exceptions,
but implies them. Nothing, however, is more common than
to blame advice (in others) because it has happened to turn

out unfortunately, or to claim credit for it (in oneself) because it has happened to succeed. Of course if the conclusion was avowedly one of a probable kind we must be prepared with complacency to accept a hostile event, or even a succession of them; it is not until the succession shows a disposition to continue over long that suspicion and doubt should arise, and then only by a comparison of the degree of the assigned probability, and the magnitude of the departure from it which experience exhibits. For any single failure the reply must be, 'the advice was sound' (supposing, that is, that it was to be justified in the long run), 'and I shall offer it again under the same circumstances.'

§ 35. The distinction drawn in the above instance deserves careful consideration; for owing to the wide difference between the kind of propositions dealt with in Probability and in ordinary Logic, and the consequent difference in the nature of the proof offered, it is quite possible for arguments of the same general appearance to be valid in the former and fallacious in the latter, and conversely.

For instance, take the well-known fallacy which consists in simply converting a universal affirmative, *i.e.* in passing from All *A* is *B* to All *B* is *A*. When, as in common Logic, the conclusion is to be as certain as the premise, there is not a word to be said for such a step. But if we look at the process with the more indulgent eye of Induction or Probability we see that a very fair case may sometimes be made out for it. The mere fact that 'Some *B* is *A*' raises a certain presumption that any particular *B* taken at random will be an *A*. There is some reason, at any rate, for the belief, though in the absence of statistics as to the relative frequency of *A* and *B* we are unable to assign a value to this belief. I suspect that there may be many cases in which a man has inferred that some particular *B* is an *A* on the

ground that All *A* is *B*, who might justly plead in his behalf
that he never meant it to be a necessary, but only a probable inference.   The same remarks will of course apply
also to the logical fallacy of Undistributed Middle.

Now for a case of the opposite kind, *i.e.* one in which
Probability fails us, whereas the circumstances seem closely
analogous to those in which ordinary inference would be
able to make a stand.   Suppose that I know that one letter
in a million is lost when in charge of the post.   I write to a
friend and get no answer.   Have I any reason to suppose
that the fault lies with him ?   Here is an event (viz. the
loss of the letter) which has certainly happened ; and we suppose that, of the only two causes to which it can be assigned,
the ' value,' *i.e.* statistical frequency, of one is accurately
assigned, does it not seem natural to suppose that something
can be inferred as to the likelihood that the other cause had
been operative ?   To say that nothing can be known about
its adequacy under these circumstances looks at first sight
like asserting that an equation in which there is only one
unknown term is theoretically insoluble.

As examples of this kind have been amply discussed in
the chapter upon Inverse rules of Probability I need do no
more here than remind the reader that no conclusion whatever can be drawn as to the likelihood that the fault lay
with my friend rather than with the Post Office.   Unless we
either know, or make some assumption about, the frequency
with which he neglects to answer the letters he receives, the
problem remains insoluble.

The reason why the apparent analogy, indicated above,
to an equation with only one unknown quantity, fails to hold
good, is that for the purposes of Probability there are really
two unknown quantities.   What we deal with are proportional or statistical propositions.   Now we are only told that

in the instance in question the letter was lost, not that they were found to be lost in such and such a proportion of cases. Had this latter information been given to us we should really have had but one unknown quantity to determine, viz. the relative frequency with which my correspondent neglects to answer his letters, and we could then have determined this with the greatest ease.

CHAPTER XV.

§ 1. IF the reader will recall to mind the fundamental postulate of the Science of Probability, established and explained in the first few chapters, and so abundantly illustrated since, he will readily recognize that the two opposite characteristics of individual irregularity and average regularity will naturally be differently estimated by different minds. To some persons the elements of uncertainty may be so painful, either in themselves or in their consequences, that they are anxious to adopt some means of diminishing them. To others the ultimate regularity of life, at any rate within certain departments, its monotony as they consider it, may be so wearisome that *they* equally wish to effect some alteration and improvement in its characteristics. We shall discuss briefly these mental tendencies, and the most simple and obvious modes of satisfying them.

To some persons, as we have said, the world is all too full of change and irregularity and consequent uncertainty. Civilization has done much to diminish these characteristics in certain directions, but it has unquestionably aggravated them in other directions, and it might not be very easy to say with certainty in which of these respects its operation has been, at present, on the whole most effective. The diminution of irregularity is exemplified, amongst other things, in the case of the staple products which supply our necessary food and clothing. With respect to them, famine and scarcity are by comparison almost unknown now, at any rate in tolerably civilized communities. As a consequence of this, and of the vast improvements in the means of transporting goods and conveying intelligence, the fluctuations in the price of such articles are much less than they once were. In other directions, however, the reverse has been the case. Fashion, for instance, now induces so many people in every large community simultaneously to desire the same thing, that great fluctuations in value may ensue. Moreover a whole group of causes (to enter upon any discussion of which would be to trench upon the ground of Political Economy) combine to produce great and frequent variations in matters concerning credit and the currency, which formerly had no existence. Bankruptcy, for instance, is from the nature of the case, almost wholly a creation of modern times. We will not attempt to strike any balance between these opposite results of modern civilization, beyond remarking that in matters of prime importance the actual uncertainties have been probably on the whole diminished, whereas in those which affect the pocket rather than the life, they have been rather increased. It might also be argued with some plausibility that in cases where the actual uncertainties have not become greater, they have for all practical purposes done so, by their consequences frequently becoming more serious, or by our estimate of these consequences becoming higher.

§ 2. However the above question, as to the ultimate balance of gain or loss, should be decided, there can be no doubt that many persons find the present amount of uncertainty in some of the affairs of life greater than suits their taste. How are they to diminish it? Something of course may be done, as regards the individual cases, by prudence and foresight. Our houses may be built with a view not to take fire so readily, or precautions may be taken that there shall be fire-engines at hand. In the warding off of death from disease and accident, something may be done by every one who chooses to live prudently. Precautions of the above kind, however, do not introduce any questions of Probability. These latter considerations only come in when we begin to invoke the regularity of the average to save us from the irregularities of the details. We cannot, it is true, remove the uncertainty in itself, but we can so act that the consequences of that uncertainty shall be less to us, or to those in whom we are interested. Take the case of Life Insurance. A professional man who has nothing but the income he earns to depend upon, knows that the whole of that income may vanish in a moment by his death. This is a state of things which he cannot prevent; and if he were the only one in such a position, or were unable or unwilling to combine with his fellow-men, there would be nothing more to be done in the matter except to live within his income as much as possible, and so leave a margin of savings.

§ 3. There is however an easy mode of escape for him. All that he has to do is to agree with a number of others, who are in the same position as himself, to make up, so to say, a common purse. They may resolve that those of their number who live to work beyond the average length of life shall contribute to support the families of those who die earlier. If a few only concurred in such a resolution they would not gain very much, for they would still be removed by but a slight step from that uncertainty which they are seeking to escape. What is essential is that a considerable number should thus combine so as to get the benefit of that comparative regularity which the average, as is well known, almost always tends to exhibit.

§ 4. The above simple considerations really contain the

essence of all insurance. Such points as the fact that the agreement for indemnity extends only to a certain definite sum of money; and that instead of calling for an occasional general contribution at the time of the death of each member they substitute a fixed annual premium, out of the proceeds of which the payment is to be made, are merely accidents of convenience and arrangement. Insurance is simply equivalent to a mutual contract amongst those who dread the consequences of the uncertainty of their life or employment, that they will employ the aggregate regularity to neutralize as far as possible the individual irregularity. They know that for every one who gains by such a contract another will lose as much; or if one gains a great deal many must have lost a little. They know also that hardly any of their number can expect to find the arrangement a 'fair' one, in the sense that they just get back again what they have paid in premiums, after deducting the necessary expenses of management; but they deliberately prefer this state of things. They consist of a body of persons who think it decidedly better to leave behind them a comparatively fixed fortune, rather than one which is extremely uncertain in amount; although they are perfectly aware that, owing to the unavoidable expenses of managing the affairs of such a society, the comparatively fixed sum, so to be left, will be a trifle less than the average fortunes which would have been left had no such system of insurance been adopted.

As this is not a regular treatise upon Insurance no more need be said upon the exact nature of such societies, beyond pointing out that they are of various different kinds. Sometimes they really are what we have compared them with, viz. mutual agreements amongst a group of persons to make up each other's losses to a certain extent. Into this category fall the Mutual Insurance Societies, Benefit Societies, Trades

Unions (in respect of some of their functions), together with innumerable other societies which go by various names. Sometimes they are companies worked by proprietors or shareholders for a profit, like any other industrial enterprise. This is the case, I believe, with the majority of the ordinary Life Insurance Societies. Sometimes, again, it is the State which undertakes the management, as in the case of our Post Office Insurance business.

§ 5. It is clear that there is no necessary limit to the range of application of this principle[1]. It is quite conceivable that the majority of the inhabitants of some nation might be so enamoured of security that they should devise a grand insurance society to cover almost every concern in life. They could not indeed abolish uncertainty, for the conditions of life are very far from permitting this, but they could without much difficulty get rid of the worst of the *consequences* of it. They might determine to insure not merely their lives, houses, ships, and other things in respect of which sudden and total loss is possible, but also to insure their business; in the sense of avoiding not only

---

[1] The question of the advisability of inoculation against the small-pox, which gave rise to much discussion amongst the writers on Probability during the last century, is a case in point of the same principles applied to a very different kind of instance. The loss against which the insurance was directed was death by small-pox, the premium paid was the illness and other inconvenience, and the very small risk of death, from the inoculation. The disputes which thence arose amongst writers on the subject involved the same difficulties as to the balance between certain moderate loss and contingent great loss. In the seventeenth century it seems to have been an occasional practice, before a journey into the Mediterranean, to insure against capture by Moorish pirates, with a view to secure having the ransom paid. (See, for an account of some extraordinary developments of the insurance principle, Walford's *Insurance Guide and Handbook*. It is not written in a very scientific spirit, but it contains much information on all matters connected with insurance.)

bankruptcy, but even casual bad years, on the same principle of commutation. Unfamiliar as such an aim may appear when introduced in this language, it is nevertheless one which under a name of suspicious import to the conservative classes has had a good deal of attention directed to it. It is really scarcely anything else than Communism, which might indeed be defined as a universal and compulsory[1] insurance society which is to take account of all departments of business, and, in some at least of its forms, to invade the province of social and domestic life as well.

Although nothing so comprehensive as this is likely to be practically carried out on any very large scale, it deserves notice that the principle itself is steadily spreading in every direction in matters of detail. It is, for instance, the great complaint against Trades Unions that they too often seek to secure these results in respect of the equalization of the workmen's wages, thus insuring to some degree against incompetence, as they rightly and wisely do against illness and loss of work. Again, there is the Tradesman's Mutual Protection Society, which insures against the occasional loss entailed by the necessity of having to conduct prosecutions at law. There are societies in many towns for the prosecution of petty thefts, with the object of escaping the same uncertain and perhaps serious loss. Amongst instances of insurance *for* the people rather than *by* them, there is of course the giant example of the English Poor Law, in which the resemblance to an initial Communistic system becomes very marked. The poor are insured against loss

---

[1] All that is meant by the above comparison is that the ideal aimed at by Communism is similar to that of Insurance. If we look at the processes by which it would be carried out, and the means for enforcing it, the matter would of course assume a very different aspect. Similarly with the action of Trades Unionism referred to in the next paragraph.

of work arising not only from illness and old age, but from any cause except wilful idleness. They do not, it is true, pay the whole premium, but since they mostly bear some portion of the burden of municipal and county taxation they must certainly be considered as paying a part of the premium. In some branches also of the public and private services the system is adopted of deducting a percentage from the wage or salary, for the purpose of a semi-compulsory insurance against death, illness or superannuation.

§ 6. Closely connected with Insurance, as an application of Probability, though of course by contrast, stands Gambling. Though we cannot, in strictness, term either of these practices the converse of the other, it seems nevertheless correct to say that they spring from opposite mental tendencies. Some persons, as has been said, find life too monotonous for their taste, or rather the region of what can be predicted with certainty is too large and predominant in their estimation. They can easily adopt two courses for securing the changes they desire. They may, for one thing, aggravate and intensify the results of events which are comparatively incapable of prevision, these events not being in themselves of sufficient importance to excite any strong emotions. The most obvious way of doing this is by betting upon them. Or again, they may invent games or other pursuits, the individual contingencies of which are entirely removed from all possible human prevision, and then make heavy money consequences depend upon these contingencies. This is gambling proper, carried on mostly by means of cards and dice and the roulette.

The gambling spirit, as we have said, seeks for the excitement of uncertainty and variety. When therefore people make a long continued practice of playing, especially if the stakes for which they play are moderate in comparison with their fortune, this uncertainty from the nature of the case begins to diminish. The thoroughly practised gambler, if he possesses more than usual skill (in games where skill counts for something), must be regarded as a man following a profession, though a profession for the most part of a risky and exciting kind, to say nothing of its ignoble and often dishonest character. If, on the other hand, his skill is below the average, or the game is one in which skill does not tell and the odds are slightly in favour of his antagonist, as in the gaming tables, one light in which he can be regarded is that of a man who is following a favourite amusement; if this amusement involves a constant annual outlay on his part, that is nothing more than what has to be said of most other amusements.

§ 7. We cannot, of course, give such a rational explanation as the above in every case. There are plenty of novices, and plenty of fanatics, who go on steadily losing in the full conviction that they will eventually come out winners. But it is hard to believe that such ignorance, or such intellectual twist, can really be so widely prevalent as would be requisite to constitute them the rule rather than the exception. There must surely be some very general impulse which is gratified by such resources, and it is not easy to see what else this can be than a love of that variety and consequent excitement which can only be found in perfection where exact prevision is impossible.

It is of course very difficult to make any generalization here as to the comparative prevalence of various motives amongst mankind; but when one considers what is the difference which most quiet ordinary whist players feel between a game for 'love' and one in which there is a small stake, one cannot but assign a high value to the influence of a wish to emphasize the excitement of loss and gain.

I would not for a moment underrate the practical dangers which are found to attend the practice of gambling. It is remarked that the gambler, if he continues to play for a long time, is under an almost irresistible impulse to increase his stakes, and so re-introduce the element of uncertainty. It is in fact this tendency to be thus led on, which makes the principal danger and mischief of the practice. Risk and uncertainty are still such normal characteristics of even civilized life, that the mere extension of such tendencies into new fields does not in itself offer any very alarming prospect. It is only to be deprecated in so far as there is a danger, which experience shows to be no trifling one, that the fascination found in the pursuit should lead men into following it up into excessive lengths[1].

§ 8.   The above general treatment of Gambling and Insurance seems to me the only rational and sound principle of division;—namely, that on which the different practices which, under various names, are known as gambling or insurance, are arranged in accordance with the spirit of which they are the outcome, and therefore of the results which they are designed to secure. If we were to attempt

---

[1] One of the best discussions that I have recently seen on these subjects, by a writer at once thoroughly competent and well informed, is in Mr Proctor's *Chance and Luck*. It appears to me however that he runs into an extreme in his denunciation not of the folly but of the dishonesty of all gambling. Surely also it is a strained use of language to speak of all lotteries as 'unfair' and even 'swindling' on the ground that the sum-total of what they distribute in prizes is less than that of what they receive in payments. The difference, in respect of information deliberately withheld and false reports wilfully spread, between most of the lotteries that have been supported, and the bubble companies which justly deserve the name of swindles, ought to prevent the same name being applied to both.

to judge and arrange them according to the names which they currently bear, we should find ourselves led to no kind of systematic division whatever; the fact being that since they all alike involve, as their essential characteristic, payments and receipts, one or both of which are necessarily uncertain in their date or amount, the names may often be interchanged.

For instance, a lottery and an ordinary insurance society against accident, if we merely look to the processes performed in them, are to all intents and purposes identical. In each alike there is a small payment which is certain in amount, and a great receipt which is uncertain in amount. A great many persons pay the small premium, whereas a few only of their number obtain a prize, the rest getting no return whatever for their outlay. In each case alike, also, the aggregate receipts and losses are intended to balance each other, after allowing for the profits of those who carry on the undertaking. But of course when we take into account the occasions upon which the insurers get their prizes, we see that there is all the difference in the world between receiving them at haphazard, as in a lottery, and receiving them as a partial set-off to a broken limb or injured constitution, as in the insurance society.

Again, the language of betting may be easily made to cover almost every kind of insurance. Indeed De Morgan has described life insurance as a bet which the individual makes with the company, that he will not live beyond a certain age. If he dies young, he is pecuniarily a gainer, if he dies late he is a loser[1]. Here, too, though the expression

---

[1] "A fire insurance is a simple bet between the office and the party, and a life insurance is a collection of wagers. There is something of the principle of a wager in every transaction in which the results of a future event are to bring gain or loss." *Penny Cyclopædia*, under the head of *Wager*.

is technically quite correct (since any such deliberate risk of money, upon an unproductive venture, may fall under the definition of a bet), there is the broadest distinction between betting with no other view whatever than that of risking money, and betting with the view of diminishing risk and loss as much as possible. In fact, if the language of sporting life is to be introduced into the matter, we ought, I presume, to speak of the insurer as 'hedging' against his death.

§ 9. Again, in Tontines we have a system of what is often called Insurance, and in certain points rightly so, but which is to all intents and purposes simply and absolutely a gambling transaction. They have been entirely abandoned, I believe, for some time, but were once rather popular, especially in France. On this plan the State, or whatever society manages the business, does not gain anything until the last member of the Tontine is dead. As the number of the survivors diminishes, the same sum-total of annuities still continues to be paid amongst them, as long as any arc left alive, so that each receives a gradually increasing sum. Hence those who die early, instead of receiving the most, as on the ordinary plan, receive the least; for at the death of each member the annuity ceases absolutely, so far as he and his relations are concerned. The whole affair therefore is to all intents and purposes a gigantic system of betting, to see which can live the longest; the State being the common stake-holder, and receiving a heavy commission for its superintendence, this commission being naturally its sole motive for encouraging such a transaction. It is recorded of one of the French Tontines[1] that a widow of 97 was left, as the last survivor, to receive an annuity of 73,500 livres during the rest of the life which she could manage to drag on after that age ;—she having originally subscribed a

---

[1] *Encyclopédie Methodique*, under the head of Tontines.

single sum of 300 livres only. It is obvious that such a system as this, though it may sometimes go by the name of insurance, is utterly opposed to the spirit of true insurance, since it tends to aggravate existing inequalities of fortune instead of to mitigate them. The insurer here bets that he will die old; in ordinary insurance he bets that he will die young.

Again, to take one final instance, common opinion often regards the bank or company which keeps a *rouge et noir* table, and the individuals who risk their money at it, as being both alike engaged in gambling. So they may be, technically, but for all practical purposes such a bank is as sure and safe a business as that of any ordinary insurance society, and probably far steadier in its receipts than the majority of ordinary trades in a manufacturing or commercial city. The bank goes in for many and small transactions, in proportion to its capital; their customers, very often, in proportion to their incomes go in for very heavy transactions. That the former comes out a gainer year after year depends, of course, upon the fact that the tables are notoriously slightly in their favour. But the *steadiness* of these gains when compared with the unsteadiness of the individual losses depends simply upon,—in fact, is merely an illustration of,—the one great permanent contrast which lies at the basis of all reasoning in Probability.

§ 10. We have so far regarded Insurance and Gambling as being each the product of a natural impulse, and as having each, if we look merely to experience, a great mass of human judgment in its favour. The popular moral judgment, however, which applauds the one and condemns the other rests in great part upon an assumption, which has doubtless much truth in it, but which is often interpreted with an absoluteness which leads to error in each direction ;—the duty of insurance being too peremptorily urged upon every one, and the practice of gambling too universally regarded as involving a sacrifice of real self-interest, as being in fact little better than a persistent blunder. The assumption in question seems to be extracted from the acknowledged advantages of insurance, and then invoked to condemn the practice of gambling. But in so doing the fact does not seem to be sufficiently recognized that the latter practice, if we merely look to the extent and antiquity of the tacit vote of mankind in its favour, might surely claim to carry the day.

It is of course obvious that in all cases with which we are concerned, the aggregate wealth is unaltered; money being merely transferred from one person to another. The loss of one is precisely equivalent to the gain of another. At least this is the approximation to the truth with which we find it convenient to start[1]. Now if the happiness which is yielded by wealth were always in direct proportion to its amount, it is not easy to see why insurance should be advocated or gambling condemned. In the case of the latter this is obvious enough. I have lost £50, say, but others (one or more as the case may be) have gained it, and the increase of their happiness would exactly balance the diminution of mine. In the case of Insurance there is a slight complication, arising from the fact that the falling in of the policy does not happen at random (otherwise, as already pointed

---

[1] Of course, if we introduce considerations of Political Economy, corrections will have to be made. For one thing, every Insurance Office is, as De Morgan repeatedly insists, a *Savings Bank* as well as an Insurance Office. The Office invests the premiums, and can therefore afford to pay a larger sum than would otherwise be the case. Again, in the case of gambling, a large loss of capital by any one will almost necessarily involve an actual destruction of wealth; to say nothing of the fact that, practically, gambling often causes a constant transfer of wealth from productive to unproductive purposes.

out, it would be simply a lottery), but is made contingent
upon some kind of loss, which it is intended as far as possible
to balance.   I insure myself on a railway journey, break my
leg in an accident, and, having paid threepence for my
ticket, receive say £200 compensation from the insurance
company.   The same remarks, however, apply here; the
happiness I acquire by this £200 would only just balance the
aggregate loss of the 16,000 who have paid their threepences
and received no return for them, were happiness always
directly proportional to wealth.

§ 11.   The practice of Insurance does not, I think, give
rise to many questions of theoretic interest, and need not
therefore detain us longer.   The fact is that it has hardly
yet been applied sufficiently long and widely, or to matters
which admit of sufficiently accurate statistical treatment,
except in one department.   This, of course, is Life Insurance;
but the subject is one which requires constant attention to
details of statistics, and is (rightly) mainly carried out in
strict accordance with routine.   As an illustration of this
we need merely refer to the works of De Morgan,—a professional actuary as well as a writer on the theory of Probability,
—who has found but little opportunity to aid his speculative
treatment of Probability by examples drawn from this class
of considerations.

With Gambling it is otherwise.   Not only have a variety
of interesting single problems been discussed (of which the
Petersburg problem is the best known) but several speculative questions of considerable importance have been raised.
One of these concerns the disadvantages of the practice of
gambling.   There have been a number of writers who, not
content with dwelling upon the obvious moral and indirect
mischief which results, in the shape of over-excitement,
consequent greed, withdrawal from the steady business

habits which alone insure prosperity in the long run, diversion of wealth into dishonest hands, &c., have endeavoured to demonstrate the necessary loss caused by the practice.

§ 12. These attempts may be divided into two classes. There are (1) those which appeal to merely numerical considerations, and (2) those which introduce what is called the 'moral' as distinguished from the mathematical value of a future contingency.

(1) For instance, an ingenious attempt has been made by Mr Whitworth to prove that gambling is necessarily disadvantageous on purely mathematical grounds.

When two persons play against each other one of the two must be ruined sooner or later, even though the game be a fair one, supposing that they go on playing long enough; the one with the smaller income having of course the worst chance of being the lucky survivor. If one of them has a finite, and the other an infinite income, it must clearly be the former who will be the ultimate sufferer if they go on long enough. It is then maintained that this is in fact every individual gambler's position, "no one is restricted to gambling with one single opponent; the speculator deals with the public at large, with a world whose resources are practically unlimited. There is a prospect that his operations may terminate to his own disadvantage, through his having nothing more to stake; but there is no prospect that it will terminate to his advantage through the exhaustion of the resources of the world. Every one who gambles is carrying on an unequal warfare: he is ranged with a restricted capital against an adversary whose means are infinite[1]."

In the above argument it is surely overlooked that the adversaries against whom he plays are not one body with a common purse, like the bank in a gambling establishment.

---

[1] *Choice and Chance*, Ed. ii. p. 208.

Each of these adversaries is in exactly the same position as he himself is, and a precisely similar proof might be employed to show that each of them must be eventually ruined which is of course a reduction to absurdity. Gambling can only transfer money from one player to another, and therefore none of it can be actually lost.

§ 13. What really becomes of the money, when they play to extremity, is not difficult to see. First suppose a limited number of players. If they go on long enough, the money will at last all find its way into the pocket of some one of their number. If their fortunes were originally equal, each stands the same chance of being the lucky survivor; in which case we cannot assert, on any numerical grounds, that the prospect of the play is disadvantageous to any one of them. If their fortunes were unequal, the one who had the largest sum to begin with can be shown to have the best chance, according to some assignable law, of being left the final winner; in which case it must be just as advantageous for him, as it was disadvantageous for his less wealthy competitors.

When, instead of a limited number of players, we suppose an unlimited number, each as he is ruined retiring from the table and letting another come in, the results are more complicated, but their general tendency can be readily distinguished. If we supposed that no one retired except when he was ruined, we should have a state of things in which all the old players were growing gradually richer. In this case the prospect before the new comers would steadily grow worse and worse, for their chance of winning against such rich opponents would be exceedingly small. But as this is an unreasonable supposition, we ought rather to assume that not only do the ruined victims retire, but also that those who have gained fortunes of a certain amount

retire also, so that the aggregate and average wealth of the
gambling body remains pretty steady.   What chance any
given player has of being ruined, and how long he may
expect to hold out before being ruined, will depend of course
upon the initial incomes of the players, the rules of the
game, the stakes for which they play, and other considerations.   But it is clear that for all that is lost by one, a
precisely equal sum must be gained by others, and that
therefore any particular gambler can only be cautioned beforehand that his conduct is not to be recommended, by
appealing to some such suppositions as those already mentioned in a former section.

§ 14. As an additional justification of this view the
reader may observe that the state of things in the last
example is one which, expressed in somewhat different
language and with a slight alteration of circumstances, is
being incessantly carried on upon a gigantic scale upon
every side of us.   Call it the competition of merchants and
traders in a commercial country, and the general results are
familiar enough.   It is true that in so far as skill comes into
the question, they are not properly gamblers; but in so far
as chance and risk do, they may be fairly so termed, and in
many branches of business this must necessarily be the case
to a very considerable extent.   Whenever business is carried
on in a reckless way, the comparison is on general grounds
fair enough.   In each case alike we find some retiring ruined,
and some making their fortunes; and in each case alike
also the chances, *cæteris paribus*, lie with those who have
the largest fortunes.   Every one is, in a sense, struggling
against the collective commercial world, but since each of his
competitors is doing the same, we clearly could not caution
any of them (except indeed the poorer ones) that their efforts
must finally end in disadvantage.

§ 15. If we wish to see this result displayed in its
most decisive form we may find a good analogy in a very
different class of events, viz. in the fate of *surnames*. We
are all gamblers in this respect, and the game is carried
out to the last farthing with a rigour unknown at New-
market or Monte Carlo. In its complete treatment the
subject is a very intricate one[1], but a simple example will
serve to display the general tendency. Suppose a colony
comprising 1000 couples of different surnames, and suppose
that each of these has four children who grow up to marry.
Approximately, one in 16 of these families will consist of
girls only; and therefore, under ordinary conventions, about
62 of the names will have disappeared for ever after the
next generation. Four again out of 16 will have but one
boy, each of whom will of course be in the same position
as his father, viz. the sole representative of his name.
Accordingly in the next generation one in 16 of these names
will again drop out, and so the process continues. The
number which disappears in each successive generation becomes smaller, as the stability of the survivors becomes
greater owing to their larger numbers. But there is no
check to the process.

§ 16. The analogy here is a very close one, the names
which thus disappear corresponding to the gamblers who
retire ruined and those which increase in number corresponding to the lucky winners. The ultimate goal in each
case alike,— of course an exceedingly remote one,—is the
exclusive survival of one at the expense of all the others.
That one surname does thus drop out after another must
have struck every one who has made any enquiry into family

---

[1] It was, I believe, first treated as
a serious problem by Mr Galton.
(See the *Journal Anthrop. Inst.* Vol.
iv. 1875, where a complete mathematical solution is indicated by Mr
H. W. Watson.)

genealogy, and various fanciful accounts have been given by those unfamiliar with the theory of probability. What is often apt to be overlooked is the extreme slightness of what may be termed the "turn of the tables" in favour of the survival at each generation. In the above numerical example we have made an extravagantly favourable supposition, by assuming that the population doubles at every generation. In an old and thickly populated country where the numbers increase very slowly, we should be much nearer the mark in assuming that the average effective family,— that is, the average number of children who live to marry,— was only *two*. In this case every family which was represented at any time by but a single male would have but three chances in four of surviving extinction, and of course the process of thinning out would be a more rapid one.

§ 17. The most interesting class of attempts to prove the disadvantages of gambling appeal to what is technically called 'moral expectation' as distinguished from 'mathematical expectation.' The latter may be defined simply as the average money value of the venture in question; that is, it is the product of the amount to be gained (or lost) and the chance of gaining (or losing) it. For instance, if I bet four to one in sovereigns against the occurrence of ace with a single die there would be, on the average of many throws, a loss of four pounds against a gain of five pounds on each set of six occurrences; i.e. there would be an average gain of three shillings and fourpence on each throw. This is called the true or mathematical expectation. The so-called 'moral expectation', on the other hand, is the subjective value of this mathematical expectation. That is, instead of reckoning a money fortune in the ordinary way, as what it *is*, the attempt is made to reckon it at what it is *felt* to be. The elements of computation therefore become, not pounds and shillings, but sums of pleasure enjoyed actually or in prospect. Accordingly when reckoning the present value of a future gain, we must now multiply, not the objective but the subjective value, by the chance we have of securing that gain.

With regard to the exact relation of this moral fortune to the physical various more or less arbitrary assumptions have been made. One writer (Buffon) considers that the moral value of any given sum varies inversely with the total wealth of the person who gains it. Another (D. Bernoulli) starting from a different assumption, which we shall presently have to notice more particularly, makes the moral value of a fortune vary as the logarithm of its actual amount[1]. A third (Cramer) makes it vary with the square root of the amount.

§ 18. Historically, these proposals have sprung from the wish to reconcile the conclusions of the Petersburg problem with the dictates of practical common sense; for, by substituting the moral for the physical estimate the total value of the expectation could be reduced to a finite sum. On this ground therefore such proposals have no great interest, for, as we have seen, there is no serious difficulty in the problem when rightly understood.

These same proposals however have been employed in

---

[1] Bernoulli himself does not seem to have based his conclusions upon actual experience. But it is a noteworthy fact that the assumption with which he starts, viz. that the subjective value of any small increment (dx) is inversely proportional to the sum then possessed (x), and which leads at once to the logarithmic law above mentioned, is identical with one which is now familiar enough to every psychologist. It is what is commonly called Fechner's Law, which he has established by aid of an enormous amount of careful experiment in the case of a number of our simple sensations. But I do not believe that he has made any claim that such a law holds good in the far more intricate dependence of happiness upon wealth.

order to prove that gambling is necessarily disadvantageous, and this to both parties. Take, for instance, Bernoulli's supposition. It can be readily shown that if two persons each with a sum of £50 to start with choose to risk, say, £10 upon an even wager there will be a loss of happiness as a result; for the pleasure gained by the possessor of £60 will not be equal to that which is lost by the man who leaves off with £40[1].

§ 19. This is the form of argument commonly adopted; but, as it stands, it does not seem conclusive. It may surely be replied that all which is thus proved is that *inequality* is bad, on the ground that two fortunes of £50 are better than one of £60 and one of £40. Conceive for instance that the original fortunes had been £60 and £40 respectively, the event may result in an increase of happiness; for this will certainly be the case if the richer man loses and the fortunes are thus equalized. This is quite true; and we are therefore obliged to show,—what can be very easily shown,—that if the other alternative had taken place and the two fortunes had been made still more unequal (viz. £65 and £35 respectively) the happiness thus lost would more than balance what would have been gained by the equalization. And since these two suppositions are equally likely there will be a loss in the long run.

The consideration just adduced seems however to show

---

[1] The formula expressive of this moral happiness is $c \log \dfrac{x}{a}$; where x stands for the physical fortune possessed at the time, and a for that small value of it at which happiness is supposed to disappear: c being an arbitrary constant. Let two persons, whose fortune is x, risk y on an even bet. Then the balance, as regards happiness, must be drawn between

$$c \log \frac{x}{a} \text{ and } \tfrac{1}{2}c \log \frac{x+y}{a} + \tfrac{1}{2}c \log \frac{x-y}{a},$$

or $\log x^2$ and $\log (x+y)(x-y)$,
or x^2 and $x^2 - y^2$,
the former of which is necessarily the greater.

that the common way of stating the conclusion is rather misleading; and that, on the assumption in question as to the law of dependence of happiness on wealth, it really is the case that the effective element in rendering gambling disadvantageous is its tendency to the increase of the inequality in the distribution of wealth.

§ 20. This raises two questions, one of some speculative interest in connection with our subject, and the other of supreme importance in the conduct of life. The first is this: quite apart from any particular assumption which we make about moral fortunes or laws of variation of happiness, is it the fact that gambling tends to increase the existing inequalities of wealth? Theoretically there is no doubt that this is so. Take the simplest case and suppose two people tossing for a pound. If their fortunes were equal to begin with there must be resultant inequality. If they were unequal there is an even chance of the inequality being increased or diminished; but since the increase is proportionally greater than the decrease, the final result remains of the same kind as when the fortunes were equal[1]. Taking a more general view the same conclusion underlies all our reasoning as to the averages of large numbers, viz. that the resultant divergencies increase absolutely (however they diminish relatively) as the numbers become greater. And of course we refer to these absolute divergencies when we are talking of the distribution of wealth.

[1] This may be seen more clearly as follows. Suppose two pair of gamblers, each pair consisting of men possessing £50 and £30 respectively. Now if we suppose the richer man to win in one case and the poorer in the other these two results will be a fair representation of the average; for there are only two alternatives and these will be equally frequent in the long run. It is obvious that we have had two fortunes of £50 and two of £30 converted into one of £20, two of £40, and one of £60. And this is clearly an increase of inequality.

§ 21.   This is the theoretic conclusion.   How far the
actual practice of gambling introduces counteracting agencies
must be left to the determination of those who are competent to pronounce.   So far as outsiders are authorised
to judge from what they read in the newspapers and other
public sources of information, it would appear that these
counteracting agencies are very considerable, and that in
consequence it is a rather insecure argument to advance
against gambling.   Many a large fortune has notoriously
been squandered on the race-course or in gambling saloons,
and most certainly a large portion, if not the major part,
has gone to swell the incomes of many who were by comparison poor.   But the solution of this question must clearly be
left to those who have better opportunities of knowing
the facts than is to be expected on the part of writers on
Probability.

§ 22.   The general conclusion to be drawn is that those
who invoked this principle of moral fortune as an argument
against gambling were really raising a much more intricate
and far-reaching problem than they were aware of.   What
they were at work upon was the question, What is the
distribution of wealth which tends to secure the maximum
of happiness ?   Is this best secured by equality or inequality?
Had they really followed out the doctrine on which their
denunciation of gambling was founded they ought to have
adopted the Socialist's ideal as being distinctly that which
tends to increase happiness.   And they ought to have
brought under the same disapprobation which they expressed against gambling all those tendencies of modern
civilized life which work in the same direction.   For instance ; keen competition, speculative operations, extended
facilities of credit, mechanical inventions, enlargement of
business operations into vast firms :—all these, and other

similar tendencies too numerous to mention here, have had some influence in the way of adding to existing inequalities. They are, or have been, in consequence denounced by socialists : are we honestly to bring them to this test in order to ascertain whether or not they are to be condemned ? The reader who wishes to see what sort of problems this assumption of 'moral fortune' ought to introduce may be recommended to read Mr F. Y. Edgeworth's *Mathematical Psychics*, the only work with which I am acquainted which treats of these questions.

CHAPTER XVI.

THE APPLICATION OF PROBABILITY TO TESTIMONY.

§ 1. ON the principles which have been adopted in this work, it becomes questionable whether several classes of problems which may seem to have acquired a prescriptive right to admission, will not have to be excluded from the science of Probability. The most important, perhaps, of these refer to what is commonly called the credibility of testimony, estimated either at first hand and directly, or as influencing a juryman, and so reaching us through his sagacity and trustworthiness. Almost every treatise upon the science contains a discussion of the principles according to which credit is to be attached to combinations of the reports of witnesses of various degrees of trustworthiness, or the verdicts of juries consisting of larger or smaller numbers. A great modern mathematician, Poisson, has written an elaborate treatise expressly upon this subject; whilst a considerable portion of the works of Laplace, De Morgan, and others, is devoted to an examination of similar enquiries. It would be presumptuous to differ from such authorities as these, except upon the strongest grounds; but I confess that the extraordinary ingenuity and mathematical ability which have been devoted to these problems, considered as questions in Probability, fails to convince me that they ought to have been so considered. The following are the principal grounds for this opinion.

§ 2. It will be remembered that in the course of the chapter on Induction we entered into a detailed investigation of the process demanded of us when, instead of the appropriate propositions from which the inference was to be made being set before us, the *individual* presented himself, and the task was imposed upon us of selecting the requisite groups or series to which to refer him. In other words, instead of calculating the chance of an event from determinate conditions of frequency of its occurrence (these being either obtained by direct experience, or deductively inferred) we have to *select* the conditions of frequency out of a plurality of more or less suitable ones. When the problem is presented to us at such a stage as this, we may of course assume that the preliminary process of obtaining the statistics which are extended into the proportional propositions has been already performed; we may suppose therefore that we are already in possession of a quantity of such propositions, our principal remaining doubt being as to which of them we should then employ. This selection was shown to be to a certain extent arbitrary; for, owing to the fact of the individual possessing a large number of different properties, he became in consequence a member of different series or groups, which might present different averages. We must now examine, somewhat more fully than we did before, the practical conditions under which any difficulty arising from this source ceases to be of importance.

§ 3. One condition of this kind is very simple and obvious. It is that the different statistics with which we are presented should not in reality offer materially different results. If, for instance, we were enquiring into the probability of a man aged forty dying within the year, we might if we pleased take into account the fact of his having red hair, or his having been born in a certain county or town.

Each of these circumstances would serve to specialize the individual, and therefore to restrict the limits of the statistics which were applicable to his case. But the consideration of such qualities as these would either leave the average precisely as it was, or produce such an unimportant alteration in it as no one would think of taking into account. Though we could hardly say with certainty of any conceivable characteristic that it has absolutely no bearing on the result, we may still feel very confident that the bearing of such characteristics as these is utterly insignificant. Of course in the extreme case of the things most perfectly suited to the Calculus of Probability, viz. games of pure chance, these subsidiary characteristics are quite irrelevant. Any further particulars about the characteristics of the cards in a really fair pack, beyond those which are familiar to all the players, would convey no information whatever about the result.

Or again; although the different sets of statistics may not as above give almost identical results, yet they may do what practically comes to very much the same thing, that is, arrange themselves into a small number of groups, all of the statistics in any one group practically coinciding in their results. If for example a consumptive man desired to insure his life, there would be a marked difference in the statistics according as we took his peculiar state of health into account or not. We should here have two sets of statistics, so clearly marked off from one another that they might almost rank with the distinctions of natural kinds, and which would in consequence offer decidedly different results. If we were to specialize still further, by taking into account insignificant qualities like those mentioned in the last paragraph, we might indeed get more limited sets of statistics applicable to persons still more closely resembling the individual in

question, but these would not differ sufficiently in their
results to make it worth our while to do so.   In other words,
the different propositions which are applicable to the case in
point arrange themselves into a limited number of groups,
which, and which only, need be taken into account; whence
the range of choice amongst them is very much diminished
in practice.

§ 4. The reasons for the conditions above described are
not difficult to detect.   Where these conditions exist the
process of selecting a series or class to which to refer any
individual is very simple, and the selection is, for the particular purposes of inference, final.   In any case of insurance,
for example, the question we have to decide is of the very
simple kind; Is *A.B.* a man of a certain age ?   If so one in
fifty in his circumstances will die in the course of the year.
If any further questions have to be decided they would be of
the following description.   Is *A.B.* a healthy man ?   Does he
follow a dangerous trade ?   But here too the classes in
question are but few, and the limits by which they are
bounded are tolerably precise ; so that the reference of an
individual to one or other of them is easy.   And when we
have once chosen our class we remain untroubled by any
further considerations; for since no other statistics are supposed to offer a materially different average, we have no
occasion to take account of any other properties than those
already noticed.

The case of games of chance, already referred to, offers
of course an instance of these conditions in an almost ideal
state of perfection ; the same circumstances which fit them
so eminently for the purposes of fair gambling, fitting them
equally to become examples in Probability.   When a die is
to be thrown, all persons alike stand on precisely the same
footing of knowledge and of ignorance about the result; the

only data to which any one could appeal being that each face turns up on an average once in six times.

§ 5. Let us now examine how far the above conditions are fulfilled in the case of problems which discuss what is called the credibility of testimony. The following would be a fair specimen of one of the elementary enquiries out of which these problems are composed;—Here is a statement made by a witness who lies once in ten times, what am I to conclude about its truth? Objections might fairly be raised against the possibility of thus assigning a man his place upon a graduated scale of mendacity. This however we will pass over, and will assume that the witness goes about the world bearing stamped somehow on his face the appropriate class to which he belongs, and consequently, the degree of credit to which he has a claim on such general grounds. But there are other and stronger reasons against the admissibility of this class of problems.

§ 6. That which has been described in the previous sections as the 'individual' which had to be assigned to an appropriate class or series of statistics is, of course, in this case, *a statement.* In the particular instance in question this individual statement is already assigned to a class, that namely of statements made by a witness of a given degree of veracity; but it is clearly optional with us whether or not we choose to confine our attention to this class in forming our judgment; at least it would be optional whenever we were practically called on to form an opinion. But in the case of this statement, as in that of the mortality of the man whose insurance we were discussing, there are a multitude of other properties observable, besides the one which is supposed to mark the given class. Just as in the latter there were (besides his age), the place of his birth, the nature of his occupation, and so on; so in the former there are (besides its being a statement by a certain kind of witness), the fact of its being uttered at a certain time and place and under certain circumstances. At the time the statement is made all these qualities or attributes of the statement are present to us, and we clearly have a right to take into account as many of them as we please. Now the question at present before us seems to be simply this;—Are the considerations, which we might thus introduce, as immaterial to the result in the case of the truth of a statement of a witness, as the corresponding considerations are in the case of the insurance of a life? There can surely be no hesitation in the reply to such a question. Under ordinary circumstances we soon know all that we can know about the conditions which determine us in judging of the prospect of a man's death, and we therefore rest content with general statistics of mortality; but no one who heard a witness speak would think of simply appealing to his figure of veracity, even supposing that this had been authoritatively communicated to us. The circumstances under which the statement is made instead of being insignificant, are of overwhelming importance. The appearance of the witness, the tone of his voice, the fact of his having objects to gain, together with a countless multitude of other circumstances which would gradually come to light as we reflect upon the matter, would make any sensible man discard the assigned average from his consideration. He would, in fact, no more think of judging in this way than he would of appealing to the Carlisle or Northampton tables of mortality to determine the probable length of life of a soldier who was already in the midst of a battle.

§ 7.   It cannot be replied that under these circumstances we still refer the witness to a class, and judge of his veracity by an average of a more limited kind; that we infer, for example, that of men who look and act like him under such circumstances, a much larger proportion, say nine-tenths, are found to lie. There is no appeal to a class in this way at all, there is no immediate reference to statistics of any kind whatever; at least none which we are conscious of using at the time, or to which we should think of resorting for justification afterwards. The decision seems to depend upon the quickness of the observer's senses and of his apprehension generally.

Statistics about the veracity of witnesses seem in fact to be permanently as inappropriate as all other statistics occasionally may be. We may know accurately the percentage of recoveries after amputation of the leg; but what surgeon would think of forming his judgment solely by such tables when he had a case before him? We need not deny, of course, that the opinion he might form about the patient's prospects of recovery might ultimately rest upon the proportions of deaths and recoveries he might have previously witnessed. But if this were the case, these data are lying, as one may say, obscurely in the background. He does not appeal to them directly and immediately in forming his judgment. There has been a far more important intermediate process of apprehension and estimation of what is essential to the case and what is not. Sharp senses, memory, judgment, and practical sagacity have had to be called into play, and there is not therefore the same direct conscious and sole appeal to statistics that there was before. The surgeon may have in his mind two or three instances in which the operation performed was equally severe, but in which the patient's constitution was different; the latter element therefore has to be properly allowed for. There may be other instances in which the constitution was similar, but the operation more severe; and so on. Hence, although the ultimate appeal may be to the statistics, it is not so directly;

their value has to be estimated through the somewhat hazy medium of our judgment and memory, which places them under a very different aspect.

§ 8.   Any one who knows anything of the game of whist may supply an apposite example of the distinction here insisted on, by recalling to mind the alteration in the nature of our inferences as the game progresses. At the commencement of the game our sole appeal is rightfully made to the theory of Probability. All the rules upon which each player acts, and therefore upon which he infers that the others will act, rest upon the observed frequency (or rather upon the frequency which calculation assures us will be observed) with which such and such combinations of cards are found to occur. Why are we told, if we have more than four trumps, to lead them out at once? Because we are convinced, on pure grounds of probability, capable of being stated in the strictest statistical form, that in a majority of instances we shall draw our opponent's trumps, and therefore be left with the command. Similarly with every other rule which is recognized in the early part of the play.

But as the play progresses all this is changed, and towards its conclusion there is but little reliance upon any rules which either we or others could base upon statistical frequency of occurrence, observed or inferred. A multitude of other considerations have come in; we begin to be influenced partly by our knowledge of the character and practice of our partner and opponents; partly by a rapid combination of a multitude of judgments, founded upon our observation of the actual course of play, the grounds of which we could hardly realize or describe at the time and which may have been forgotten since. That is, the particular combination of cards, now before us, does not readily fall into any well-marked class to which alone it can

reasonably be referred by every one who has the facts before
him.

§ 9.　A criticism somewhat resembling the above has
been given by Mill (*Logic*, Bk. III. Chap. xviii. § 3) upon
the applicability of the theory of Probability to the credibility of witnesses.　But he has added other reasons which
do not appear to me to be equally valid ; he says " common
sense would dictate that it is impossible to strike a general
average of the veracity, and other qualifications for true
testimony, of mankind or any class of them ; and if it were
possible, such an average would be no guide, the credibility of
almost every witness being either below or above the average."
The latter objection would however apply with equal force
to estimating the length of a man's life from tables of mortality ; for the credibility of different witnesses can scarcely
have a wider range of variation than the length of different
lives.　If statistics of credibility could be obtained, and
could be conveniently appealed to when they were obtained,
they might furnish us in the long run with as accurate
inferences as any other statistics of the same general description.　These statistics would however in practice naturally and rightly be neglected, because there can hardly fail
to be circumstances in each individual statement which would
more appropriately refer it to some new class depending on
different statistics, and affording a far better chance of our
being right in that particular case.　In most instances of
the kind in question, indeed, such a change is thus produced
in the mode of formation of our opinion, that, as already
pointed out, the mental operation ceases to be in any proper
sense founded on appeal to statistics[1].

[1] It may be remarked also that
there is another reason which tends
to dissuade us from appealing to
principles of Probability in the
majority of the cases where testimony has to be estimated.　It often,

§ 10. The Chance problems which are concerned with testimony are not altogether confined to such instances as those hitherto referred to. Though we must, as it appears to me, reject all attempts to estimate the credibility of any particular witness, or to refer him to any assigned class in respect of his trustworthiness, and consequently abandon as unsuitable any of the numerous problems which start from such data as 'a witness who is wrong once in ten times,' yet it does not follow that testimony may not to a slight extent be treated by our science in a somewhat different manner. We may be quite unable to estimate, except in the roughest possible way, the veracity of any particular witness, and yet it may be possible to form some kind of opinion upon the veracity of certain classes of witnesses; to say, for instance, that Europeans are superior in this way to Orientals. So we might attempt to explain why, and to what extent, an opinion in which the judgments of ten persons, say jurors, concur, is superior to one in which five only concur. Something may also be done towards laying down the principles in accordance with which we are to decide whether, and why, extraordinary stories deserve less credence than ordinary ones, even if we cannot arrive at any precise and definite decision upon the point. This last question is further discussed in the course of the next chapter.

§ 11. The change of view in accordance with which it follows that questions of the kind just mentioned need not be entirely rejected from scientific consideration, presents it-

---

perhaps usually happens, that we are not absolutely forced to come to a decision; at least so far as the acquitting of an accused person may be considered as avoiding a decision. It may be of much greater importance to us to attain not merely truth on the average, but truth in each individual instance, so that we had rather not form an opinion at all than form one of which we can only say in its justification that it will tend to lead us right in the long run.

self in other directions also. It has, for instance, been already pointed out that the individual characteristics of any sick man's disease would be quite sufficiently important in most cases to prevent any surgeon from judging about his recovery by a genuine and direct appeal to statistics, however such considerations might indirectly operate upon his judgment. But if an opinion had to be formed about a considerable number of cases, say in a large hospital, statistics might again come prominently into play, and be rightly recognized as the principal source of appeal. We should feel able to compare one hospital, or one method of treatment, with another. The ground of the difference is obvious. It arises from the fact that the characteristics of the individuals, which made us so ready to desert the average when we had to judge of them separately, do not produce the same disturbance when we have to judge about a group of cases. The averages then become the most secure and available ground on which to form an opinion, and therefore Probability again becomes applicable.

But although some resort to Probability may be admitted in such cases as these, it nevertheless does not appear to me that they can ever be regarded as particularly appropriate examples to illustrate the methods and resources of the theory. Indeed it is scarcely possible to resist the conviction that the refinements of mathematical calculation have here been pushed to lengths utterly unjustifiable, when we bear in mind the impossibility of obtaining any corresponding degree of accuracy and precision in the data from which we have to start. To cite but one instance. It would be hard to find a case in which love of consistency has prevailed over common sense to such an extent as in the admission of the conclusion that it is unimportant what are the numbers for and against a particular statement, provided the actual majority is the same. That is, the unanimous judgment of a jury of eight is to count for the same as a majority of ten to two in a jury of twelve. And yet this conclusion is admitted by Poisson. The assumptions under which it follows will be indicated in the course of the next chapter.

Again, perfect independence amongst the witnesses or jurors is an almost necessary postulate. But where can this be secured? To say nothing of direct collusion, human beings are in almost all instances greatly under the influence of sympathy in forming their opinions. This influence, under the various names of political bias, class prejudice, local feeling, and so on, always exists to a sufficient degree to induce a cautious person to make many of those individual corrections which we saw to be necessary when we were estimating the trustworthiness, in any given case, of a single witness; that is, they are sufficient to destroy much, if not all, of the confidence with which we resort to statistics and averages in forming our judgment. Since then this Essay is mainly devoted to explaining and establishing the general principles of the science of Probability, we may very fairly be excused from any further treatment of this subject, beyond the brief discussions which are given in the next chapter.

CHAPTER XVII.

ON THE CREDIBILITY OF EXTRAORDINARY STORIES.

§ 1. IT is now time to recur for fuller investigation to an enquiry which has been already briefly touched upon more than once; that is, the validity of testimony to establish, as it is frequently expressed, an otherwise improbable story. It will be remembered that in a previous chapter (the twelfth) we devoted some examination to an assertion by Butler, which seemed to be to some extent countenanced by Mill, that a great improbability before the proof might become but a very small improbability after the proof. In opposition to this it was pointed out that the different estimates which we undoubtedly formed of the credibility of the examples adduced, had nothing to do with the fact of the event being past or future, but arose from a very different cause; that the conception of the event which we entertain at the moment (which is all that is then and there actually present to us, and as to the correctness of which as a representation of facts we have to make up our minds) comes before us in two very different ways. In one instance it was a mere guess of our own which we knew from statistics would be right in a certain proportion of cases; in the other instance it was the assertion of a witness, and therefore the appeal was not now primarily to statistics of the event, but to the trustworthiness of the witness. The conception, or 'event' if we will so term it, had in fact passed out of the category of guesses (on statistical grounds), into that of assertions (most likely resting on some specific evidence), and would therefore be naturally regarded in a very different light.

§ 2. But it may seem as if this principle would lead us to somewhat startling conclusions. For, by transferring the appeal from the frequency with which the event occurs to the trustworthiness of the witness who makes the assertion, is it not implied that the probability or improbability of an assertion depends solely upon the veracity of the witness? If so, ought not any story whatever to be believed when it is assorted by a truthful person?

In order to settle this question we must look a little more closely into the circumstances under which such testimony is commonly presented to us. As it is of course necessary, for clearness of exposition, to take a numerical example, let us suppose that a given statement is made by a witness who, on the whole and in the long run, is right in what he says nine times out of ten[1]. Here then is an average given to us, an average veracity that is, which includes all the particular statements which the witness has made or will make.

§ 3. Now it has been abundantly shown in a former chapter (Ch. IX. §§ 14—32) that the mere fact of a par-

---

[1] Reasons were given in the last chapter against the propriety of applying the rules of Probability with any strictness to such examples as these. But although all approach to numerical accuracy is unattainable, we do undoubtedly recognize in ordinary life a distinction between the credibility of one witness and another; such a rough practical distinction will be quite sufficient for the purposes of this chapter. For convenience, and to illustrate the theory, the examples are best stated in a numerical form, but it is not intended thereby to imply that any such accuracy is really attainable in practice.

ticular average having been assigned, is no reason for our being forced invariably to adhere to it, even in those cases in which our most natural and appropriate ground of judgment is found in an appeal to statistics and averages. The general average may constantly have to be corrected in order to meet more accurately the circumstances of particular cases. In statistics of mortality, for instance, instead of resorting to the wider tables furnished by people in general of a given age, we often prefer the narrower tables furnished by men of a particular profession, abode, or mode of life. The reader may however be conveniently reminded here that in so doing we must not suppose that we are able, by any such device, in any special or peculiar way to secure truth. The general average, if persistently adhered to throughout a sufficiently wide and varied experience, would in the long run tend to give us the truth; all the advantage which the more special averages can secure for us is to give us the same tendency to the truth with fewer and slighter aberrations.

§ 4. Returning then to our witness, we know that if we have a very great many statements from him upon all possible subjects, we may feel convinced that in nine out of ten of these he will tell us the truth, and that in the tenth case he will go wrong. This is nothing more than a matter of definition or consistency. But cannot we do better than thus rely upon his general average? Cannot we, in almost any given case, specialize it by attending to various characteristic circumstances in the nature of the statement which he makes; just as we specialize his prospects of mortality by attending to circumstances in his constitution or mode of life?

Undoubtedly we may do this; and in any of the practical contingencies of life, supposing that we were at all guided

by considerations of this nature, we should act very foolishly
if we did not adopt some such plan.   Two methods of thus
correcting the average may be suggested : one of them being
that which practical sagacity would be most likely to employ,
the other that which is almost universally adopted by writers
on Probability.   The former attempts to make the correction
by the following considerations : instead of relying upon the
witness' general average, we assign to it a sort of conjectural
correction to meet the case before us, founded on our experience or observation ;   that is, we appeal to experience to
establish that stories of such and such a kind are more or
less likely to be true, as the case may be, than stories in
general.   The other proceeds upon a different and somewhat more methodical plan.   It is here endeavoured to
show, by an analysis of the nature and number of the
sources of error in the cases in question, that such and such
kinds of stories must be more or less likely to be correctly
reported, and this in certain numerical proportions.

§ 5.   Before proceeding to a discussion of these methods
a distinction must be pointed out to which writers upon the
subject have not always attended, or at any rate to which
they have not generally sufficiently directed their readers'
attention[1].   There are, broadly speaking, two different ways
in which we may suppose testimony to be given.   It may, in
the first place, take the form of a reply to an alternative
question, a question, that is, framed to be answered by *yes*
or *no*.   Here, of course, the possible answers are mutually
contradictory, so that if one of them is not correct the other
must be so :—Has *A* happened, yes or no ?   The common
mode of illustrating this kind of testimony numerically is by

---

[1] I must plead guilty to this
charge myself, in the first edition
of this work.   The result was to
make the treatment of this part of
the subject obscure and imperfect,
and in some respects erroneous.

supposing a lottery with a prize and blanks, or a bag of balls of two colours only, the witness knowing that there are only two, or at any rate being confined to naming one or other of them. If they are black and white, and he errs when black is drawn, he must say 'white.' The reason for the prominence assigned to examples of this class is, probably, that they correspond to the very important case of verdicts of juries; juries being supposed to have nothing else to do than to say 'guilty' or 'not guilty.'

On the other hand, the testimony may take the form of a more original statement or piece of information. Instead of saying, Did A happen? we may ask, What happened? Here if the witness speaks truth he must be supposed, as before, to have but one way of doing so; for the occurrence of some specific event was of course contemplated. But if he errs he has many ways of going wrong, possibly an infinite number. Ordinarily however his possible false statements are assumed to be limited in number, as must generally be more or less the result in practice. This case is represented numerically by supposing the balls in the bag not to be of two colours only, but to be all distinct from each other; say by their being all numbered successively. It may of course be objected that a large number of the statements that are made in the world are not in any way answers to questions, either of the alternative or of the open kind. For instance, a man simply asserts that he has drawn the seven of spades from a pack of cards; and we do not know perhaps whether he had been asked 'Has that card been drawn?' or 'What card has been drawn?' or indeed whether he had been asked anything at all. Still more might this be so in the case of any ordinary historical statement.

This objection is quite to the point, and must be recognized as constituting an additional difficulty. All that we

can do is to endeavour, as best we may, to ascertain, from
the circumstances of the case, what number of alternatives
the witness may be supposed to have had before him. When
he simply testifies to some matter well known to be in dispute, and does not go much into detail, we may fairly consider that there were practically only the two alternatives
before him of saying 'yes' or 'no.' When, on the other hand,
he tells a story of a more original kind, or (what comes to
much the same thing) goes into details, we must regard him
as having a wide comparative range of alternatives before
him.

These two classes of examples, viz. that of the black and
white balls, in which only one form of error is possible, and
the numbered balls, in which there may be many forms of
error, are the only two which we need notice. In practice it
would seem that they may gradually merge into each other,
according to the varying ways in which we choose to frame
our question. Besides asking, Did you see A strike B? and,
What did you see? we may introduce any number of intermediate leading questions, as, What did A do? What did
he do to B? and so on. In this way we may gradually narrow
the possible openings to wrong statement, and so approach
to the direct alternative question. But it is clear that all
these cases may be represented numerically by a supposed
diminution in the number of the balls which are thus distinguished from each other.

§ 6. Of the two plans mentioned in § 4 we will begin
with the latter, as it is the only methodical and scientific one
which has been proposed. Suppose that there is a bag with
1000 balls, only one of which is white, the rest being all
black. A ball is drawn at random, and our witness whose
veracity is $\frac{9}{10}$ reports that the white ball was drawn. Take
a great many of his statements upon this particular subject,

say 10,000; that is, suppose that 10,000 balls having been successively drawn out of this bag, or bags of exactly the same kind, he makes his report in each case. His 10,000 statements being taken as a fair sample of his general average, we shall find, by supposition, that 9 out of every 10 of them are true and the remaining one false. What will be the nature of these false statements? Under the circumstances in question, he having only one way of going wrong, the answer is easy. In the 10,000 drawings the white ball would come out 10 times, and therefore be rightly asserted 9 times, whilst on the one of these occasions on which he goes wrong he has nothing to say but 'black.' So with the 9990 occasions on which black is drawn; he is right and says black on 8991 of them, and is wrong and therefore says white on 999 of them. On the whole, therefore, we conclude that out of every 1008 times on which he says that white is drawn he is wrong 999 times and right only 9 times. That is, his special veracity, as we may term it, for cases of this description, has been reduced from $\frac{9}{10}$ to $\frac{9}{1008}$. As it would commonly be expressed, the latter fraction represents the chance that this particular statement of his is true[1].

---

[1] The generalized algebraical form of this result is as follows. Let p be the à priori probability of an event, and x be the credibility of the witness. Then, if he asserts that the event happened, the probability that it really did happen is

$$\frac{px}{px + (1-p)(1-x)};$$

whilst if he asserts that it did *not* happen the probability that it did happen is $\dfrac{p(1-x)}{p(1-x) + (1-p)x}$.

In illustration of some remarks to be presently made, the reader will notice that on making either of these expressions $= p$, we obtain in each case $x = \frac{1}{2}$. That is, a witness whose veracity $= \frac{1}{2}$ leaves the à priori probability of an event (of this kind) unaffected.

If, on the other hand, we make these expressions equal to x and $1 - x$ respectively, we obtain in each case $p = \frac{1}{2}$. That is, when an event (of this kind) is as likely to happen as not, the ordinary veracity of the witness in respect of it remains unaffected.

§ 7. We will now take the case in which the witness has many ways of going wrong, instead of merely one. Suppose that the balls were all numbered, from 1 to 1,000, and the witness knows this fact. A ball is drawn, and he tells me that it was numbered 25, what are the odds that he is right? Proceeding as before, in 10,000 drawings this ball would be obtained 10 times, and correctly named 9 times. But on the 9990 occasions on which it was not drawn there would be a difference, for the witness has now many openings for error before him. It is, however, generally considered reasonable to assume that his errors will all take the form of announcing wrong numbers; and that, there being no apparent reason why he should choose one number rather than another, he will be likely to announce all the wrong ones equally often. Hence his 999 errors, instead of all leading him now back again to one spot, will be uniformly spread over as many distinct ways of going wrong. On one only of these occasions, therefore, will he mention 25 as having been drawn. It follows therefore that out of every 10 times that he names 25 he is right 9 times; so that in this case his average or general truthfulness applies equally well to the special case in point.

§ 8. With regard to the truth of these conclusions, it must of course be admitted that if we grant the validity of the assumptions about the limits within which the blundering or mendacity of the witness are confined, and the complete impartiality with which his answers are disposed within those limits, the reasoning is perfectly sound. But are not these assumptions extremely arbitrary, that is, are not our lotteries and bags of balls rendered perfectly precise in many respects in which, in ordinary life, the conditions supposed to correspond to them are so vague and uncertain that no such method of reasoning becomes practically available? Suppose

that a person whom I have long known, and of whose measure of veracity and judgment I may be supposed therefore
to have acquired some knowledge, informs me that there is
something to my advantage if I choose to go to certain
trouble or expense in order to secure it. As regards the
general veracity of the witness, then, there is no difficulty;
we suppose that this is determined for us. But as regards
his story, difficulty and vagueness emerge at every point.
What is the number of balls in the bag here ? What in fact
are the nature and contents of the bag out of which we suppose the drawing to have been made ? It does not seem
that the materials for any rational judgment exist here.
But if we are to get at any such amended figure of veracity
as those attained in the above example, these questions must
necessarily be answered with some degree of accuracy; for
the main point of the method consists in determining how
often the event must be considered *not* to happen, and thence
inferring how often the witness will be led wrongly to assert
that it has happened.

It is not of course denied that considerations of the kind
in question have some influence upon our decision, but only
that this influence could under any ordinary circumstances
be submitted to numerical determination. We are doubtless liable to have information given to us that we have
come in for some kind of fortune, for instance, when no
such good luck has really befallen us ; and this not once
only but repeatedly. But who can give the faintest intimation of the nature and number of the occasions on which,
a blank being thus really drawn, a prize will nevertheless
be falsely announced ? It appears to me therefore that
numerical results of any practical value can seldom, if ever,
be looked for from this method of procedure.

§ 9. Our conclusion in the case of the lottery, or, what

comes to the same thing, in the case of the bag with black
and white balls, has been questioned or objected to[1] on the
ground that it is contrary to all experience to suppose that
the testimony of a moderately good witness could be so
enormously depreciated under such circumstances. I should
prefer to base the objection on the ground that experience
scarcely ever presents such circumstances as those supposed ;
but if we postulate their existence the given conclusion seems
correct enough. Assume that a man is merely required to
say *yes* or *no ;* assume also a group or succession of cases in
which *no* should rightly be said very much oftener than
yes. Then, assuming almost any general truthfulness of the
witness, we may easily suppose the rightful occasions for
denial to be so much the more frequent that a majority of
his affirmative answers will actually occur as false ' noes '
rather than as correct ' ayes.' This of course lowers the
average value of his ' ayes,' and renders them comparatively
untrustworthy.

Consider the following example. I have a gardener whom
I trust as to all ordinary matters of fact. If he were to
tell me some morning that my dog had run away I should
fully believe him. He tells me however that the dog has
gone mad. Surely I should accept the statement with much
hesitation, and on the grounds indicated above. It is not
that he is more likely to be wrong when the dog *is* mad ;
but that experience shows that there are other complaints
(e.g. fits) which are far more common than madness, and
that most of the assertions of madness are erroneous assertions referring to these. This seems a somewhat parallel
case to that in which we find that most of the assertions
that a white ball had been drawn are really false assertions
referring to the drawing of a black ball. Practically I do

[1] Todhunter's *History*, p. 400. *Philosophical Magazine*, July, 1864.

not think that any one would feel a difficulty in thus ex-
orbitantly discounting some particular assertion of a witness
whom in most other respects he fully trusted.

§ 10.   There is one particular case which has been regarded as a difficulty in the way of this treatment of the
problem, but which seems to me to be a decided confirmation of it; always, be it understood, within the very narrow
and artificial limits to which we must suppose ourselves to
be confined.   This is the case of a witness whose veracity is
just one-half; that is, one who, when a mere *yes* or *no* is
demanded of him, is as often wrong as right.   In the case of
any other assigned degree of veracity it is extremely difficult
to get anything approaching to a confirmation from practical judgment and experience.   We are not accustomed to
estimate the merits of witnesses in this way, and hardly appreciate what is meant by his numerical degree of truthfulness.   But as regards the man whose veracity is one-half, we
are (as Mr C. J. Monro has very ingeniously suggested) only
too well acquainted with such witnesses, though under a
somewhat different name; for this is really nothing else than
the case of a person confidently answering a question about
a subject-matter of which he knows nothing, and can therefore only give a mere guess.

Now in the case of the lottery with one prize, when the
witness whose veracity is one-half tells us that we have
gained the prize, we find on calculation that his testimony
goes for absolutely nothing; the chances that we have got
the prize are just the same as they would be if he had never
opened his lips, viz. $\frac{1}{1000}$.   But clearly this is what ought
to be the result, for the witness who knows nothing about
the matter leaves it exactly as he found it.   He is indeed,
in strictness, scarcely a witness at all; for the natural function of a witness is to examine the matter, and so to add

confirmation, more or less, according to his judgment and probity, but at any rate to offer an improvement upon the mere guesser. If, however, we will give heed to his mere guess we are doing just the same thing as if we were to guess ourselves, in which case of course the odds that we are right are simply measured by the frequency of occurrence of the events.

We cannot quite so readily apply the same rule to the other case, namely to that of the numbered balls, for there the witness who is right every other time may really be a very fair, or even excellent, witness. If he has many ways of going wrong, and yet is right in half his statements, it is clear that he must have taken some degree of care, and cannot have merely guessed. In a case of *yes* or *no*, any one can be right every other time, but it is different where truth is single and error is manifold. To represent the case of a simply worthless witness when there were 1000 balls and the drawing of one assigned ball was in question, we should have to put his figure of veracity at $\frac{1}{1000}$. If this were done we should of course get a similar result.

§ 11. It deserves notice therefore that the figure of veracity, or fraction representing the general truthfulness of a witness, is in a way relative, not absolute; that is, it depends upon, and varies with, the general character of the answer which he is supposed to give. Two witnesses of equal intrinsic veracity and worth, one of whom confined himself to saying *yes* and *no*, whilst the other ventured to make more original assertions, would be represented by different fractions; the former having set himself a much easier task than the latter. The real caution and truthfulness of the witness are only one factor, therefore, in his actual figure of veracity; the other factor consists of the nature of his assertions, as just pointed out. The ordinary plan therefore, in such problems, of assigning an average truthfulness to the witness, and accepting this alike in the case of each of the two kinds of answers, though convenient, seems scarcely sound. This consideration would however be of much more importance were not the discussions upon the subject mainly concerned with only one description of answer, namely that of the 'yes or no' kind.

§ 12. So much for the methodical way of treating such a problem. The way in which it would be taken in hand by those who had made no study of Probability is very different. It would, I apprehend, strike them as follows. They would say to themselves, Here is a story related by a witness who tells the truth, say, nine times out of ten. But it is a story of a kind which experience shows to be very generally made untruly, say 99 times out of 100. Having then these opposite inducements to belief, they would attempt in some way to strike a balance between them. Nothing in the nature of a strict rule could be given to enable them to decide how they might escape out of the difficulty. Probably, in so far as they did not judge at haphazard, they would be guided by still further resort to experience, or unconscious recollections of its previous teachings, in order to settle which of the two opposing inductions was better entitled to carry the day in the particular case before them. The reader will readily see that any general solution of the problem, when thus presented, is impossible. It is simply the now familiar case (Chap. IX. §§ 14—32) of an individual which belongs equally to two distinct, or even, in respect of their characteristics, opposing classes. We cannot decide offhand to which of the two its characteristics most naturally and rightly refer it. A fresh induction is needed in order to settle this point.

§ 13. Rules have indeed been suggested by various

writers in order to extricate us from the difficulty. The controversy about miracles has probably been the most fertile occasion for suggestions of this kind on one side or the other. It is to this controversy, presumably, that the phrase is due, so often employed in discussions upon similar subjects, 'a contest of opposite improbabilities.' What is meant by such an expression is clearly this: that in forming a judgment upon the truth of certain assertions we may find that they are comprised in two very distinct classes, so that, according as we regarded them as belonging to one or the other of these distinct classes, our opinion as to their truth would be very different. Such an assertion belongs to one class, of course, by its being a statement of a particular witness, or kind of witness; it belongs to the other by its being a particular kind of story, one of what is called an improbable nature. Its belonging to the former class is so far favourable to its truth, its belonging to the latter is so far hostile to its truth. It seems to be assumed, in speaking of a contest of opposite improbabilities, that when these different sources of conviction co-exist together, they would each in some way retain their probative force so as to produce a contest, ending generally in a victory to one or other of them. Hume, for instance, speaks of our *deducting* one probability from the other, and apportioning our belief to the remainder[1]. Thomson, in his *Laws of Thought*, speaks of one probability as entirely superseding the other.

§ 14. It does not appear to me that the slightest philosophical value can be attached to any such rules as these. They doubtless may, and indeed will, hold in individual

---

[1] "When therefore these two kinds of experience are contrary, we have nothing to do but subtract the one from the other, and embrace an opinion, either on one side or the other, with that assurance which arises from the remainder." (Essay on Miracles.)

cases, but they cannot lay claim to any generality. Even
the notion of a contest, as any necessary ingredient in the
case, must be laid aside. For let us refer again to the way
in which the perplexity arises, and we shall readily see, as
has just been remarked, that it is nothing more than a particular exemplification of a difficulty which has already been
recognized as incapable of solution by any general *à priori*
method of treatment. All that we are supposed to have before
us is a statement. On this occasion it is made by a witness
who lies, say, once in ten times in the long run; that is, who
mostly tells the truth. But on the other hand, it is a statement which experience, derived from a variety of witnesses on
various occasions, assures us is mostly false; stated numerically
it is found, let us suppose, to be false 99 times in a hundred.

Now, as was shown in the chapter on Induction, we are
thus brought to a complete dead lock. Our science offers no
principles by which we can form an opinion, or attempt to
decide the matter one way or the other; for, as we found,
there are an indefinite number of conclusions which are all
equally possible. For instance, all the witness' extraordinary
assertions may be true, or they may all be false, or they may
be divided into the true and the false in any proportion
whatever. Having gone so far in our appeal to statistics as
to recognize that the witness is generally right, but that his
story is generally false, we cannot stop there. We ought to
make still further appeal to experience, and ascertain how it
stands with regard to his stories when they are of that
particular nature: or rather, for this would be to make a
needlessly narrow reference, how it stands with regard to
stories of that kind when advanced by witnesses of his
general character, position, sympathies, and so on[1].

---

[1] Considerations of this kind have
indeed been introduced into the
mathematical treatment of the subject. The common algebraical solu-

§ 15. That extraordinary stories are in many cases, probably in a great majority of cases, less trustworthy than others must be fully admitted. That is, if we were to make two distinct classes of such stories respectively, we should find that the same witness, or similar witnesses, were proportionally more often wrong when asserting the former than when asserting the latter. But it does not by any means appear to me that this must always be the case. We may well conceive, for instance, that with some people the mere fact of the story being of a very unusual character may make them more careful in what they state, so as actually to add to their veracity. If this were so we might be ready to accept their extraordinary stories with even more readiness than their ordinary ones.

Such a supposition as that just made does not seem to me by any means forced. Put such a case as this : let us suppose that two persons, one of them a man of merely ordinary probity and intelligence, the other a scientific naturalist, make a statement about some common event. We believe

tion of the problem in § 5 (to begin with the simplest case) is of course as follows. Let p be the antecedent probability of the event, and t the measure of the truthfulness of the witness; then the chance of his statement being true is $\dfrac{pt}{pt+(1-p)(1-t)}$. This supposes him to lie as much when the event does not happen as when it does. But we may meet the cases supposed in the text by assuming that t' is the measure of his veracity when the event does not happen, so that the above formula becomes $\dfrac{pt}{pt+(1-p)(1-t')}$.

Here t' and t measure respectively his trustworthiness in usual and unusual events. As a formal solution this certainly meets the objections stated above in §§ 14 and 15. The determination however of t' would demand, as I have remarked, continually renewed appeal to experience. In any case the practical methods which would be adopted, if any plans of the kind indicated above were resorted to, seem to me to differ very much from that adopted by the mathematicians, in their spirit and plan.

them both.   Let them now each report some extraordinary *lusus naturæ* or monstrosity which they profess to have seen. Most persons, we may presume, would receive the statement of the naturalist in this latter case almost as readily as in the former: whereas when the same story came from the unscientific observer it would be received with considerable hesitation.   Whence arises the difference?   From the conviction that the naturalist will be far more careful, and therefore to the full as accurate, in matters of this kind as in those of the most ordinary description, whereas with the other man we feel by no means the same confidence.   Even if any one is not prepared to go this length, he will probably admit that the difference of credit which he would attach to the two kinds of story, respectively, when they came from the naturalist, would be much less than what it would be when they came from the other man.

§ 16.   Whilst we are on this part of the subject, it must be pointed out that there is considerable ambiguity and consequent confusion about the use of the term 'an extraordinary story.'   Within the province of pure Probability it ought to mean simply a story which asserts an *unusual* event. At least this is the view which has been adopted and maintained, it is hoped consistently, throughout this work.   So long as we adhere to this sense we know precisely what we mean by the term.   It has a purely objective reference; it simply connotes a very low degree of relative statistical frequency, actual or prospective.   Out of a great number of events we suppose a selection of some particular kind to be contemplated, which occurs relatively very seldom, and this is termed an unusual or extraordinary event.   It follows, as was abundantly shown in a former chapter, that owing to the rarity of the event we are very little disposed to expect its occurrence in any given case.   Our guess about it, in case we thus anticipated it, would very seldom be justified, and we are therefore apt to be much surprised when it does occur. This, I take it, is the only legitimate sense of 'extraordinary' so far as Probability is concerned.

But there is another and very different use of the word, which belongs to Induction, or rather to the science of evidence in general, more than to that limited portion of it termed Probability. In this sense the 'extraordinary,' and still more the 'improbable,' event is not merely one of extreme statistical rarity, which we could not expect to guess aright, but which on moderate evidence we may pretty readily accept; it is rather one which possesses, so to say, an actual evidence-resisting power. It may be something which affects the credibility of the witness at the fountain-head, which makes, that is, his statements upon such a subject essentially inferior to those on other subjects. This is the case, for instance, with anything which excites his prejudices or passions or superstitions. In these cases it would seem unreasonable to attempt to estimate the credibility of the witness by calculating (as in § 6) how often his errors would mislead us through his having been wrongly brought to an affirmation instead of adhering correctly to a negation. We should rather be disposed to put our correction on the witness' average veracity at once.

§ 17. In true Probability, as has just been remarked, every event has its own definitely recognizable degree of frequency of occurrence. It may be excessively rare, rare to any extreme we like to postulate, but still every one who understands and admits the data upon which its occurrence depends will be able to appreciate within what range of experience it may be expected to present itself. We do not expect it in any individual case, nor within any brief range, but we do confidently expect it within an adequately exten-

sive range. How therefore can miraculous stories be similarly taken account of, when the disputants, on one side at
least, are not prepared to admit their actual occurrence anywhere or at any time ? How can any arrangement of bags
and balls, or other mechanical or numerical illustrations of
unlikely events, be admitted as fairly illustrative of miraculous occurrences, or indeed of many of those which come
under the designation of 'very extraordinary' or 'highly
improbable'? Those who contest the occurrence of a particular miracle, as reported by this or that narrator, do not
admit that miracles are to be confidently expected sooner or
later. It is not a question as to whether what must happen
sometimes has happened some particular time, and therefore
no illustration of the kind can be regarded as apposite.

How unsuitable these merely rare events, however excessive their rarity may be, are as examples of miraculous
events, will be evident from a single consideration. No one,
I presume, who admitted the occasional occurrence of an exceedingly unusual combination, would be in much doubt if
he considered that he had actually seen it himself[1]. On the
other hand, few men of any really scientific turn would
readily accept a miracle even if it appeared to happen under
their very eyes. They might be staggered at the time, but

---

[1] Laplace, for instance (*Essai*, ed.
1825, p. 149), says that if we saw
100 dies (known of course to be fair
ones) all give the same face, we
should be bewildered at the time,
and need confirmation from others,
but that, after due examination, no
one would feel obliged to postulate
hallucination in the matter. But
the chance of this occurrence is
represented by a fraction whose
numerator is 1, and denominator
contains 77 figures, and is therefore
utterly inappreciable by the imagination. It must be admitted, though,
that there is something hypothetical
about such an example, for we could
not really know that the dies were
fair with a confidence even distantly
approaching such prodigious odds.
In other words, it is difficult here to
keep apart those different aspects of
the question discussed in Chap. XIV.
§§ 28—33.

they would probably soon come to discredit it afterwards, or so explain it as to evacuate it of all that is meant by miraculous.

§ 18. It appears to me therefore, on the whole, that very little can be made of these problems of testimony in the way in which it is generally intended that they should be treated; that is, in obtaining specific rules for the estimation of the testimony under any given circumstances. Assuming that the veracity of the witness can be measured, we encounter the real difficulty in the utter impossibility of determining the limits within which the failures of the event in question are to be considered to lie, and the degree of explicitness with which the witness is supposed to answer the enquiry addressed to him; both of these being characteristics of which it is necessary to have a numerical estimate before we can consider ourselves in possession of the requisite data.

Since therefore the practical resource of most persons, viz. that of putting a direct and immediate correction, of course of a somewhat conjectural nature, upon the general trustworthiness of the witness, by a consideration of the nature of the circumstances under which his statement is made, is essentially unscientific and irreducible to rule; it really seems to me that there is something to be said in favour of the simple plan of trusting in all cases alike to the witness' general veracity[1]. That is, whether his story is ordinary or extraordinary, we may resolve to put it on the same footing of credibility, provided of course that the event is fully recognized as one which does or may occa-

---

[1] In the first edition this was stated, as it now seems to me, in decidedly too unqualified a manner. It must be remembered, however, that (as was shown in § 7) this plan is really the best theoretical one which can be adopted in certain cases.

sionally happen. It is true that we shall thus go constantly astray, and may do so to a great extent, so that if there were any rational and precise method of specializing his trustworthiness, according to the nature of his story, we should be on much firmer ground. But at least we may thus know what to expect on the average. Provided we have a sufficient number and variety of statements from him, and always take them at the same constant rate or degree of trustworthiness, we may succeed in balancing and correcting our conduct in the long run so as to avoid any ruinous error.

§ 19. A few words may now be added about the combination of testimony. No new principles are introduced here, though the consequent complication is naturally greater. Let us suppose two witnesses, the veracity of each being $\frac{9}{10}$. Now suppose 100 statements made by the pair; according to the plan of proceeding adopted before, we should have them both right 81 times and both wrong once, in the remaining 18 cases one being right and the other wrong. But since they are both supposed to give the same account, what we have to compare together are the number of occasions on which they agree and are right, and the total number on which they agree whether right or wrong. The ratio of the former to the latter is the fraction which expresses the trustworthiness of their combination of testimony in the case in question.

In attempting to decide this point the only difficulty is in determining how often they will be found to agree when they are both wrong, for clearly they must agree when they are both right. This enquiry turns of course upon the number of ways in which they can succeed in going wrong. Suppose first the case of a simple *yes* or *no* (as in § 6), and take the same example, of a bag with 1000 balls, in which one only is white. Proceeding as before, we should find that out of 100,000 drawings (the number required in order to obtain a complete cycle of all possible occurrences, as well as of all possible reports about them) the two witnesses agree in a correct report of the appearance of white in 81, and agree in a wrong report of it in 999. The Probability therefore of the story when so attested is $\frac{81}{1080}$; the fact therefore of two such witnesses of equal veracity having concurred makes the report nearly 9 times as likely as when it rested upon the authority of only one of them[1].

§ 20. When however the witnesses have many ways of going wrong, the fact of their agreeing makes the report far more likely to be true. For instance, in the case of the 1000 numbered balls, it is very unlikely that when they both mistake the number they should (without collusion) happen to make the same misstatement. Whereas, in the last case, every combined misstatement necessarily led them both to the assertion that the event in question had happened, we should now find that only once in 999 × 999 times would they both be led to assert that *some given number* (say, as before, 25) had been drawn. The odds in favour of the

---

[1] It is on this principle that the remarkable conclusion mentioned on p. 105 is based. Suppose an event whose probability is p; and that, of a number of witnesses of the same veracity (y), m assert that it happened, and n deny this. Generalizing the arithmetical reasoning given above we see that the chance of the event being asserted varies as

$$py^m(1-y)^n + (1-p)y^n(1-y)^m;$$

(viz. as the chance that the event happens, and that m are right and n are wrong; *plus* the chance that it does not happen, and that n are right and m are wrong). And the chance of its being rightly asserted as $py^m(1-y)^n$. Therefore the chance that when we have an assertion before us it is a true one is

$$\frac{py^m(1-y)^n}{py^m(1-y)^n + (1-p)y^n(1-y)^m},$$

which is equal to

$$\frac{py^{m-n}}{py^{m-n} + (1-p)(1-y)^{m-n}}.$$

But this last expression represents the probability of an assertion which is unanimously supported by $m-n$ such witnesses.

event in fact now become $\frac{80919}{80920}$, which are enormously greater than when there was only one witness.

It appears therefore that when two, and of course still more when many, witnesses agree in a statement in a matter about which they might make many and various errors, the combination of their favourable testimony adds enormously to the likelihood of the event; provided always that there is no chance of collusion. And in the extreme case of the opportunities for error being, as they well may be, practically infinite in number, such combination would produce almost perfect certainty. But then this condition, viz. absence of collusion, very seldom can be secured. Practically our main source of error and suspicion is in the possible existence of some kind of collusion. Since we can seldom entirely get rid of this danger, and when it exists it can never be submitted to numerical calculation, it appears to me that combination of testimony, in regard to detailed accounts, is yet more unfitted for consideration in Probability than even that of single testimony.

§ 21. The impossibility of any adequate or even appropriate consideration of the credibility of miraculous stories by the rules of Probability has been already noticed in § 17. But, since the grounds of this impossibility are often very insufficiently appreciated, a few pages may conveniently be added here with a view to enforcing this point. If it be regarded as a digression, the importance of the subject and the persistency with which various writers have at one time or another attempted to treat it by the rules of our science must be the excuse for entering upon it.

A necessary preliminary will be to decide upon some definition of a miracle. It will, we may suppose, be admitted by most persons that in calling a miracle 'a suspension of a law of causation,' we are giving what, though it may not amount

to an adequate definition, is at least true as a description.
It is true, though it may not be the whole truth. Whatever
else the miracle may be, this is its physical aspect: this is the
point at which it comes into contact with the subject-matter
of science. If it were not considered that any suspension of
causation were involved, the event would be regarded merely
as an ordinary one to which some special significance was
attached, that is, as a type or symbol rather than a miracle.
It is this aspect moreover of the miracle which is now exposed to the main brunt of the attack, and in support of
which therefore the defence has generally been carried on.

Now it is obvious that this, like most other definitions or
descriptions, makes some assumption as to matters of fact,
and involves something of a theory. The assumption clearly
is, that laws of causation prevail universally, or almost universally, throughout nature, so that infractions of them are
marked and exceptional. This assumption is made, but it
does not appear that anything more than this is necessarily
required; that is, there is nothing which need necessarily
make us side with either of the two principal schools which
are divided as to the nature of these laws of causation. The
definition will serve equally well whether we understand by
law nothing more than uniformity of antecedent and consequent, or whether we assert that there is some deeper and
more mysterious tie between the events than mere sequence.
The use of the term 'causation' in this minimum of signification is common to both schools, though the one might
consider it inadequate; we may speak, therefore, of 'suspen-
sions of causation' without committing ourselves to either.

§ 22. It should be observed that the aspect of the question suggested by this definition is one from which we can
hardly escape. Attempts indeed have been sometimes made
to avoid the necessity of any assumption as to the universal

prevalence of law and order in nature, by defining a miracle from a different point of view. A miracle may be called, for instance, 'an immediate exertion of creative power,' 'a sign of a revelation,' or, still more vaguely, an 'extraordinary event.' But nothing would be gained by adopting any such definitions as these. However they might satisfy the theologian, the student of physical science would not rest content with them for a moment. He would at once assert his own belief, and that of other scientific men, in the existence of universal law, and enquire what was the connection of the definition with this doctrine. An answer would imperatively be demanded to the question, Does the miracle, as you have described it, imply an infraction of one of these laws, or does it not ? And an answer must be given, unless indeed we reject his assumption by denying our belief in the existence of this universal law, in which case of course we put ourselves out of the pale of argument with him. The necessity of having to recognize this fact is growing upon men day by day, with the increased study of physical science. And since this aspect of the question has to be met some time or other, it is as well to place it in the front. The difficulty, in its scientific form, is of course a modern one, for the doctrine out of which it arises is modern. But it is only one instance, out of many that might be mentioned, in which the growth of some philosophical conception has gradually affected the nature of the dispute, and at last shifted the position of the battle-ground, in some discussion with which it might not at first have appeared to have any connection whatever.

§ 23. So far our path is plain. Up to this point disciples of very different schools may advance together; for in laying down the above doctrine we have carefully abstained from implying or admitting that it contains the whole truth. But from this point two paths branch out before us, paths as different from each other in their character, origin, and direction, as can well be conceived. As this enquiry is only a digression, we may confine ourselves to stating briefly what seem to be the characteristics of each, without attempting to give the arguments which might be used in their support.

(I.) On the one hand, we may assume that this principle of causation is the ultimate one. By so terming it, we do not mean that it is one from which we consciously start in our investigations, as we do from the axioms of geometry, but rather that it is the final result towards which we find ourselves drawn by a study of nature. Finding that, throughout the scope of our enquiries, event follows event in never-failing uniformity, and finding moreover (some might add) that this experience is supported or even demanded by a tendency or law of our nature (it does not matter here how we describe it), we may come to regard this as the one fundamental principle on which all our enquiries should rest.

(II.) Or, on the other hand, we may admit a class of principles of a very different kind. Allowing that there is this uniformity so far as our experience extends, we may yet admit what can hardly be otherwise described than by calling it a Superintending Providence, that is, a Scheme or Order, in reference to which Design may be predicated without using merely metaphorical language. To adopt an aptly chosen distinction, it is not to be understood as *over-ruling* events, but rather as *underlying* them.

§ 24. Now it is quite clear that according as we come to the discussion of any particular miracle or extraordinary story under one or other of these prepossessions, the question of its credibility will assume a very different aspect. It is sometimes overlooked that although a difference about *facts* is one of the conditions of a *bonâ fide* argument, a difference which reaches to ultimate principles is fatal to all argument. The possibility of present conflict is banished in such a case as absolutely as that of future concord. A large amount of popular literature on the subject of miracles seems to labour under this defect. Arguments are stated and examined for and against the credibility of miraculous stories without the disputants appearing to have any adequate conception of the chasm which separates one side from the other.

§ 25. The following illustration may serve in some degree to show the sort of inconsistency of which we are speaking. A sailor reports that in some remote coral island of the Pacific, on which he had landed by himself, he had found a number of stones on the beach disposed in the exact form of a cross. Now if we conceive a debate to arise about the truth of his story, in which it is attempted to decide the matter simply by considerations about the validity of testimony, without introducing the question of the existence of inhabitants, and the nature of their customs, we shall have some notion of the unsatisfactory nature of many of the current arguments about miracles. All illustrations of this subject are imperfect, but a case like this, in which a supposed trace of human agency is detected interfering with the orderly sequence of other and non-intelligent natural causes, is as much to the point as any illustration can be. The thing omitted here from the discussion is clearly the one important thing. If we suppose that there is no inhabitant, we shall probably disbelieve the story, or consider it to be grossly exaggerated. If we suppose that there are inhabitants, the question is at once resolved into a different and somewhat more intricate one. The credibility of the witness is not the only element, but we should necessarily have to take into consideration the character of the supposed inhabitants, and the object of such an action on their part.

§ 26. Considerations of this character are doubtless often introduced into the discussion, but it appears to me that they are introduced to a very inadequate extent. It is often urged, after Paley, ' Once believe in a God, and miracles are not incredible.' Such an admission surely demands some modification and extension. It should rather be stated thus, Believe in a God whose working may be traced throughout the whole moral and physical world. It amounts, in fact, to this ;—Admit that there may be a *design* which we can trace somehow or other in the course of things; admit that we are not wholly confined to tracing the connection of events, or following out their effects, but that we can form some idea, feeble and imperfect though it be, of a *scheme*[1]. Paley's advice sounds too much like saying, Admit that there are fairies, and we can account for our cups being cracked. The admission is not to be made in so off-hand a manner. To any one labouring under the difficulty we are speaking of, this belief in a God almost out of any constant relation to nature, whom we then imagine to occasionally manifest himself in a perhaps irregular manner, is altogether impossible. The only form under which belief in the Deity can gain entrance into his mind is as the controlling Spirit of an infinite and orderly system. In fact, it appears to me, paradoxical as the suggestion may appear, that it might even be more easy for a person thoroughly imbued with the spirit of Inductive science, though an atheist, to believe in a miracle which formed a part of a vast system, than for such a person, as a theist, to accept an isolated miracle.

§ 27. It is therefore with great prudence that Hume, and others after him, have practically insisted on commencing with a discussion of the credibility of the single miracle,

---

[1] The stress which Butler lays upon this notion of a scheme is, I think, one great merit of his *Analogy*.

treating the question as though the Christian Revelation could be adequately regarded as a succession of such events. As well might one consider the living body to be represented by the aggregate of the limbs which compose it. What is to be complained of in so many popular discussions on the subject is the entire absence of any recognition of the different ground on which the attackers and defenders of miracles are so often really standing. Proofs and illustrations are produced in endless number, which involving, as they almost all do in the mind of the disputants on one side at least, that very principle of causation, the absence of which in the case in question they are intended to establish, they fail in the single essential point. To attempt to induce any one to disbelieve in the existence of physical causation, in a given instance, by means of illustrations which to him seem only additional examples of the principle in question, is like trying to make a dam, in order to stop the flow of a river, by shovelling in snow. Such illustrations are plentiful in times of controversy, but being in reality only modified forms of that which they are applied to counteract, they change their shape at their first contact with the disbeliever's mind, and only help to swell the flood which they were intended to check.

CHAPTER XVIII.

ON THE NATURE AND USE OF AN AVERAGE, AND ON THE DIFFERENT KINDS OF AVERAGE[1].

§ 1.　WE have had such frequent occasion to refer to *averages*, and to the kind of uniformity which they are apt to display in contrast with individual objects or events, that it will now be convenient to discuss somewhat more minutely what are the different kinds of available average, and what exactly are the functions they perform.

[1] There is much need of some good account, accessible to the ordinary English reader, of the nature and properties of the principal kinds of Mean. The common text-books of Algebra suggest that there are only three such, viz. the arithmetical, the geometrical and the harmonical:— thus including two with which the statistician has little or nothing to do, and excluding two or more with which he should have a great deal to do. The best three references I can give the reader are the following. (1) The article *Moyenne* in the *Dictionnaire des Sciences Médicales*, by Dr Bertillon. This is written somewhat from the Quetelet point of view. (2) A paper by Fechner in the *Abhandlungen d. Math. phys. Classe d. Kön. Sächs. Gesellschaft d. Wiss.* 1878; pp. 1—76. This contains a very interesting discussion, especially for the statistician, of a number of different kinds of mean. His account of the median is remarkably full and valuable. But little mathematical knowledge is demanded. (3) A paper by Mr F. Y. Edgeworth in the *Camb. Phil. Trans.* for 1885, entitled *Observations and Statistics*. This demands some mathematical knowledge. Instead of dealing, as such investigations generally do, with only one Law of Error and with only one kind of mean, it covers a wide field of investigation.

The first vague notion of an average, as we now understand it, seems to me to involve little more than that of a
something *intermediate* to a number of objects. The objects
must of course resemble each other in certain respects, otherwise we should not think of classing them together; and
they must also differ in certain respects, otherwise we should
not distinguish between them. What the average does for
us, under this primitive form, is to enable us conveniently to
retain the group together as a whole. That is, it furnishes a
sort of representative value of the quantitative aspect of the
things in question, which will serve for certain purposes to
take the place of any single member of the group.

It would seem then that the first dawn of the conception
which science reduces to accuracy under the designation of
an average or mean, and then proceeds to subdivide into
various distinct species of means, presents itself as performing some of the functions of a general name. For what
is the main use of a general name? It is to reduce a plu-
larity of objects to unity; to group a number of things
together by reference to some qualities which they possess
in common. The ordinary general name rests upon a considerable variety of attributes, mostly of a qualitative
character, whereas the average, in so far as it serves the
same sort of purpose, rests rather upon a single quantitative
attribute. It directs attention to a certain kind and degree
of magnitude. When the grazier says of his sheep that 'one
with another they will fetch about 50 shillings,' or the
farmer buys a lot of poles which 'run to about 10 feet,' it is
true that they are not strictly using the equivalent of either
a general or a collective name. But they are coming very
near to such use, in picking out a sort of type or specimen of
the magnitude to which attention is to be directed, and in
classing the whole group by its resemblance to this type.

The grazier is thinking of his sheep: not in a merely general
sense, as sheep, and therefore under that name or conception, but as sheep of a certain approximate money value.
Some will be more, some less, but they are all near enough
to the assigned value to be conveniently classed together as
if by a name. Many of our rough quantitative designations
seem to be of this kind, as when we speak of 'eight-day
clocks' or 'twelve-stone men,' &c.; unless of course we intend (as we sometimes do in these cases) to assign a maximum
or minimum value. It is not indeed easy to see how else we
could readily convey a merely general notion of the quantitative aspect of things, except by selecting a type as above,
or by assigning certain limits within which the things are
supposed to lie.

§ 2. So far there is not necessarily any idea introduced
of comparison,—of comparison, that is, of one group with
another,—by aid of such an average. As soon as we begin
to think of this we have to be more precise in saying what
we mean by an average. We can easily see that the number
of possible kinds of average, in the sense of intermediate
values, is very great ; is, in fact, indefinitely great. Out of
the general conception of an intermediate value, obtained by
some treatment of the original magnitudes, we can elicit as
many subdivisions as we please, by various modes of treatment. There are however only three or four which for our
purposes need be taken into account.

(1) In the first place there is the arithmetical average
or mean. The rule for obtaining this is very simple : add
all the magnitudes together, and divide the sum by their
number. This is the only kind of average with which the
unscientific mind is thoroughly familiar. But we must not
let this simplicity and familiarity blind us to the fact that
there are definite reasons for the employment of this average,

and that it is therefore appropriate only in definite circumstances. The reason why it affords a safe and accurate
intermediate value for the actual divergent values, is that
for many of the ordinary purposes of life, such as purchase
and sale, we come to exactly the same result, whether we
take account of those existent divergences, or suppose all
the objects equated to their average. What the grazier
must be understood to mean, if he wishes to be accurate, by
saying that the average price of his sheep is 50 shillings, is,
that so far as that flock is concerned (and so far as he is
concerned), it comes to exactly the same thing, whether they
are each sold at different prices, or are all sold at the ' average ' price. Accordingly, when he compares his sales of one
year with those of another; when he says that last year the
sheep averaged 48 shillings against the 50 of this year; the
employment of this representative or average value is a great
simplification, and is perfectly accurate for the purpose in
question.

§ 3. (2) Now consider this case. A certain population is
found to have doubled itself in 100 years: can we talk of an
' average ' increase here of 1 per cent. annually ? The circumstances are not quite the same as in the former case, but
the analogy is sufficiently close for our purpose. The answer
is decidedly, No. If 100 articles of any kind are sold for £100,
we say that the average price is £1. By this we mean that
the total amount is the same whether the entire lot are sold
for £100, or whether we split the lot up into individuals
and sell each of these for £1. The average price here is a
convenient fictitious substitute, which can be applied for
each individual without altering the aggregate total. If
therefore the question be, Will a supposed increase of 1 p. c.
in each of the 100 years be equivalent to a total increase to
double the original amount? we are proposing a closely

analogous question. And the answer, as just remarked, must
be in the negative. An annual increase of 1 p. c. continued
for 100 years will more than double the total; it will multiply
it by about 2·7. The true annual increment required is measured by $\sqrt[100]{2}$; that is, the population may be said to have
increased 'on the average' 0·7 p. c. annually.

We are thus directed to the second kind of average discussed in the ordinary text-books of algebra, viz. the geometrical. When only two quantities are concerned, with a single
intermediate value between them, the geometrical mean constituting this last is best described as the mean proportional
between the two former. Thus, since $3 : \sqrt{15} :: \sqrt{15} : 5$,
$\sqrt{15}$ is the geometrical mean between 3 and 5. When a
number of geometrical means have to be interposed between
two quantities, they are to be so chosen that every term in
the entire succession shall bear the same constant ratio to
its predecessor. Thus, in the example in the last paragraph,
99 intermediate steps were to be interposed between 1 and 2,
with the condition that the 100 ratios thus produced were to
be all equal.

It would seem therefore that wherever accurate quantitative results are concerned, the selection of the appropriate
kind of average must depend upon the answer to the question, What particular intermediate value may be safely
substituted for the actual variety of values, so far as the
precise object in view is concerned? This is an aspect of
the subject which will have to be more fully considered in
the next chapter. But it may safely be laid down that for
purposes of general comparison, where accurate numerical
relations are not required, almost any kind of intermediate
value will answer our purpose, provided we adhere to the
same throughout. Thus, if we want to compare the statures
of the inhabitants of different counties or districts in Eng-

land, or of Englishmen generally with those of Frenchmen, or to ascertain whether the stature of some particular class or district is increasing or diminishing, it really does not seem to matter what sort of average we select provided, of course, that we adhere to the same throughout our investigations. A very large amount of the work performed by averages is of this merely comparative or non-quantitative description ; or, at any rate, nothing more than this is really required. This being so, we should naturally resort to the arithmetical average ; partly because, having been long in the field, it is universally understood and appealed to, and partly because it happens to be remarkably simple and easy to calculate.

§ 4. The arithmetical mean is for most ordinary purposes the simplest and best. Indeed, when we are dealing with a small number of somewhat artificially selected magnitudes, it is the only mean which any one would think of employing. We should not, for instance, apply any other method to the results of a few dozen measurements of lengths or estimates of prices.

When, however, we come to consider the results of a very large number of measurements of the kind which can be grouped together into some sort of 'probability curve' we begin to find that there is more than one alternative before us. Begin by recurring to the familiar curve represented on p. 29 ; or, better still, to the initial form of it represented in the next chapter (p. 476). We see that there are three different ways in which we may describe the vertex of the curve. We may call it the position of the *maximum* ordinate ; or that of the *centre* of the curve ; or (as will be seen hereafter) the point to which the arithmetical average of all the different values of the variable magnitude directs us. These three are all distinct ways of describing a position ;

but when we are dealing with a symmetrical curve at all
resembling the binomial or exponential form they all three
coincide in giving the same result : as they obviously do in
the case in question.

As soon, however, as we come to consider the case of
asymmetrical, or lop-sided curves, the indications given by
these three methods will be as a rule quite distinct; and
therefore the two former of these deserve brief notice as
representing different kinds of means from the arithmetical
or ordinary one. We shall see that there is something about
each of them which recommends it to common sense as being
in some way natural and appropriate.

§ 5. (3) The first of these selects from amongst the
various different magnitudes that particular one which is
most frequently represented. It has not acquired any technical designation[1], except in so far as it is referred to, by
its graphical representation, as the "maximum ordinate"
method. But I suspect that some appeal to such a mean
or standard is really far from uncommon, and that if we
could draw out into clearness the conceptions latent in the
judgments of the comparatively uncultivated, we should find
that there were various classes of cases in which this mean
was naturally employed. Suppose, for instance, that there
was a fishery in which the fish varied very much in size

---

[1] This kind of mean is called by
Fechner and others the "*dichteste
Werth.*" The most appropriate appeal to it that I have seen is by Prof.
Lexis (*Massenerscheinungen*, p. 42)
where he shows that it indicates
clearly a sort of normal length of
human life, of about 70 years ; a
result which is almost entirely masked when we appeal to the arithmetical average.

This mean *ought* to be called the
'probable' value (a name however in
possession of another) on the ground
that it indicates the point of likeliest
occurrence ; i.e. if we compare all
the indefinitely small and equal units
of variation, the one corresponding
to this will tend to be most frequently represented.

but in which the commonest size was somewhat near the
largest or the smallest. If the men were in the habit of
selling their fish by *weight*, it is probable that they would
before long begin to acquire some kind of notion of what
is meant by the arithmetical mean or average, and would
perceive that this was the most appropriate test. But if the
fish were sorted into sizes, and sold by numbers in each of
these sizes, I suspect that this appeal to a maximum ordinate would begin to take the place of the other. That is,
the most numerous class would come to be selected as a
sort of type by which to compare the same fishery at one
time and another, or one fishery with others. There is also,
as we shall see in the next chapter, some scientific ground
for the preference of this kind of mean in peculiar cases;
viz. where the quantities with which we deal are true
'errors,' in the estimate of some magnitude, and where also
it is of much more importance to be exactly right, or very
nearly right, than to have merely a low average of error.

§ 6. (4) The remaining kind of mean is that which is
now coming to be called the "median." It is one with
which the writings of Mr Galton have done so much to
familiarize statisticians, and is best described as follows.
Conceive all the objects in question to be marshalled in the
order of their magnitude; or, what comes to the same thing,
conceive them sorted into a number of equally numerous
classes; then the middle one of the row, or the middle one
in the middle class, will be the *median*. I do not think
that this kind of mean is at all generally recognized at
present, but if Mr Galton's scheme of natural measurement
by what he calls "per-centiles" should come to be generally adopted, such a test would become an important one.
There are some conspicuous advantages about this kind of
mean. For one thing, in most statistical enquiries, it is

far the simplest to calculate; and, what is more, the process
of determining it serves also to assign another important
element to be presently noticed, viz. the 'probable error.'
Then again, as Fechner notes, whereas in the arithmetical
mean a few exceptional and extreme values will often cause
perplexity by their comparative preponderance, in the case
of the median (where their number only and not their extreme magnitude is taken into account) the importance of
such disturbance is diminished.

§ 7. A simple illustration will serve to indicate how these
three kinds of mean coalesce into one when we are dealing
with symmetrical Laws of Error, but become quite distinct
as soon as we come to consider those which are unsymmetrical.

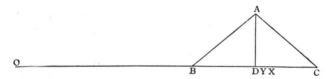

Suppose that, in measuring a magnitude along *OBDC*,
where the extreme limits are *OB* and *OC*, the law of error
is represented by the triangle *BAC*: the length *OD* will
be at once the arithmetical mean, the median, and the most
frequent length: its frequency being represented by the
maximum ordinate *AD*. But now suppose, on the other
hand, that the extreme lengths are *OD* and *OC*, and that
the triangle *ADC* represents the law of error. The most
frequent length will be the same as before, *OD*, marked by
the maximum ordinate *AD*. But the mean value will now
be *OX*, where $DX = \frac{1}{3}DC$; and the median will be *OY*,
where $DY = \left(1 - \frac{1}{\sqrt{2}}\right)DC.$

Another example, taken from natural phenomena, may be found in the heights of the barometer as taken at the same hour on successive days. So far as 4857 of these may be regarded as furnishing a sufficiently stable basis of experience, it certainly seems that the resulting curve of frequency is asymmetrical. The mean height here was found to be 29·98: the median was 30·01: the most frequent height was 30·05. The close approximation amongst these is an indication that the asymmetry is slight[1].

§ 8. It must be clearly understood that the average, of whatever kind it may be, from the mere fact of its being a single substitute for an actual plurality of observed values, must let slip a considerable amount of information. In fact it is only introduced for economy. It may entail no loss when used for some one assigned purpose, as in our example about the sheep; but for purposes in general it cannot possibly take the place of the original diversity, by yielding all the information which they contained. If all this is to be retained we must resort to some other method. Practically we generally do one of two things: either (1) we put all the figures down in statistical tables, or (2) we appeal to a diagram. This last plan is convenient when the data are very numerous, or when we wish to display or to discover the nature of the law of facility under which they range.

The mere assignment of an average lets drop nearly all of this, confining itself to the indication of an intermediate

---

[1] A diagram illustrative of this number of results was given in *Nature* (Sept. 1, 1887). In calculating, as above, the different means, I may remark that the original results were given to three decimal places; but, in classing them, only one place was noted. That is, 29·9 includes all values between 29·900 and 29·999. Thus the value most frequently entered in my tables was 30·0, but on the usual principles of interpolation this is reckoned as 30·05.

value. It gives a "middle point" of some kind, but says
nothing whatever as to how the original magnitudes were
grouped about this point. For instance, whether two magnitudes had been respectively 25 and 27, or 15 and 37, they
would yield the same arithmetical average of 26.

§ 9. To break off at this stage would clearly be to leave
the problem in a very imperfect condition. We therefore
naturally seek for some simple test which shall indicate
how closely the separate results were grouped about their
average, so as to recover some part of the information which
had been let slip.

If any one were approaching this problem entirely anew,—
that is, if he had no knowledge of the mathematical exigencies which attend the theory of "Least Squares,"—I ap
prehend that there is but one way in which he would set
about the business. He would say, The average which we
have already obtained gave us a rough indication, by assigning an intermediate point amongst the original magnitudes. If we want to supplement this by a rough indication as to how near together these magnitudes lie, the
best way will be to treat their departures from the mean
(what are technically called the "errors") in precisely the
same way, viz. by assigning *their* average. Suppose there
are 13 men whose heights vary by equal differences from
5 feet to 6 feet, we should say that their average height
was 66 inches, and their average departure from this average
was $3\frac{3}{13}$ inches.

Looked at from this point of view we should then proceed to try how each of the above-named averages would
answer the purpose. Two of them,—viz. the arithmetical
mean and the median,—will answer perfectly; and, as we
shall immediately see, are frequently used for the purpose.
So too we could, if we pleased, employ the geometrical

mean, though such employment would be tedious, owing
to the difficulty of calculation. The 'maximum ordinate'
clearly would not answer, since it would generally (v. the
diagram on p. 443) refer us back again to the average
already obtained, and therefore give no information.

The only point here about which any doubt could arise
concerns what is called in algebra the *sign* of the errors.
Two equal and opposite errors, added algebraically, would
cancel each other. But when, as here, we are regarding
the errors as substantive quantities, to be considered on
their own account, we attend only to their real magnitude,
and then these equal and opposite errors are to be put upon
exactly the same footing.

§ 10. Of the various means already discussed, two, as
just remarked, are in common use. One of these is familiarly known, in astronomical and other calculations, as
the 'Mean Error,' and is so absolutely an application of the
same principle of the arithmetical mean to the errors, that
has been already applied to the original magnitudes, that it
needs no further explanation. Thus in the example in the
last section the mean of the heights was 66 inches, the
mean of the errors was $3\frac{3}{13}$ inches.

The other is the Median, though here it is always known
under another name, i.e. as the 'Probable Error';—a technical and decidedly misleading term. It is briefly defined
as that error which we are as likely to exceed as to fall
short of: otherwise phrased, if we were to arrange all the
errors in the order of their magnitude, it corresponds to that
one of them which just bisects the row. It is therefore the
'median' error: or, if we arrange all the magnitudes in successive order, and divide them into four equally numerous
classes,—what Mr Galton calls 'quartiles,'—the first and
third of the consequent divisions will mark the limits of

the 'probable error' on each side, whilst the middle one will mark the 'median.' This median, as was remarked, coincides, in symmetrical curves, with the arithmetical mean.

It is best to stand by accepted nomenclature, but the reader must understand that such an error is not in any strict sense 'probable.' It is indeed highly improbable that in any particular instance we should happen to get just this error: in fact, if we chose to be precise and to regard it as one exact magnitude out of an infinite number, it would be infinitely unlikely that we should hit upon it. Nor can it be said to be probable that we shall be *within* this limit of the truth, for, by definition, we are just as likely to exceed as to fall short. As already remarked (see note on p. 441), the 'maximum ordinate' would have the best right to be regarded as indicating the really most probable value.

§ 11. (5) *The error of mean square.* As previously suggested, the plan which would naturally be adopted by any one who had no concern with the higher mathematics of the subject, would be to take the 'mean error' for the purpose of the indication in view. But a very different kind of average is generally adopted in practice to serve as a test of the amount of divergence or dispersion. Suppose that we have the magnitudes $x_1, x_2, \ldots x_n$; their ordinary average is $\frac{1}{n} (x_1 + x_2 + \ldots + x_n)$, and their 'errors' are the differences between this and $x_1, x_2 \ldots x_n$. Call these errors $e_1, e_2, \ldots e_n$, then the arithmetical mean of these errors (irrespective of sign) is $\frac{1}{n} (e_1 + e_2 + \ldots + e_n)$. The Error of Mean Square[1], on the other hand, is the square root of $\frac{1}{n} (e_1^2 + e_2^2 + \ldots + e_n^2)$.

---

[1] There is some ambiguity in the phraseology in use here. Thus Airy commonly uses the expression 'Error of Mean Square' to represent, as

The reasons for employing this latter kind of average in preference to any of the others will be indicated in the following chapter. At present we are concerned only with the general logical nature of an average, and it is therefore sufficient to point out that any such intermediate value will answer the purpose of giving a rough and summary indication of the degree of closeness of approximation which our various measures display to each other and to their common average. If we were to speak respectively of the 'first' and the 'second average,' we might say that the former of these assigns a rough single substitute for the plurality of original values, whilst the latter gives a similar rough estimate of the degree of their departure from the former.

§ 12. So far we have only been considering the general nature of an average, and the principal kinds of average practically in use. We must now enquire more particularly what are the principal purposes for which averages are employed.

In this respect the first thing we have to do is to raise doubts in the reader's mind on a subject on which he perhaps has not hitherto felt the slightest doubt. Every one is more or lest familiar with the practice of appealing to an average in order to secure accuracy. But distinctly what we begin by doing is to sacrifice accuracy; for in place of the plurality of actual results we get a single result which

here, $\sqrt{\dfrac{\Sigma e^2}{n}}$. Galloway commonly speaks of the 'Mean Square of the Errors' to represent $\dfrac{\Sigma e^2}{n}$. I shall adhere to the former usage and represent it briefly by E. M. S. Still more unfortunate (to my thinking) is the employment, by Mr Merriman and others, of the expression 'Mean Error,' (widely in use in its more natural signification,) as the equivalent of this E. M. S.

The technical term 'Fluctuation' is applied by Mr F. Y. Edgeworth to the expression $\dfrac{2\Sigma e^2}{n}$.

very possibly does not agree with any one of them. If I find
the temperature in different parts of a room to be different,
but say that the average temperature is 61°, there may perhaps be but few parts of the room where this exact temperature is realized. And if I say that the average stature of
a certain small group of men is 68 inches, it is probable that
no one of them will present precisely this height.

The principal way in which accuracy can be thus secured
is when what we are really aiming at is not the magnitudes
before us but something else of which they are an indication.
If they are themselves 'inaccurate,'—we shall see presently
that this needs some explanation,—then the single average,
which in itself agrees perhaps with none of them, may be
much more nearly what we are actually in want of. We shall
find it convenient to subdivide this view of the subject into
two parts; by considering first those cases in which quantitative considerations enter but slightly, and in which no determination of the particular Law of Error involved is demanded,
and secondly those in which such determination cannot be
avoided. The latter are only noticed in passing here, as a
separate chapter is reserved for their fuller consideration.

§ 13. The process, as a practical one, is familiar enough
to almost everybody who has to work with measures of any
kind. Suppose, for instance, that I am measuring any object
with a brass rod which, as we know, expands and contracts
according to the temperature. The results will vary slightly,
being sometimes a little too great and sometimes a little too
small. All these variations are physical facts, and if what
we were concerned with was the properties of brass they
would be the one important fact for us. But when we are
concerned with the length of the object measured, these facts
become superfluous and misleading. What we want to do is
to escape their influence, and this we are enabled to effect by

taking their (arithmetical) average, provided only they are as often in excess as in defect[1]. For this purpose all that is necessary is that equal excesses and defects should be equally prevalent. It is not necessary to know what is the law of variation, or even to be assured that it is of one particular kind. Provided only that it is in the language of the diagram on p. 29, symmetrical, then the arithmetical average of a suitable and suitably varied number of measurements will be free from this source of disturbance. And what holds good of this cause of variation will hold good of all others which obey the same general conditions. In fact the equal prevalence of equal and opposite errors seems to be the sole and sufficient justification of the familiar process of taking the average in order to secure accuracy.

§ 14. We must now make the distinction to which attention requires so often to be drawn in these subjects between the cases in which there respectively is, and is not, some objective magnitude aimed at: a distinction which the common use of the same word "errors" is so apt to obscure. When we talked, in the case of the brass rod, of excesses and defects being equal, we meant exactly what we said, viz. that for every case in which the 'true' length (i.e. that determined by the authorized standard) is exceeded by a given fraction of an inch, there will be a corresponding case in which there is an equal defect.

On the other hand, when there is no such fixed objective standard of reference, it would appear that all that we mean by equal excesses and defects is permanent symmetry of arrangement. In the case of the measuring rod we were

---

[1] Practically, of course, we should allow for the expansion or contraction. But for purposes of logical explanation we may conveniently take this variation as a specimen of one of those disturbances which may be neutralised by resort to an average.

able to start with something which existed, so to say, before
its variations; but in many cases any starting point which
we can find is solely determined by the average.

Suppose, for instance, we take a great number of observations of the height of the barometer at a certain place,
at all times and seasons and in all weathers, we should
generally consider that the average of all these showed the
'true' height for that place. What we really mean is that
the height at any moment is determined partly (and principally) by the height of the column of air above it, but partly
also by a number of other agencies such as local temperature,
moisture, wind, &c. These are sometimes more and sometimes less effective, but their range being tolerably constant, and their distribution through this range being
tolerably symmetrical, the average of one large batch of
observations will be almost exactly the same as that of any
other. This constancy of the average *is* its truth. I am
quite aware that we find it difficult not to suppose that
there must be something more than this constancy, but we
are probably apt to be misled by the analogy of the other
class of cases, viz. those in which we are really aiming at
some sort of mark.

§ 15. As regards the practical methods available for
determining the various kinds of average there is very little
to be said; as the arithmetical rules are simple and definite,
and involve nothing more than the inevitable drudgery
attendant upon dealing with long rows of figures. Perhaps
the most important contribution to this part of the subject is
furnished by Mr Galton's suggestion to substitute the median
for the mean, and thus to elicit the average with sufficient
accuracy by the mere act of grouping a number of objects
together. Thus he has given an ingenious suggestion for
obtaining the average height of a number of men without

the trouble and risk of measuring them all. "A barbarian chief might often be induced to marshall his men in the order of their heights, or in that of the popular estimate of their skill in any capacity; but it would require some apparatus and a great deal of time to measure each man separately, even supposing it possible to overcome the usually strong repugnance of uncivilized people to any such proceeding" (*Phil. Mag.* Jan. 1875), That is, it being known from wide experience that the heights of any tolerably homogeneous set of men are apt to group themselves symmetrically,—the condition for the coincidence of the three principal kinds of mean,—the middle man of a row thus arranged in order will represent the mean or average man, and him we may subject to measurement. Moreover, since the intermediate heights are much more thickly represented than the extreme ones, a moderate error in the selection of the central man of a long row will only entail a very small error in the selection of the corresponding height.

§ 16. We can now conveniently recur to a subject which has been already noticed in a former chapter, viz. the attempt which is sometimes made to establish a distinction between an average and a mean. It has been proposed to confine the former term to the cases in which we are dealing with a fictitious result of our own construction, that is, with a mere arithmetical deduction from the observed magnitudes, and to apply the latter to cases in which there is supposed to be some objective magnitude peculiarly representative of the average.

Recur to the three principal classes, of things appropriate to Probability, which were sketched out in Ch. II. § 4. The first of these comprised the results of games of chance. Toss a die ten times: the total number of pips on the upper side may vary from ten up to sixty. Suppose it to be thirty. We then say that the average of this batch of ten is three. Take another set of ten throws, and we may get another average, say four. There is clearly nothing objective peculiarly corresponding in any way to these averages. No doubt if we go on long enough we shall find that the averages tend to centre about 3·5 : we then call this *the* average, or the 'probable' number of points; and this ultimate average might have been pretty constantly asserted beforehand from our knowledge of the constitution of a die. It has however no other truth or reality about it of the nature of a type : it is simply the limit towards which the averages tend.

The next class is that occupied by the members of most natural groups of objects, especially as regards the characteristics of natural species. Somewhat similar remarks may be repeated here. There is very frequently a 'limit' towards which the averages of increasing numbers of individuals tend to approach; and there is certainly some temptation to regard this limit as being a sort of type which all had been intended to resemble as closely as possible. But when we looked closer, we found that this view could scarcely be justified; all which could be safely asserted was that this type represented, for the time being, the most numerous specimens, or those which under existing conditions could most easily be produced.

The remaining class stands on a somewhat different ground. When we make a succession of more or less successful attempts of any kind, we get a corresponding series of deviations from the mark at which we aimed. These we may treat arithmetically, and obtain their averages, just as in the former cases. These averages are fictions, that is to say, they are artificial deductions of our own which need not necessarily have anything objective corresponding to them. In fact, if they be averages of a *few* only they most probably will not have anything thus corresponding to them. Anything answering to a type can only be sought in the 'limit' towards which they ultimately tend, for this limit coincides with the fixed point or object aimed at.

§ 17. Fully admitting the great value and interest of Quetelet's work in this direction,—he was certainly the first to direct public attention to the fact that so many classes of natural objects display the same characteristic property,—it nevertheless does not seem desirable to attempt to mark such a distinction by any special use of these technical terms. The objections are principally the two following.

In the first place, a single antithesis, like this between an average and a mean, appears to suggest a very much simpler state of things than is actually found to exist in nature. A reference to the three classes of things just mentioned, and a consideration of the wide range and diversity included in each of them, will serve to remind us not only of the very gradual and insensible advance from what is thus regarded as 'fictitious' to what is claimed as 'real;' but also of the important fact that whereas the 'real type' may be of a fluctuating and evanescent character, the 'fiction' may (as in games of chance) be apparently fixed for ever. Provided only that the conditions of production remain stable, averages of large numbers will always practically present much the same general characteristics. The far more important distinction lies between the average of a few, with its fluctuating values and very imperfect and occasional attainment of its ultimate goal, and the average of many and its gradually close approximation to its ultimate value : i.e. to its objective point of aim if there happen to be such.

Then, again, the considerations adduced in this chapter

will show that within the field of the average itself there is
far more variety than Quetelet seems to have recognized.
He did not indeed quite ignore this variety, but he practically confined himself almost entirely to those symmetrical
arrangements in which three of the principal means coalesce
into one. We should find it difficult to carry out his distinction in less simple cases. For instance, when there is
some degree of asymmetry, it is the 'maximum ordinate'
which would have to be considered as a 'mean' to the
exclusion of the others; for no appeal to an arithmetical
average would guide us to this point, which however is to
be regarded, if any can be so regarded, as marking out the
position of the ultimate type.

§ 18. We have several times pointed out that it is a
characteristic of the things with which Probability is concerned to present, in the long run, a continually intensifying
uniformity. And this has been frequently described as what
happens 'on the average.' Now an objection may very
possibly be raised against regarding an arrangement of
things by virtue of which order thus emerges out of disorder
as deserving any special notice, on the ground that from the
nature of the arithmetical average it could not possibly be
otherwise. The process by which an average is obtained, it
may be urged, insures this tendency to equalization amongst
the magnitudes with which it deals. For instance, let there
be a party of ten men, of whom four are tall and four are
short, and take the average of any five of them. Since this
number cannot be made up of tall men only, or of short men
only, it stands to reason that the averages cannot differ so
much amongst themselves as the single measures can. Is
not then the equalizing process, it may be asked, which is
observable on increasing the range of our observations,
one which can be shown to follow from necessary laws of

arithmetic, and one therefore which might be asserted à priori ?

Whatever force there may be in the above objection arises principally from the limitations of the example selected, in which the number chosen was so large a proportion of the total as to exclude the bare possibility of only extreme cases being contained within it. As much confusion is often felt here between what is necessary and what is matter of experience, it will be well to look at an example somewhat more closely, in order to determine exactly what are the really necessary consequences of the averaging process.

§ 19. Suppose then that we take ten digits at random from a table (say) of logarithms. Unless in the highly unlikely case of our having happened upon the same digit ten times running, the average of the ten *must* be intermediate between the possible extremes. Every conception of an average of any sort not merely involves, but actually means, the taking of something intermediate between the extremes. The average therefore of the ten must lie closer to 4·5 (the average of the extremes) than did some of the single digits.

Now suppose we take 1000 such digits instead of 10. We can say nothing more about the larger number, with demonstrative certainty, than we could before about the smaller. If they were unequal to begin with (i.e. if they were not all the same) then the average *must* be intermediate, but more than this cannot be proved arithmetically. By comparison with such purely arithmetical considerations there is what may be called a physical fact underlying our confidence in the growing stability of the average of the larger number. It is that the constituent elements from which the average is deduced will themselves betray a growing uniformity:—that the proportions in which the different digits come out will become more and more nearly equal as we take larger numbers of them. If the proportions in which the 1000 digits were distributed were the same as those of the 10 the averages would be the same. It is obvious therefore that the arithmetical process of obtaining an average goes a very little way towards securing the striking kind of uniformity which we find to be actually presented.

§ 20. There is another way in which the same thing may be put. It is sometimes said that whatever may have been the arrangement of the original elements the process of continual averaging will necessarily produce the peculiar binomial or exponential law of arrangement. This statement is perfectly true (with certain safeguards) but it is not in any way opposed to what has been said above. Let us take for consideration the example above referred to. The arrangement of the individual digits in the long run is the simplest possible. It would be represented, in a diagram, not by a curve but by a finite straight line, for each digit occurs about as often as any other, and this exhausts all the 'arrangement' that can be detected. Now, when we consider the results of taking averages of ten such digits, we see at once that there is an opening for a more extensive arrangement. The totals may range from 0 up to 100, and therefore the average will have 100 values from 0 to 9; and what we find is that the frequency of these numbers is determined according to the Binomial[1] or Exponential Law. The most frequent result is the true mean, viz. 4·5, and from this they diminish in each direction towards 0 and 10, which will each occur but once (on the average) in 10^{10} occasions.

The explanation here is of the same kind as in the former case. The resultant arrangement, so far as the averages are

---

[1] More strictly *multinomial :* the relative frequency of the different numbers being indicated by the coefficients of the powers of x in the development of

$$(1 + x + x^2 + \ldots + x^9)^{10}.$$

concerned, is only 'necessary' in the sense that it is a necessary result of certain physical assumptions or experiences. If all the digits tend to occur with equal frequency, and if they are 'independent' (i.e. if each is associated indifferently with every other), then it is an arithmetical consequence that the averages when arranged in respect of their magnitude and prevalence will display the Law of Facility above indicated. Experience, so far as it can be appealed to, shows that the true randomness of the selection of the digits,—i.e. their equally frequent recurrence, and the impartiality of their combination,—is very fairly secured in practice. Accordingly the theoretic deduction that whatever may have been the original Law of Facility of the individual results we shall always find the familiar Exponential Law asserting itself as the law of the averages, is fairly justified by experience in such a case.

The further discussion of certain corrections and refinements is reserved to the following chapter.

§ 21. In regard to the three kinds of average employed to test the amount of dispersion,—i.e. the mean error, the probable error, and the error of mean square,—two important considerations must be borne in mind. They will both recur for fuller discussion and justification in the course of the next chapter, when we come to touch upon the Method of Least Squares, but their significance for logical purposes is so great that they ought not to be entirely passed by at present.

(1) In the first place, then, it must be remarked that in order to know what in any case is the real value of an error we ought in strictness to know what is the position of the limit or ultimate average, for the amount of an error is always theoretically measured from this point. But this is information which we do not always possess. Recurring

once more to the three principal classes of events with which
we are concerned, we can readily see that in the case of
games of chance we mostly do possess this knowledge. Instead of appealing to experience to ascertain the limit, we
practically deduce it by simple mechanical or arithmetical
considerations, and then the 'error' in any individual case or
group of cases is obviously found by comparing the results
thus obtained with that which theory informs us would ultimately be obtained in the long run. In the case of deliberate efforts at an aim (the third class) we may or may
not know accurately the value or position of this aim. In
astronomical observations we do not know it, and the method
of Least Squares is a method for helping us to ascertain it as
well as we can; in such experimental results as firing at a
mark we do know it, and may thus test the nature and
amount of our failure by direct experience. In the remaining case, namely that of what we have termed natural kinds
or groups of things, not only do we not know the ultimate
limit, but its existence is always at least doubtful, and in
many cases may be confidently denied. Where it does exist,
that is, where the type seems for all practical purposes permanently fixed, we can only ascertain it by a laborious resort
to statistics. Having done this, we may then test by it the
results of observations on a small scale. For instance, if we
find that the ultimate proportion of male to female births is
about 106 to 100, we may then compare the statistics of
some particular district or town and speak of the consequent
'error,' viz. the departure, in that particular and special
district, from the general average.

What we have therefore to do in the vast majority of
practical cases is to take the average of a finite number of
measurements or observations,—of all those, in fact, which
we have in hand,—and take *this* as our starting point in

order to measure the errors. The errors in fact are not known for certain but only probably calculated. This however is not so much of a theoretic defect as it may seem at first sight; for inasmuch as we seldom have to employ these methods,—for purposes of calculation, that is, as distinguished from mere illustration,—except for the purpose of discovering what the ultimate average is, it would be a sort of petitio principii to assume that we had already secured it. But it is worth while considering whether it is desirable to employ one and the same term for 'errors' known to be such, and whose amount can be assigned with certainty, and for 'errors' which are only probably such and whose amount can be only probably assigned. In fact it has been proposed[1] to employ the two terms 'error' and 'residual' respectively to distinguish between the magnitudes thus determined, that is, between the (generally unknown) actual error and the observed error.

§ 22. (2) The other point involves the question to what extent either of the first two tests (pp. 446, 7) of the closeness with which the various results have grouped themselves about their average is trustworthy or complete. The answer is that they are necessarily incomplete. No single estimate or magnitude can possibly give us an adequate account of a number of various magnitudes. The point is a very important one; and is not, I think, sufficiently attended to, the consequence being, as we shall see hereafter, that it is far too summarily assumed that a method which yields the result with the least 'error of mean square' must necessarily be the best result for all purposes. It is not however by any means clear that a test which answers best for one purpose must do so for all.

It must be clearly understood that each of these tests is

---

[1] By Mr Merriman, in his work on *Least Squares.*

an 'average,' and that every average necessarily rejects a mass of varied detail by substituting for it a single result. We had, say, a lot of statures: so many of 60 inches, so many of 61, &c. We replace these by an 'average' of 68, and thereby drop a mass of information. A portion of this we then seek to recover by reconsidering the 'errors' or departures of these statures from their average. As before, however, instead of giving the full details we substitute an average of the errors. The only difference is that instead of taking the same kind of average (i.e. the arithmetical) we often prefer to adopt the one called the 'error of mean square.'

§ 23. A question may be raised here which is of sufficient importance to deserve a short consideration. When we have got a set of measurements before us, why is it generally held to be sufficient simply to assign: (1) the mean value; and (2) the mean departure from this mean? The answer is, of course, partly given by the fact that we are only supposed to be in want of a rough approximation: but there is more to be said than this. A further justification is to be found in the fact that we assume that we need only contemplate the possibility of a single Law of Error, or at any rate that the departures from the familiar Law will be but trifling. In other words, if we recur to the figure on p. 29, we assume that there are only two unknown quantities or disposable constants to be assigned; viz. first, the position of the centre, and, secondly, the degree of eccentricity, if one may so term it, of the curve. The determination of the mean value directly and at once assigns the former, and the determination of the mean error (in either of the ways referred to already) indirectly assigns the latter by confining us to one alone of the possible curves indicated in the figure.

Except for the assumption of one such Law of Error the

determination of the mean error would give but a slight intimation of the sort of outline of our Curve of Facility. We might then have found it convenient to adopt some plan of successive approximation, by adding a third or fourth 'mean.' Just as we assign the mean value of the magnitude, and its mean departure from this mean; so we might take this mean error (however determined) as a fresh starting point, and assign the mean departure from it. If the point were worth further discussion we might easily illustrate by means of a diagram the sort of successive approximations which such indications would yield as to the ultimate form of the Curve of Facility or Law of Error.

As this volume is written mainly for those who take an interest in the logical questions involved, rather than as an introduction to the actual processes of calculation, mathematical details have been throughout avoided as much as possible. For this reason comparatively few references have been made to the exponential equation of the Law of Error, or to the corresponding 'Probability integral,' tables of which are given in several handbooks on the subject. There are two points however in connection with these particular topics as to which difficulties are, or should be, felt by so many students that some notice may be taken of them here

(1) In regard to the ordinary algebraical expression for the law of error, viz. $y = \dfrac{h}{\sqrt{\pi}} e^{-h^2 x^2}$, it will have been observed that I have always spoken of y as being *proportional* to the number of errors of the particular magnitude x. It would hardly be correct to say, absolutely, that y *represents* that number, because of course the actual number of errors of any precise magnitude, where continuity of possibility is assumed, must be indefinitely small. If therefore we want to pass from the continuous to the discrete, by ascertaining the actual number of errors between two consecutive divisions of our scale, when, as usual in measurements, all within certain limits are referred to some one precise point, we must modify our formula. In accordance with the usual differential notation, we must say that the number of errors falling into one subdivision (dx) of our scale *is* $dx \dfrac{h}{\sqrt{\pi}} e^{-h^2 x^2}$, where dx is a (small) unit of length, in which both h^{-1} and x must be measured.

The difficulty felt by most students is in applying the formula to actual statistics, in other words in putting in the correct units. To take an actual numerical example, suppose that 1460 men have been measured in regard to their height "true to the nearest inch," and let it be known that the modulus here is 3·6 inches. Then $dx = 1$ (inch); $h^{-1} = 3·6$ inches. Now

$$\sum \frac{h}{\sqrt{\pi}} e^{-h^2 x^2} dx = 1\,;$$ that is, the sum of all the consecutive possible values

is equal to *unity*. When therefore we want the sum, as here, to be 1460, we must express the formula thus: $y = \dfrac{1460}{\sqrt{\pi \times 3·6}} e^{-\left(\frac{x}{36}\right)^2}$, or $y = 228\, e^{-\left(\frac{x}{36}\right)^2}$.

Here x stands for the number of inches measured from the central or mean height, and y stands for the number of men referred to that height in our statistical table. (The values of e^{-t^2} for successive values of t are given in the handbooks.)

For illustration I give the calculated numbers by this formula for values of x from 0 to 8 inches, with the actual numbers observed in the Cambridge measurements recently set on foot by Mr Galton.

inches	calculated	observed
$x = 0$	$y = 228$	$= 231$
$x = 1$	$y = 212$	$= 218$
$x = 2$	$y = 166$	$= 170$
$x = 3$	$y = 111$	$= 110$
$x = 4$	$y = 82$	$= 66$
$x = 5$	$y = 32$	$= 31$
$x = 6$	$y = 11$	$= 10$
$x = 7$	$y = 4$	$= 6$
$x = 8$	$y = 1$	$= 3$

Here the average height was 69 inches: dx, as stated, $= 1$ inch. By saying, 'put $x = 0$,' we mean, calculate the number of men who are assigned to 69 inches; i.e. who fall between 68·5 and 69·5. By saying, 'put $x = 4$,' we mean, calculate the number who are assigned to 65 or to 73; i.e. who lie between 64·5 and 65·5, or between 72·5 and 73·5. The observed results, it will be seen, keep pretty close to the calculated: in the case of the former the *means* of equal and opposite divergences from the mean have been taken, the actual results not being always the same in opposite directions.

(2) The other point concerns the interpretation of the familiar probability integral, $\dfrac{2}{\sqrt{\pi}} \displaystyle\int_0^t e^{-t^2} dt$. Every one who has calculated the chance of an event, by the help of the tables of this integral given in so many handbooks, knows that if we assign any numerical value to t, the corresponding value of the above expression assigns the chance that an

error taken at random shall lie within that same limit, viz. t. Thus put $t = 1\cdot5$, and we have the result $\cdot96$; that is, only 4 *per cent.* of the errors will exceed 'one and a half.' But when we ask, 'one and a half' *what?* the answer would not always be very ready. As usual, the main difficulty of the beginner is not to manipulate the formulæ, but to be quite clear about his units.

It will be seen at once that this case differs from the preceding in that we cannot now choose our unit as we please. Where, as here, there is only one variable (t), if we were allowed to select our own unit, the inch, foot, or whatever it might be, we might get quite different results. Accordingly some comparatively natural unit must have been chosen for us in which we are bound to reckon, just as in the circular measurement of an angle as distinguished from that by degrees.

The answer is that the unit here is the *modulus*, and that to put '$t = 1\cdot5$' is to say, 'suppose the error half as great again as the modulus'; the modulus itself being an error of a certain assignable magnitude depending upon the nature of the measurements or observations in question. We shall see this better if we put the integral in the form $\dfrac{2}{\sqrt{\pi}}\displaystyle\int_{0}^{hx} e^{-h^2x^2}\,d(hx)$; which is precisely equivalent, since the value of a definite integral is independent of the particular variable employed. Here hx is the same as $x : \dfrac{1}{h}$; i.e. it is the ratio of x to $\dfrac{1}{h}$, or x measured in terms of $\dfrac{1}{h}$. But $\dfrac{1}{h}$ is the modulus in the equation $\left(y = \dfrac{h}{\sqrt{\pi}} e^{-h^2x^2}\right)$ for the law of error. In other words the numerical value of an error in this formula, is the number of times, whole or fractional, which it contains the modulus.

CHAPTER XIX.

THE THEORY OF THE AVERAGE AS A MEANS OF APPROXIMATION TO THE TRUTH.

§ 1.   IN the last chapter we were occupied with the Average mainly under its qualitative rather than its quantitative aspect.   That is, we discussed its general nature, its principal varieties, and the main uses to which it could be put in ordinary life or in reasoning processes which did not claim to be very exact.   It is now time to enter more minutely into the specific question of the employment of the average in the way peculiarly appropriate to Probability.   That is, we must be supposed to have a certain number of measurements,—in the widest sense of that term,—placed before us, and to be prepared to answer such questions as ; Why do we take their average ?   With what degree of confidence ? Must we in all cases take the average, and, if so, one always of the same kind ?

The subject upon which we are thus entering is one which, under its most general theoretic treatment, has perhaps given rise to more profound investigation, to a greater variety of opinion, and in consequence to a more extensive history and literature, than any other single problem within the range of mathematics[1].   But, in spite of this, the main

---

[1] Mr Mansfield Merriman published in 1877 (*Trans. of the Connecticut Acad.*) a list of 408 writings on the subject of Least Squares.

logical principles underlying the methods and processes in question are not, I apprehend, particularly difficult to grasp : though, owing to the extremely technical style of treatment adopted even in comparatively elementary discussions of the subject, it is far from easy for those who have but a moderate command of mathematical resources to disentangle these principles from the symbols in which they are clothed. The present chapter contains an attempt to remove these difficulties, so far as a general comprehension of the subject is concerned. As the treatment thus adopted involves a considerable number of subdivisions, the reader will probably find it convenient to refer back occasionally to the table of contents at the commencement of this volume.

§ 2. The subject, in the form in which we shall discuss it, will be narrowed to the consideration of the *average*, on account of the comparative simplicity and very wide prevalence of this aspect of the problem. The problem is however very commonly referred to, even in non-mathematical treatises, as the Rule or Method of Least Squares ; the fact being that, in such cases as we shall be concerned with, the Rule of Least Squares resolves itself into the simpler and more familiar process of taking the arithmetical average. A very simple example,—one given by Herschel,—will explain the general nature of the task under a slightly wider treatment, and will serve to justify the familiar designation.

Suppose that a man had been firing for some time with a pistol at a small mark, say a wafer on a wall. We may take it for granted that the shot-marks would tend to group themselves about the wafer as a centre, with a density varying in some way inversely with the distance from the centre. But now suppose that the wafer which marked the centre was removed, so that we could see nothing but the surface of the wall spotted with the shot-marks ; and that we were

asked to guess the position of the wafer. Had there been
only *one* shot, common sense would suggest our assuming
(of course very precariously) that this marked the real centre.
Had there been two, common sense would suggest our taking
the mid-point between them. But if three or more were
involved, common sense would be at a loss. It would feel
that some intermediate point ought to be selected, but
would not see its way to a more precise determination, because its familiar reliance,—the arithmetical average,—does
not seem at hand here. The rule in question tells us how to
proceed. It directs us to select that point which will render
the sum of the squares of all the distances of the various
shot-marks from it the least possible [1].

This is merely by way of illustration, and to justify the
familiar designation of the rule. The sort of cases with
which we shall be exclusively occupied are those comparatively simple ones in which only linear magnitude, or some
quality which can be adequately represented by linear magnitude, is the object under consideration. In respect of these
the Rule of Least Squares reduces itself to the process of
taking the average, in the most familiar sense of that term,
viz. the arithmetical mean; and a single Law of Error, or its
graphical equivalent, a Curve of Facility, will suffice accurately to indicate the comparative frequency of the different
amounts of the one variable magnitude involved.

---

[1] In other words, we are to take
the " centre of gravity " of the shot-
marks, regarding them all as of equal
weight. This is, in reality, the ' average' of all the marks, as the elementary geometrical construction for
obtaining the centre of gravity of a
system of points will show; but it is
not familiarly so regarded. Of course,
when we are dealing with such cases
as occur in Mensuration, where we
have to combine or reconcile three or
more inconsistent equations, some
such rule as that of Least Squares
becomes imperative. No taking of
an average will get us out of the
difficulty.

§ 3. We may conveniently here again call attention to a misconception or confusion which has been already noticed in a former chapter. It is that of confounding the Law of Error with the Method of Least Squares. These are things of an entirely distinct kind. The former is of the nature of a physical fact, and its production is one which in many cases is entirely beyond our control. The latter,—or any simplified application of it, such as the arithmetical average,— is no law whatever in the physical sense. It is rather a precept or rule for our guidance. The Law states, in any given case, how the errors tend to occur in respect of their magnitude and frequency. The Method directs us how to treat these errors when any number of them are presented to us. No doubt there is a relation between the two, as will be pointed out in the course of the following pages; but there is nothing really to prevent us from using the same method for different laws of error, or different methods for the same law. In so doing, the question of distinct right and wrong would seldom be involved, but rather one of more or less propriety.

§ 4. The reader must understand,—as was implied in the illustration about the pistol shots,—that the ultimate problem before us is an *inverse* one. That is, we are sup- posed to have a moderate number of 'errors' before us and we are to undertake to say whereabouts is the centre from which they diverge. This resembles the determination of a cause from the observation of an effect. But, as mostly happens in inverse problems, we must commence with the consideration of the direct problem. In other words, so far as concerns the case before us, we shall have to begin by supposing that the ultimate object of our aim,—that is, the true centre of our curve of frequency,—is already known to us: in which case all that remains to be done is to study the

consequences of taking averages of the magnitudes which
constitute the errors.

§ 5. We shall, for the present, confine our remarks to
what must be regarded as the typical case where considerations of Probability are concerned; viz. that in which
the law of arrangement or development is of the Binomial
kind. The nature of this law was explained in Chap. II.,
where it was shown that the frequency of the respective
numbers of occurrences was regulated in accordance with
the magnitude of the successive terms of the expansion of
the binomial $(1 + 1)^n$. It was also pointed out that when n
becomes very great, that is, when the number of influencing
circumstances is very large, and their relative individual
influence correspondingly small, the form assumed by a
curve drawn through the summits of ordinates representing
these successive terms of the binomial tends towards that
assigned by the equation

$$y = A e^{-h^2 x^2}.$$

For all practical purposes therefore we may talk indifferently of the Binomial or Exponential law; if only on
the ground that the arrangement of the actual phenomena
on one or other of these two schemes would soon become
indistinguishable when the numbers involved are large.
But there is another ground than this. Even when the
phenomena themselves represent a continuous magnitude,
our measurements of them,—which are all with which we
can deal,—are discontinuous. Suppose we had before us the
accurate heights of a million adult men. For all practical
purposes these would represent the variations of a continuous magnitude, for the differences between two successive magnitudes, especially near the mean, would be
inappreciably small. But our tables will probably represent

them only to the nearest inch. We have so many assigned
as 69 inches; so many as 70; and so on. The tabular
statement in fact is of much the same character as if we
were assigning the number of 'heads' in a toss of a handful
of pence; that is, as if we were dealing with discontinuous
numbers on the binomial, rather than with a continuous
magnitude on the exponential arrangement.

§ 6. Confining ourselves then, for the present, to this
general head, of the binomial or exponential law, we must
distinguish two separate cases in respect of the knowledge
we may possess as to the generating circumstances of the
variable magnitudes.

(1) There is, first, the case in which the conditions of
the problem are determinable à priori: that is, where we are
able to say, prior to specific experience, how frequently each
combination will occur in the long run. In this case the
main or ultimate object for which we are supposing that the
average is employed,—i.e. that of discovering the true mean
value,—is superseded. We are able to say what the mean
or central value in the long run will be; and therefore there
is no occasion to set about determining it, with some trouble
and uncertainty, from a small number of observations. Still
it is necessary to discuss this case carefully, because its
assumption is a necessary link in the reasoning in other
cases.

This comparatively à priori knowledge may present itself
in two different degrees as respects its completeness. In the
first place it may, so far as the circumstances in question
are concerned, be absolutely complete. Consider the results
when a handful of ten pence is repeatedly tossed up. We
know precisely what the mean value is here, viz. equal
division of heads and tails: we know also the chance of six
heads and four tails, and so on. That is, if we had to plot

out a diagram showing the relative frequency of each combination, we could do so without appealing to experience. We could draw the appropriate binomial curve from the generating conditions given in the statement of the problem.

But now consider the results of firing at a target consisting of a long and narrow strip, of which one point is marked as the centre of aim[1]. Here (assuming that there are no causes at work to produce permanent bias) we know that this centre will correspond to the mean value. And we know also, in a general way, that the dispersion on each side of this will follow *a* binomial law. But if we attempted to plot out the proportions, as in the preceding case, by erecting ordinates which should represent each degree of frequency as we receded further from the mean, we should find that we could not do so. Fresh data must be given or inferred. A good marksman and a bad marksman will both distribute their shot according to the same general law; but the rapidity with which the shots thin off as we recede from the centre will be different in the two cases. Another 'constant' is demanded before the curve of frequency could be correctly traced out.

§ 7. (2) The second division, to be next considered, corresponds for all logical purposes to the first. It comprises the cases in which though we have no à priori knowledge as to the situation about which the values will tend to cluster in the long run, yet we have sufficient experience at hand to assign it with practical certainty. Consider for instance the tables of human stature. These are often very extensive, including tens or hundreds of thousands. In such cases the mean or central value is determinable with just as

---

[1] The only reason for supposing this exceptional shape is to secure simplicity. The ordinary target, allowing errors in two dimensions, would yield slightly more complicated results.

great certainty as by any à priori rule. That is, if we took
another hundred thousand measurements from the same
class of population, we should feel secure that the average
would not be altered by any magnitude which our measuring
instruments could practically appreciate.

§ 8.   But the mere assignment of the mean or central
value does not here, any more than in the preceding case,
give us all that we want to know.   It *might* so happen that
the mean height of two populations was the same, but that
the law of dispersion about that mean was very different:
so that a man who in one series was an exceptional giant or
dwarf should, in the other, be in no wise remarkable.

To explain the process of thus determining the actual
magnitude of the dispersion would demand too much mathematical detail; but some indication may be given.   What
we have to do is to determine the constant h in the equation[1]

$$y = \frac{h}{\sqrt{\pi}} \, e^{-h^2 x^2}.$$ In technical language, what we have to do is

to determine the *modulus* of this equation.   The quantity $\frac{1}{h}$

in the above expression is called the modulus.   It measures
the degree of contraction or dispersion about the mean
indicated by this equation.   When it is large the dispersion
is considerable; that is the magnitudes are not closely

---

[1] When first referred to, the *general*
form of this equation was given (v. p.
29).   The special form here assigned,
in which $\dfrac{h}{\sqrt{\pi}}$ is substituted for A, is
commonly employed in Probability,
because the integral of $y\,dx$, between
$+ \infty$ and $- \infty$, becomes equal to unity.
That is, the sum of all the mutually
exclusive possibilities is represented,
as usual, by unity.   In this form of
expression h is a quantity of the
order x^{-1}; for hx is to be a numerical
quantity, standing as it does as an
index.   The modulus, being the reci-
procal of this, is of the same order
of quantities as the errors themselves.
In fact, if we multiply it by ·4769...
we have the so-called 'probable
error.'

crowded up towards the centre, when it is small they are thus crowded up. The smaller the modulus in the curve representing the thickness with which the shot-marks clustered about the centre of the target, the better the marksman.

§ 9. There are several ways of determining the modulus. In the first of the cases discussed above, where our theoretical knowledge is complete, we are able to calculate it à priori from our knowledge of the chances. We should naturally adopt this plan if we were tossing up a large handful of pence.

The usual à posteriori plan, when we have the measurements of the magnitudes or observations before us, is this:— Take the mean square of the errors, and double this; the result gives the square of the modulus. Suppose, for instance, that we had the five magnitudes, 4, 5, 6, 7, 8. The mean of these is 6: the 'errors' are respectively 2, 1, 0, 1, 2. Therefore the 'modulus squared' is equal to $\frac{10}{5}$; i.e. the modulus is $\sqrt{2}$. Had the magnitudes been 2, 4, 6, 8, 10; representing the same mean (6) as before, but displaying a greater dispersion about it, the modulus would have been larger, viz. $\sqrt{8}$ instead of $\sqrt{2}$.

Mr Galton's method is more of a graphical nature. It is described in a paper on Statistics by Intercomparison (*Phil. Mag.* 1875), and elsewhere. It may be indicated as follows. Suppose that we were dealing with a large number of measurements of human stature, and conceive that all the persons in question were marshalled in the order of their height. Select the average height, as marked by the central man of the row. Suppose him to be 69 inches. Then raise (or depress) the scale from this point until it stands at such a height as just to include one half of the men above (or below) the mean. (In practice this would be found to require about 1·71 inches: that is, one quarter of any large group of such men will fall between 69 and 70·71 inches.) Divide this number by ·4769 and we have the modulus. In the case in question it would be equal to about 3·6 inches.

Under the assumption with which we start, viz. that the law of error displays itself in the familiar binomial form, or in some form approximating to this, the three methods indicated above will coincide in their result. Where there is any doubt on this head, or where we do not feel able to calculate beforehand what will be the rate of dispersion, we must adopt the second plan of determining the modulus. This is the only universally applicable mode of calculation: in fact that it should yield the modulus is a truth of definition; for in determining the error of mean square we are really doing nothing else than determining the modulus, as was pointed out in the last chapter.

§ 10.   The position then which we have now reached is this.   Taking it for granted that the Law of Error will fall into the symbolic form expressed by the equation $y = \dfrac{h}{\sqrt{\pi}} e^{-h^2 x^2}$, we have rules at hand by which h may be determined.   We therefore, for the purposes in question, know all about the curve of frequency: we can trace it out on paper: given one value,—say the central one,—we can determine any other value at any distance from this.   That is, knowing how many men in a million, say, are 69 inches high, we can determine without direct observation how many will be 67, 68, 70, 71, and so on.

We can now adequately discuss the principal question of logical interest before us; viz. *why* do we take averages or means?   What is the exact nature and amount of the advantage gained by so doing? The advanced student would of course prefer to work out the answers to these questions by appealing at once to the Law of Error in its ultimate or exponential form. But I feel convinced that the best method for those who wish to gain a clear conception of the logical nature of the process involved, is to begin by treating it as a question of combinations such as we are familiar with in elementary algebra; in other words to take a finite number of errors and to see what comes of averaging these. We can then proceed to work out arithmetically the results of combining two or more of the errors together so as to get a new series, not contenting ourselves with the general character merely of the new law of error, but actually calculating what it is in the given case. For the sake of simplicity we will not take a series with a very large number of terms in it, but it will be well to have enough of them to secure that our law of error shall roughly approximate in its form to the standard or exponential law.

For this purpose the law of error or divergence given by supposing our effort to be affected by ten causes, each of which produces an equal error, but which error is equally likely to be positive and negative (or, as it might perhaps be expressed, 'ten equal and indifferently additive and subtractive causes') will suffice. This is the lowest number formed according to the Binomial law, which will furnish to the eye a fair indication of the limiting or Exponential law[1]. The whole number of possible cases here is 2^{10} or 1024; that is, this is the number required to exhibit not only all the cases which can occur (for there are but eleven really distinct cases), but also the relative frequency with which each of these cases occurs in the long run. Of this total, 252 will

[1] See, for the explanation of this, and of the graphical method of illustrating it, the note on p. 29.

be situated at the mean, representing the 'true' result, or that given when five of the causes of disturbance just neutralize the other five. Again, 210 will be at what we will call one unit's distance from the mean, or that given by six causes combining against four; and so on; until at the extreme distance of five places from the mean we get but one result, since in only one case out of the 1024 will all the causes combine together in the same direction. The set of 1024 efforts is therefore a fair representation of the distribution of an infinite number of such efforts. A graphical representation of the arrangement is given here.

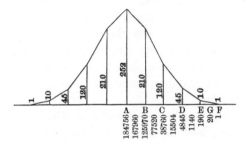

§ 11. This representing a complete set of single observations or efforts, what will be the number and arrangement in the corresponding set of combined or reduced observations, say of two together? With regard to the number we must bear in mind that this is not a case of the combinations of things which cannot be repeated; for any given error, say the extreme one at *F*, can obviously be repeated twice running. Such a repetition would be a piece of very bad luck no doubt, but being possible it must have its place in the set. Now the possible number of ways of combining 1024 things two together, where the same thing may be repeated twice running, is 1024 × 1024 or 1048576.

This then is the number in a complete cycle of the results taken two and two together.

§ 12. So much for their number; now for their arrangement or distribution. What we have to ascertain is, firstly, how many times each possible pair of observations will present itself; and, secondly, where the new results, obtained from the combination of each pair, are to be placed. With regard to the first of these enquiries;—it will be readily seen that on one occasion we shall have F repeated twice; on 20 occasions we shall have F combined with E (for F coming first we may have it followed by any one of the 10 at E, or any one of these may be followed by F); E can be repeated in 10×10, or 100 ways, and so on.

Now for the position of each of these reduced observations, the relative frequency of whose component elements has thus been pointed out. This is easy to determine, for when we take two errors there is (as was seen) scarcely any other mode of treatment than that of selecting the mid-point between them; this mid-point of course becoming identical with each of them when the two happen to coincide. It will be seen therefore that F will recur once on the new arrangement, viz. by its being repeated twice on the old one. G, midway between E and F, will be given 20 times. E, on our new arrangement, can be got at in two ways, viz. by its being repeated twice (which will happen 100 times), and by its being obtained as the mid-point between D and F (which will happen 90 times). Hence E will occur 190 times altogether.

The reader who chooses to take the trouble may work out the frequency of all possible occurrences in this way, and if the object were simply to illustrate the principle in accordance with which they occur, this might be the best way of proceeding. But as he may soon be able to observe, and as the mathematician would at once be able to prove, the new 'law of facility of error' can be got at more quickly deductively, viz. by taking the successive terms of the expansion of $(1+1)^{20}$. They are given, below the line, in the figure on p. 476.

§ 13. There are two apparent obstacles to any direct comparison between the distribution of the old set of simple observations, and the new set of combined or reduced ones. In the first place, the number of the latter is much greater. This, however, is readily met by reducing them both to the same scale, that is by making the same total number of each. In the second place, half of the new positions have no representatives amongst the old, viz. those which occur midway between F and E, E and D, and so on. This can be met by the usual plan of interpolation, viz. by filling in such gaps by estimating what would have been the number at the missing points, on the same scale, had they been occupied. Draw a curve through the vertices of the ordinates at A, B, C, &c., and the lengths of the ordinates at the intermediate points will very fairly represent the corresponding frequency of the errors of those magnitudes respectively. When the gaps are thus filled up, and the numbers thus reduced to the same scale, we have a perfectly fair basis of comparison. (See figure on next page.)

Similarly we might proceed to group or 'reduce' three observations, or any greater number. The number of possible groupings naturally becomes very much larger, being $(1024)^3$ when they are taken three together. As soon as we get to three or more observations, we have (as already pointed out) a variety of possible modes of treatment or reduction, of which that of taking the arithmetical mean is but one.

§ 14. The following figure is intended to illustrate the nature of the advantage secured by thus taking the arithmetical mean of several observations.

The curve *ABCD* represents the arrangement of a given number of 'errors' supposed to be disposed according to the binomial law already mentioned, when the angles have been smoothed off by drawing a curve through them. *A'CD'* represents the similar arrangement of the same number when given not as simple errors, but as averages of pairs of errors. *A"BD"*, again, represents the similar arrangement obtained as averages of errors taken three together. They are drawn as carefully to scale as the small size of the figure permits.

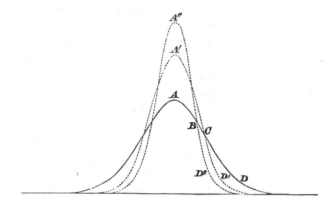

§ 15. A glance at the above figure will explain to the reader, better than any verbal description, the full significance of the statement that the result of combining two or more measurements or observations together and taking the average of them, instead of stopping short at the single elements, is to make large errors comparatively more scarce. The advantage is of the same general description as that of fishing in a lake where, of the same number of fish, there are more big and fewer little ones than in another water : of dipping in a bag where of the same number of coins there are more sovereigns and fewer shillings; and so on. The extreme importance, however, of obtaining a perfectly clear conception of the subject may render it desirable to work this out a little more fully in detail.

For one thing, then, it must be clearly understood that the result of a set of 'averages' of errors is nothing else than another set of 'errors.' No device can make the attainment of the true result certain,—to suppose the contrary would be to misconceive the very foundations of Probability,—no device even can obviate the possibility of being actually worse off as the result of our labour. The average of two, three, or any larger number of single results, *may* give a worse result, i.e. one further from the ultimate average, than was given by the first observation we made. We must simply fall back upon the justification that big deviations are rendered scarcer in the long run.

Again; it may be pointed out that though, in the above investigation, we have spoken only of the arithmetical average as commonly understood and employed, the same general results would be obtained by resorting to almost any symmetrical and regular mode of combining our observations or errors. The two main features of the regularity displayed by the Binomial Law of facility were (1) ultimate symmetry about the central or true result, and (2) increasing relative frequency as this centre was approached. A very little consideration will show that it is no peculiar prerogative of the arithmetical mean to retain the former of these and to increase the latter. In saying this, however, a distinction must be attended to for which it will be convenient to refer to a figure.

§ 16. Suppose that O, in the line $D'OD$, was the point aimed at by any series of measurements; or, what comes to

the same thing for our present purpose, was the ultimate
average of all the measurements made. What we mean by

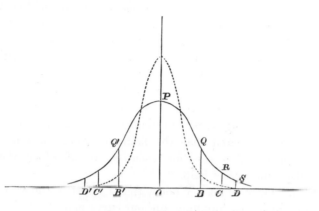

a symmetrical arrangement of the values in regard to O, is
that for every error OB, there shall be in the long run a precisely corresponding opposite one OB'; so that when we erect
the ordinate BQ, indicating the frequency with which B is
yielded, we must erect an equal one $B'Q'$. Accordingly the
two halves of the curve on each side of P, viz. PQ and PQ'
are precisely alike.

It then readily follows that the secondary curve, viz.
that marking the law of frequency of the averages of two or
more simple errors, will also be symmetrical. Consider any
three points B, C, D: to these correspond another three
B', C', D'. It is obvious therefore that any regular and symmetrical mode of dealing with all the groups, of which BCD
is a sample, will result in symmetrical arrangement about
the centre O. The ordinary familiar arithmetical average is
but one out of many such modes. One way of describing it is
by saying that the average of B, C, D, is assigned by choosing
a point such that the sum of the squares of its distances from

$B, C, D,$ is a minimum. But we might have selected a point such that the cubes, or the fourth powers, or any higher powers should be a minimum. These would all yield curves resembling in a general way the dotted line in our figure. Of course there would be insuperable practical objections to any such courses as these; for the labour of calculation would be enormous, and the results so far from being better would be worse than those afforded by the employment of the ordinary average. But so far as concerns the general principle of dealing with discordant and erroneous results, it must be remembered that the familiar average is but one out of innumerable possible resources, all of which would yield the same sort of help.

§ 17. Once more. We saw that a resort to the average had the effect of 'humping up' our curve more towards the centre, expressive of the fact that the errors of averages are of a better, i.e. smaller kind. But it must be noticed that exactly the same characteristics will follow, as a general rule, from any other such mode of dealing with the individual errors. No strict proof of this fact can be given here, but a reference to one of the familiar results of taking combinations of things will show whence this tendency arises. Extreme results, as yielded by an average of any kind, can only be got in one way, viz. by repetitions of extremes in the individuals from which the averages were obtained. But intermediate results can be got at in two ways, viz. either by intermediate individuals, or by combinations of individuals in opposite directions. In the case of the Binomial Law of Error this tendency to thicken towards the centre was already strongly predominant in the individual values before we took them in hand for our average; but owing to this characteristic of combinations we may lay it down (broadly speaking) that any sort of average applied to any sort of law of distribution will give a result which bears the same general relation to the individual values that the dotted lines above bear to the black line[1].

§ 18.   This being so, the speculative advantages of one method of combining, or averaging, or reducing, our observations, over another method,—irrespective, that is, of the practical conveniences in carrying them out,—will consist solely in the degree of rapidity with which it tends thus to cluster the result about the centre. We shall have to subject this merit to a somewhat further analysis, but for the present purpose it will suffice to say that if one kind of average gave the higher dotted line in the figure on p. 479 and another gave the lower dotted line, we should say that the former was the better one. The advantage is of the same general kind as that which is furnished in algebraical calculation, by a series which converges rapidly towards the true value as compared with one which converges slowly. We can do the work sooner or later by the aid of either; but we get nearer the truth by the same amount of labour, or get as near by a less amount of labour, on one plan than on the other.

As we are here considering the case in which the individual observations are supposed to be grouped in accordance

---

[1] Broadly speaking, we may say that the above remarks hold good of any law of frequency of error in which there are actual limits, however wide, to the possible magnitude of an error. If there are no limits to the possible errors, this characteristic of an average to heap its results up towards the centre will depend upon circumstances. When, as in the exponential curve, the approximation to the base, as asymptote, is exceed- ingly rapid,—that is, when the extreme errors are relatively very few,— it still holds good. But if we were to take as our law of facility such an equation as $y = \dfrac{\pi}{1 + x^2}$, (as hinted by De Morgan and noted by Mr Edgeworth : *Camb. Phil. Trans.* vol. x. p. 184, and vol. xiv. p. 160) it does not hold good. The result of averaging is to *diminish* the tendency to cluster towards the centre.

with the Binomial Law, it will suffice to say that in this case
there is no doubt that the arithmetical average is not only
the simplest and easiest to deal with, but is also the best in
the above sense of the term.   And since this Binomial Law,
or something approximating to it, is of very wide prevalence,
a strong primâ facie case is made out for the general employment of the familiar average.

§ 19.   The analysis of a few pages back carried the
results of the averaging process as far as could be conveniently done by the help of mere arithmetic.   To go
further we must appeal to higher mathematics, but the
following indication of the sort of results obtained will
suffice for our present purpose.   After all, the successive
steps, though demanding intricate reasoning for their proof,
are nothing more than generalizations of processes which
could be established by simple arithmetic[1].   Briefly, what we
do is this :—

(1)   We first extend the proof from the binomial form,
with its finite number of elements, to the limiting or exponential form.   Instead of confining ourselves to a small
number of discrete errors, we then recognize the possibility
of any number of errors of any magnitude whatever.

(2)   In the next place, instead of confining ourselves to
the consideration of an average of two or three only,—
already, as we have seen, a tedious piece of arithmetic,—we
calculate the result of an average of any number, n.   The
actual result is extremely simple.   If the modulus of the
single errors is c, that of the average of n of these will be
$c \div \sqrt{n}$.

(3)   Finally we draw similar conclusions in reference to
the *sum or difference* of two averages of any numbers.   Sup-

[1] The reader will find the proofs   in Galloway *on Probability*, and in
of these and other similar formulæ   Airy *on Errors*.

pose, for instance, that m errors were first taken and averaged, and then n similarly taken and averaged. These averages will be nearly, but not quite, equal. Their sum or difference,—these, of course, are indistinguishable in the end, since positive and negative errors are supposed to be equal and opposite,—will itself be an 'error', every magnitude of which will have a certain assignable probability or facility of occurrence. What we do is to assign the modulus of *these* errors. The actual result again is simple. If c had been the modulus of the single errors, that of the sum or difference of the averages of m and n of them will be

$$c\sqrt{\frac{1}{m}+\frac{1}{n}}.$$

§ 20. So far, the problem under investigation has been of a direct kind. We have supposed that the ultimate mean value or central position has been given to us; either à priori (as in many games of chance), or from more immediate physical considerations (as in aiming at a mark), or from extensive statistics (as in tables of human stature). In all such cases therefore the main desideratum is already taken for granted, and it may reasonably be asked what remains to be done. The answers are various. For one thing we may want to estimate the value of an average of many when compared with an average of a few. Suppose that one man has collected statistics including 1000 instances, and another has collected 4000 similar instances. Common sense can recognize that the latter are better than the former; but it has no idea *how much* better they are. Here, as elsewhere, quantitative precision is the privilege of science. The answer we receive from this quarter is that, in the long run, the modulus,—and with this the probable error, the mean error, and the error of mean square, which all vary in proportion,—

diminishes inversely as the square root of the number of
measurements or observations. (This follows from the second
of the above formulæ.) Accordingly the probable error of
the more extensive statistics here is one half that of the less
extensive. Take another instance. Observation shows that
"the mean height of 2,315 criminals differs from the mean
height of 8,585 members of the general adult population by
about two inches" (v. Edgeworth, Methods of Statistics:
Stat. Soc. Journ. 1885). As before, common sense would feel
little doubt that such a difference was significant, but it
could give no numerical estimate of the significance. Appealing to science, we see that this is an illustration of the
third of the above formulæ. What we really want to know
is the odds against the averages of two large batches differing
by an assigned amount: in this case by an amount equalling
twenty-five times the modulus of the variable quantity.
The odds against this are many billions to one.

§ 21. The number of direct problems which will thus
admit of solution is very great, but we must confine ourselves
here to the main inverse problem to which the foregoing
discussion is a preliminary. It is this. Given *a few only* of
one of these groups of measurements or observations; what
can we do with these, in the way of determining that mean
about which they would ultimately be found to cluster?
Given a large number of them, they would betray the position of their ultimate centre with constantly increasing
certainty : but we are now supposing that there are only a
few of them at hand, say half a dozen, and that we have no
power at present to add to the number.

In other words,—expressing ourselves by the aid of
graphical illustration, which is perhaps the best method
for the novice and for the logical student,—in the direct
problem we merely have to draw the curve of frequency from

a knowledge of its determining elements; viz. the position
of the centre, and the numerical value of the modulus.   In
the inverse problem, on the other hand, we have three elements at least, to determine.   For not only must we, (1), as
before, determine whereabouts the centre may be assumed to
lie; and (2), as before, determine the value of the modulus
or degree of dispersion about this centre.   This does not
complete our knowledge.   Since neither of these two elements is assigned with certainty, we want what is always
required in the Theory of Chances, viz. some estimate of their
probable truth.   That is, after making the best assignment
we can as to the value of these elements, we want also to
assign numerically the 'probable error' committed in such
assignment.   Nothing more than this can be attained in Probability, but nothing less than this should be set before us.

§ 22.   (1) As regards the first of these questions, the
answer is very simple.   Whether the number of measurements or observations be few or many, we must make the
assumption that their average *is* the point we want; that is,
that the average of the few will coincide with the ultimate
average.   This is the best, in fact the only assumption we
can make.   We should adopt this plan, of course, in the
extreme case of there being only *one* value before us, by just
taking that one; and our confidence increases slowly with
the number of values before us.   The only difference therefore here between knowledge resting upon such data, and
knowledge resting upon complete data, lies not in the result
obtained but in the confidence with which we entertain it.

§ 23.   (2) As regards the second question, viz. the determination of the modulus or degree of dispersion about the
mean, much the same may be said.   That is, we adopt the
same rule for the determination of the E.M.S. (error of mean
square) by which the modulus is assigned, as we should

adopt if we possessed full information. Or rather we are confined to *one* of the rules given on p. 473, viz. the second, for by supposition we have neither the à priori knowledge which would be able to supply the first, nor a sufficient number of observations to justify the third. That is, we reckon the errors, measured from the average, and calculate their mean square: twice this is equal to the square of the modulus of the probable curve of facility[1].

§ 24. (3) The third question demands for its solution somewhat advanced mathematics; but the results can be indicated without much difficulty. A popular way of stating our requirement would be to say that we want to know how likely it is that the mean of the few, which we have thus accepted, shall coincide with the true mean. But this would be to speak loosely, for the chances are of course indefinitely great against such precise coincidence. What we really do is to assign the 'probable error'; that is, to assign a limit which it is as likely as not that the discrepancy between the inferred mean and the true mean should exceed[2]. To take a numerical example: suppose we had made several

---

[1] The formula commonly used for the E.M.S. in this case is $\dfrac{\Sigma e^2}{n-1}$ and not $\dfrac{\Sigma e^2}{n}$. The difference is trifling, unless n be small; the justification has been offered for it that since the sum of the squares measured from the true centre is a minimum (that centre being the ultimate arithmetical mean) the sum of the squares measured from the somewhat incorrectly assigned centre will be somewhat larger.

[2] It appears to me that in strict logical propriety we should like to know the probable error committed in *both* the assignments of the preceding two sections. But the profound mathematicians who have discussed this question, and who alone are competent to treat it, have mostly written with the practical wants of Astronomy in view; and for this purpose it is sufficient to take account of the one great desideratum, viz. the true values sought. Accordingly the only rules commonly given refer to the probable error of the mean.

measurements of a wall with a tape, and that the average of these was 150 feet. The scrupulous surveyor would give us this result, with some such correction as this added,—'probable error 3 inches'. All that this means is that we may assume that the true value is 150 feet, with a confidence that in half the cases (of this description) in which we did so, we should really be within three inches of the truth.

The expression for this probable error is a simple multiple of the modulus: it is the modulus multiplied by ·4769... That it should be some function of the modulus, or E.M.S., seems plausible enough; for the greater the errors,—in other words the wider the observed discrepancy amongst our measurements,—the less must be the confidence we can feel in the accuracy of our determination of the mean. But, of course, without mathematics we should be quite unable to attempt any numerical assignment.

§ 25. The general conclusion therefore is that the determination of the curve of facility,—and therefore ultimately of every conclusion which rests upon a knowledge of this curve,—where only a few observations are available, is of just the same kind as where an infinity are available. The rules for obtaining it are the same, but the confidence with which it can be accepted is less.

The knowledge, therefore, obtainable by an average of a small number of measurements of any kind, hardly differs except in degree from that which would be attainable by an indefinitely extensive series of them. We know the same sort of facts, only we are less certain about them. But, on the other hand, the knowledge yielded by an average even of a small number differs in kind from that which is yielded by a single measurement. Revert to our marksman, whose bullseye is supposed to have been afterwards removed. If he had fired only a single shot, not only should we be less

certain of the point he had aimed at, but we should have no
means whatever of guessing at the quality of his shooting, or
of inferring in consequence anything about the probable
remoteness of the next shot from that which had gone before.
But directly we have a plurality of shots before us, we not
merely feel more confident as to whereabouts the centre of
aim was, but we also gain some knowledge as to how the
future shots will cluster about the spot thus indicated. The
quality of his shooting begins at once to be betrayed by the
results.

§ 26. Thus far we have been supposing the Law of
Facility to be of the Binomial type. There are several
reasons for discussing this at such comparative length. For
one thing it is the only type which,—or something approximately resembling which,—is actually prevalent over a wide
range of phenomena. Then again, in spite of its apparent
intricacy, it is really one of the simplest to deal with ; owing
to the fact that every curve of facility derived from it by
taking averages simply repeats the same type again. The
curve of the average only differs from that of the single
elements in having a smaller modulus ; and its modulus is
smaller in a ratio which is exceedingly easy to give. If that
of the one is c, that of the other (derived by averaging
n single elements) is $\dfrac{c}{\sqrt{n}}$.

But for understanding the theory of averages we must
consider other cases as well. Take then one which is intrinsically as simple as it possibly can be, viz. that in which all
values within certain assigned limits are equally probable.
This is a case familiar enough in abstract Probability, though,
as just remarked, not so common in natural phenomena. It
is the state of things when we act at random directly upon

the objects of choice[1]; as when, for instance, we choose digits
at random out of a table of logarithms.

The reader who likes to do so can without much labour
work out the result of taking an average of two or three
results by proceeding in exactly the same way which we
adopted on p. 476. The 'curve of facility' with which we
have to start in this case has become of course simply a
finite straight line. Treating the question as one of simple
combinations, we may divide the line into a number of equal
parts, by equidistant points; and then proceed to take these
two and two together in every possible way, as we did in the
case discussed some pages back.

If we did so, what we should find would be this. When
an average of *two* is taken, the 'curve of facility' of the
average becomes a triangle with the initial straight line for
base; so that the ultimate mean or central point becomes
the likeliest result even with this commencement of the
averaging process. If we were to take averages of three,
four, and so on, what we should find would be that the
Binomial law begins to display itself here. The familiar bell
shape of the exponential curve would be more and more
closely approximated to, until we obtained something quite
indistinguishable from it.

§ 27. The conclusion therefore is that when we are
dealing with averages involving a considerable number it is
not necessary, in general, to presuppose the binomial law of
distribution in our original data. The law of arrangement of
what we may call the derived curve, viz. that corresponding
to the averages, will not be appreciably affected thereby.
Accordingly we seem to be justified in bringing to bear all

---

[1] i.e. as distinguished from acting
upon them indirectly. This latter
proceeding, as explained in the chapter on Randomness, may result in
giving a non-uniform distribution.

the same apparatus of calculation as in the former case. We
take the initial average as the probable position of the true
centre or ultimate average : we estimate the probability that
we are within an assignable distance of the truth in so doing
by calculating the 'error of mean square'; and we appeal
to this same element to determine the modulus, i.e. the
amount of contraction or dispersion, of our derived curve of
facility.

The same general considerations will apply to most other
kinds of Law of Facility. Broadly speaking,—we shall come
to the examination of certain exceptions immediately,—
whatever may have been the primitive arrangement (i.e.
that of the single results) the arrangement of the derived
results (i.e. that of the averages) will be more crowded up
towards the centre. This follows from the characteristic of
combinations already noticed, viz. that extreme values can
only be got at by a repetition of several extremes, whereas
intermediate values can be got at either by repetition of
intermediates or through the counteraction of opposite extremes. Provided the original distribution be symmetrical
about the centre, and provided the limits of possible error be
finite, or if infinite, that the falling off of frequency as we
recede from the mean be very rapid, then the results of
taking averages will be better than those of trusting to
single results.

§ 28. We will now take notice of an exceptional case.
We shall do so, not because it is one which can often
actually occur, but because the consideration of it will force
us to ask ourselves with some minuteness what we mean in
the above instances by calling the results of the averages
'better' than those of the individual values. A diagram will
bring home to us the point of the difficulty better than any
verbal or symbolic description.

The black line represents a Law of Error easily stated in
words, and one which, as we shall subsequently see, can be

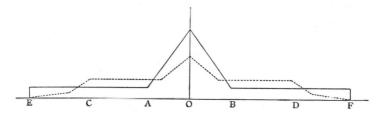

conceived as occurring in practice. It represents a state of
things under which up to a certain distance from 0, on each
side, viz. to *A* and *B*, the probability of an error diminishes
uniformly with the distance from 0; whilst beyond these
points, up to *E* and *F*, the probability of error remains constant. The dotted line represents the resultant Law of Error
obtained by taking the average of the former two and two
together. Now is the latter 'better' than the former?
Under it, certainly, great errors are less frequent and intermediate ones more frequent; but then on the other hand
the *small* errors are less frequent: is this state of things on
the whole an improvement or not? This requires us to re-
consider the whole question.

§ 29. In all the cases discussed in the previous sections
the superiority of the curve of averages over that of the
single results showed itself at every point. The big errors
were scarcer and the small errors were commoner; it was
only just at one intermediate point that the two were on
terms of equality, and this point was not supposed to possess
any particular significance or importance. Accordingly we
had no occasion to analyse the various cases included under
the general relation. It was enough to say that one was
better than the other, and it was sufficient for all purposes to

take the 'modulus' as the measure of this superiority. In fact we are quite safe in simply saying that the *average* of those average results is better than that of the individual ones.

When however we proceed in what Hume calls "the sifting humour," and enquire *why* it is sufficient thus to trust to the average; we find, in addition to the considerations hitherto advanced, that some postulate was required as to the *consequences* of the errors we incur. It involved an estimate of what is sometimes called the 'detriment' of an error. It seemed to take for granted that large and small errors all stand upon the same general footing of being mischievous in their consequences, but that their evil effects increase in a greater ratio than that of their own magnitude.

§ 30. Suppose, for comparison, a case in which the importance of an error is directly proportional to its magnitude (of course we suppose positive and negative errors to balance each other in the long run): it does not appear that any advantage would be gained by taking averages. Something of this sort may be considered to prevail in cases of mere purchase and sale. Suppose that any one had to buy a very large number of yards of cloth at a constant price per yard : that he had to do this, say, five times a day for many days in succession. And conceive that the measurement of the cloth was roughly estimated on each separate occasion, with resultant errors which are as likely to be in excess as in defect. Would it make the slightest difference to him whether he paid separately for each piece ; or whether the five estimated lengths were added together, their average taken, and he were charged with this average price for each piece ? In the latter case the errors which will be made in the estimation of each piece will of course be less in the long run than they would be in the former : will this be of any

consequence? The answer surely is that it will not make
the slightest difference to either party in the bargain. In
the long run, since the same parties are concerned, it will not
matter whether the intermediate errors have been small or
large.

Of course nothing of this sort can be regarded as the
general rule. In almost every case in which we have to
make measurements we shall find that large errors are much
more mischievous than small ones, that is, mischievous in a
greater ratio than that of their mere magnitude. Even in
purchase and sale, where *different* purchasers are concerned,
this must be so, for the pleasure of him who is overserved
will hardly equal the pain of him who is underserved. And
in many cases of scientific measurement large errors may be
simply fatal, in the sense that if there were no reasonable
prospect of avoiding them we should not care to undertake
the measurement at all.

§ 31. If we were only concerned with practical considerations we might stop at this point; but if we want to
realize the full logical import of average-taking as a means
to this particular end, viz. of estimating some assigned
magnitude, we must look more closely into such an exceptional case as that which was indicated in the figure on
p. 493. What we there assumed was a state of things in
reference to which extremely small errors were very frequent, but that when once we got beyond a certain small
range all other errors, within considerable limits, were equally
likely.

It is not difficult to imagine an example which will aptly
illustrate the case in point: at worst it may seem a little far-
fetched. Conceive then that some firm in England received
a hurried order to supply a portion of a machine, say a
steam-engine, to customers at a distant place; and that it

was absolutely essential that the work should be true to the
tenth of an inch for it to be of any use.   But conceive also
that two specifications had been sent, resting on different
measurements, in one of which the length of the requisite
piece was described as sixty and in the other sixty-one
inches.   On the assumption of any ordinary law of error,
whether of the binomial type or not, there can be no doubt
that the firm would make the best of a very bad job by constructing a piece of 60 inches and a half: i.e. they would
have a better chance of being within the requisite tenth of
an inch by so doing, than by taking either of the two specifications at random and constructing it accurately to this.
But if the law were of the kind indicated in our diagram[1],
then it seems equally certain that they would be less likely
to be within the requisite narrow margin by so doing.   As a
mere question of probability,—that is, if such estimates were
acted upon again and again,—there would be fewer failures
encountered by simply choosing one of the conflicting
measurements at random and working exactly to this, than
by trusting to the average of the two.

This suggests some further reflections as to the taking of
averages.   We will turn now to another exceptional case,
but one involving somewhat different considerations than
those which have been just discussed.   As before, it may be
most conveniently introduced by commencing with an example.

[1] There is no difficulty in conceiving circumstances under which a
law very closely resembling this
would prevail. Suppose, e.g., that
one of the two measurements had
been made by a careful and skilled
mechanic, and the other by a man
who to save himself trouble had put
in the estimate at random (within
certain limits),—the firm having a
knowledge of this fact but being of
course unable to assign the two to
their authors,—we should get very
much such a Law of Error as is supposed above.

§ 32. Suppose then that two scouts were sent to take
the calibre of a gun in a hostile fort,—we may conceive that
the fort was to be occupied next day, and used against the
enemy, and that it was important to have a supply of shot or
shell,—and that the result is that one of them reports the
calibre to be 8 inches and the other 9. Would it be wise to
assume that the mean of these two, viz. 8½ inches, was a
likelier value than either separately?

The answer seems to be this. If we have reason to
suppose that the possible calibres partake of the nature of a
continuous magnitude,—i.e. that all values, with certain
limits, are to be considered as admissible, (an assumption
which we always make in our ordinary inverse step from an
observation or magnitude to the thing observed or measured)
—then we should be justified in selecting the average as the
likelier value. But if, on the other hand, we had reason to
suppose that *whole* inches are always or generally preferred,
as is in fact the case now with heavy guns, we should do
better to take, even at hazard, one of the two estimates set
before us, and trust this alone instead of taking an average
of the two.

§ 33. The principle upon which we act here may be
stated thus. Just as in the direct process of calculating or
displaying the 'errors', whether in an algebraic formula or in
a diagram, we generally assume that their possibility is
continuous, i.e. that all intermediate values are possible; so,
in the inverse process of determining the probable position of
the original from the known value of two or more errors, we
assume that that position is capable of falling at any point
whatever between certain limits. In such an example as the
above, where we know or suspect a discontinuity of that
possibility of position, the value of the average may be
entirely destroyed.

In the above example we were supposed to know that
the calibre of the guns was likely to run in English inches or
in some other recognized units.   But if the battery were in
China or Japan, and we knew nothing of the standards of
length in use there, we could no longer appeal to this
principle.   It is doubtless highly probable that those calibres
are not of the nature of continuously varying magnitudes;
but in an entire ignorance of the standards actually adopted,
we are to all intents and purposes in the same position as if
they were of that continuous nature.   When this is so the
objections to trusting to the average would no longer hold
good, and if we had only one opportunity, or a very few
opportunities, we should do best to adhere to the customary
practice.

§ 34.   When however we are able to collect and compare
a large number of measurements of various objects, this
consideration of the probable discontinuity of the objects we
thus measure,—that is, their tendency to assume some one or
other of a finite number of distinct magnitudes, instead of
showing an equal readiness to adapt themselves to all intermediate values,—again assumes importance.   In fact, given
a sufficient number of measurable objects, we can actually
deduce with much probability the standard according to
which the things in question were made.

This is the problem which Mr Flinders Petrie has attacked with so much acuteness and industry in his work on
Inductive Metrology, a work which, merely on the ground of
its speculative interest, may well be commended to the
student of Probability.   The main principles on which the
reasoning is based are these two:—(1) that all artificers are
prone to construct their works according to round numbers,
or simple fractions, of their units of measurement; and (2)
that, aiming to secure this, they will stray from it in toler-

able accordance with the law of error. The result of these two assumptions is that if we collect a very large number of measurements of the different parts and proportions of some ancient building,—say an Egyptian temple,—whilst no assignable length is likely to be permanently unrepresented, yet we find a marked tendency for the measurements to cluster about certain determinate points in our own, or any other standard scale of measurement. These points mark the length of the standard, or of some multiple or submultiple of the standard, employed by the old builders. It need hardly be said that there are a multitude of practical considerations to be taken into account before this method can be expected to give trustworthy results, but the leading principles upon which it rests are comparatively simple.

§ 35. The case just considered is really nothing else than the recurrence, under a different application, of one which occupied our attention at a very early stage. We noticed (Chap. II.) the possibility of a curve of facility which instead of having a single vertex like that corresponding to the common law of error, should display two humps or vertices. It can readily be shown that this problem of the measurements of ancient buildings, is nothing more than the reopening of the same question, in a slightly more complex form, in reference to the question of the functions of an average.

Take a simple example. Suppose an instance in which great errors, of a certain approximate magnitude, are distinctly more likely to be committed than small ones, so that the curve of facility, instead of rising into one peak towards the centre, as in that of the familiar law of error, shows a depression or valley there. Imagine, in fact, two binomial curves, with a short interval between their centres. Now if we were to calculate the result of taking averages here we

should find that this at once tends to fill up the valley; and
if we went on long enough, that is, if we kept on taking
averages of sufficiently large numbers, a peak would begin to
arise in the centre. In fact the familiar single binomial
curve would begin to make its appearance.

§ 36. The question then at once suggests itself, ought we
to do this? Shall we give the average free play to perform
its allotted function of thus crowding things up towards the
centre? To answer this question we must introduce a distinction. If that peculiar double-peaked curve had been, as
it conceivably might, a true error-curve,—that is, if it had
represented the divergences actually made in aiming at the
real centre,—the result would be just what we should want.
It would furnish an instance of the advantages to be gained
by taking averages even in circumstances which were originally unfavourable. It is not difficult to suggest an appropriate illustration. Suppose a man firing at a mark from
some sheltered spot, but such that the range crossed a broad
exposed valley up or down which a strong wind was generally
blowing. If the shotmarks were observed we should find
them clustering about two centres to the right and left of
the bullseye. And if the results were plotted out in a curve
they would yield such a double-peaked curve as we have
described. But if the winds were equally strong and prevalent in opposite directions, we should find that the averaging
process redressed the consequent disturbance.

If however the curve represented, as it is decidedly more
likely to do, some outcome of natural phenomena in which
there was, so to say, a real double aim on the part of nature,
it would be otherwise. Take, for instance, the results of
measuring a large number of people who belonged to two
very heterogeneous races. The curve of facility would here
be of the kind indicated on p. 45, and if the numbers of the

two commingled races were equal it would display a pair of
twin peaks. Again the question arises, 'ought' we to involve the whole range within the scope of a single average?
The answer is that the obligation depends upon the purpose
we have in view. If we want to compare that heterogeneous
race, as a whole, with some other, or with itself at some
other time, we shall do well to average without analysis.
All statistics of population, as we have already seen (v. p. 47),
are forced to neglect a multitude of discriminating characteristics of the kind in question. But if our object were to
interpret the causes of this abnormal error-curve we should
do well to break up the statistics into corresponding parts,
and subject these to analysis separately.

Similarly with the measurements of the ancient buildings.
In this case if all our various 'errors' were thrown together
into one group of statistics we should find that the resultant
curve of facility displayed, not two peaks only, but a succession of them; and these of various magnitudes, corresponding to the frequency of occurrence of each particular
measurement. We *might* take an average of the whole, but
hardly any rational purpose could be subserved in so doing;
whereas each separate point of maximum frequency of occurrence has something significant to teach us.

§ 37. One other peculiar case may be noticed in conclusion. Suppose a distinctly asymmetrical, or lopsided curve
of facility, such as this :—

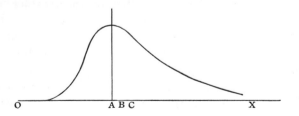

Laws of error, of which this is a graphical representation, are, I apprehend, far from uncommon. The curve in question, is, in fact, but a slight exaggeration of that of barometrical heights as referred to in the last chapter; when it was explained that in such cases the mean, the median, and the maximum ordinate would show a mutual divergence. The doubt here is not, as in the preceding instances, whether or not a single average should be taken, but rather what kind of average should be selected. As before, the answer must depend upon the special purpose we have in view. For all ordinary purposes of comparison between one time or place and another, any average will answer, and we should therefore naturally take the arithmetical, as the most familiar, or the median, as the simplest.

§ 38. Cases might however arise under which other kinds of average could justify themselves, with a momentary notice of which we may now conclude. Suppose, for instance, that the question involved here were one of desirability of climate. The ordinary mean, depending as it does so largely upon the number and magnitude of extreme values, might very reasonably be considered a less appropriate test than that of judging simply by the relatively most frequent value : in other words, by the maximum ordinate. And various other points of view can be suggested in respect of which this particular value would be the most suitable and significant.

In the foregoing case, viz. that of the weather curve, there was no objective or 'true' value aimed at. But a curve closely resembling this would be representative of that particular class of estimates indicated by Mr Galton, and for which, as he has pointed out, the *geometrical* mean becomes the only appropriate one. In this case the curve of facility ends abruptly at O : it resembles a much foreshortened modification of the common exponential form. Its characteristics have been discussed in the paper by Dr Macalister already referred to, but any attempt to examine its properties here would lead us into far too intricate details.

§ 39. The general conclusion from all this seems quite in accordance with the nature and functions of an average as pointed out in the last chapter. Every average, it was urged, is but a single representative intermediate value substituted for a plurality of actual values. It must accordingly let slip the bulk of the information involved in these latter. Occasionally, as in most ordinary measurements, the one thing which it represents is obviously the thing we are in want of; and then the only question can be, which mean will most accord with the 'true' value we are seeking. But when, as may happen in most of the common applications of statistics, there is really no 'true value' of an objective kind behind the phenomena, the problem may branch out in various directions. We may have a variety of purposes to work out, and these may demand some discrimination as regards the average most appropriate for them. Whenever therefore we have any doubt whether the familiar arithmetical average is suitable for the purpose in hand we must first decide precisely what that purpose is.

INDEX.

CHELSEA

SCIENTIFIC

BOOKS

THE CALCULUS OF FINITE DIFFERENCES
By G. BOOLE

A standard work on the subject of finite differences and difference equations by one of the seminal minds in the field of finite mathematics.

Some of the topics covered are: *Interpolation, Finite Integration, Summation of Series, General Theory of Difference and Differential Equations of First Order, Linear DEqns with Variable Coefficients, Linear DEqns, Geometrical Applications.* Numerous exercises with answers.

—Fourth edition. 1958. xii + 336 pp. 5x8. [121] Cloth **$3.95**
[148] Paper **$1.39**

A TREATISE ON DIFFERENTIAL EQUATIONS
By G. BOOLE

Including the Supplementary Volume.

—Fifth edition. 1959. xxiv + 735 pp. 5¼x8. [128] **$6.00**

THEORY OF FUNCTIONS
By C. CARATHÉODORY

Translated by F. STEINHARDT. The recent, and already famous textbook, *Funktionentheorie.*

Partial Contents: **Part One.** Chap. I. Algebra of Complex Numbers. II. Geometry of Complex Numbers. III. Euclidean, Spherical, and Non-Euclidean Geometry. **Part Two.** Theorems from Point Set Theory and Topology. Chap. I. Sequences and Continuous Complex Functions. II. Curves and Regions. III. Line Integrals. **Part Three.** Analytic Functions. Chap. I. Foundations. II. The Maximum-modulus principle. III. Poisson Integral and Harmonic Functions. IV. Meromorphic Functions. **Part Four.** Generation of Analytic Functions by Limiting Processes. Chap. I. Uniform Convergence. II. Normal Families of Meromorphic Functions. III. Power Series. IV. Partial Fraction Decomposition and the Calculus of Residues. **Part Five.** Special Functions. Chap. I. The Exponential Function and the Trigonometric Functions. II. Logarithmic Function. III. Bernoulli Numbers and the Gamma Function.

Vol. II.: **Part Six.** Foundations of Geometric Function Theory. Chap. I. Bounded Functions. II. Conformal Mapping. III. The Mapping of the Boundary. **Part Seven.** The Triangle Function and Picard's Theorem. Chap. I. Functions of Several Complex Variables. II. Conformal Mapping of Circular-Arc Triangles. III. The Schwarz Triangle Functions and the Modular Function. IV. Essential Singularities and Picard's Theorems.

"A book by a master . . . Carathéodory himself regarded [it] as his finest achievement . . . written from a catholic point of view."—*Bulletin of A.M.S.*

—Vol. I. Second edition. 1958. 310 pp. 6x9. [97] **$4.95**
—Vol. II. Second edition. 1960. 220 pp. 6x9. [106] **$4.95**

ARITHMETISCHE UNTERSUCHUNGEN
By C. F. GAUSS

The German translation of his *Disquisitiones Arithmeticae.*
—Repr. of 1st German ed. 860 pp. 5⅜x8.   [150]   **In prep.**

THEORY OF PROBABILITY
By B. V. GNEDENKO

Translated from the second Russian edition, with additions and revisions by Prof. Gnedenko.

Partial Contents: I. The Concept of Probability (Different approaches to the definition. Field of events. Geometrical Probability. Statistical definition. Axiomatic construction . . .). II. Sequences of Independent Trials. III. Markov Chains. IV. Random Variables and Distribution Functions (Continuous and discrete distributions. Multidimensional d. functions. Functions of random variables. Stieltjes integral). V. Numerical Characteristics of Random Variables (Mathematical expectation. Variance . . . Moments). VI. Law of Large Numbers (Mass phenomena. Tchebychev's form of law. Strong law of large numbers . . .). VII. Characteristic Functions (Properties. Inversion formula and uniqueness theorem. Helly's theorems. Limit theorems. Char. functs. for multidimensional random variables . . .). VIII. Classical Limit Theorem (Liapunov's theorem. Local limit theorem). IX. Theory of Infinitely Divisible Distribution Laws. X. Theory of Stochastic Processes (Generalized Markov equation. Continuous S. processes. Purely discontinuous S. processes. Kolmogorov-Feller equations. Homogeneous S. processes with independent increments. Stationary S. process. Stochastic integral. Spectral theorem of S. processes. Birkhoff-Khinchine ergodic theorem). XI. Elements of Statistics (Some problems. Variational series and empirical distribution functions. Glivenko's theorem and Kolmogorov's compatibility criterion. Two-sample problem. Critical region. Comparison of two statistical hypotheses . . . Confidence limits). TABLES. BIBLIOGRAPHY.

—Ready, 1961-1962.

LES INTÉGRALES DE STIELTJES et leurs Applications aux Problèmes de la Physique Mathématique
By N. GUNTHER
—1932. 498 pp. 5½x8.   [63]   **$5.95**

Grundzüge Einer Allgemeinen Theorie der
LINEAREN INTEGRALGLEICHUNGEN
By D. HILBERT

—306 pp. 5½x8¼.   [91]   **$4.50**

PRINCIPLES OF MATHEMATICAL LOGIC
By D. HILBERT and W. ACKERMANN

The famous *Grundüge der Theoretischen Logik* translated into English, with added notes and revisions by PROF. R. E. LUCE.

"The best textbook in a Western European language for a student wishing a fairly thorough treatment."—*Bulletin of the A. M. S.*

—1950-59. xii + 172 pp. 6x9.   [69]   **$3.75**

GEOMETRY AND THE IMAGINATION
By D. HILBERT and S. COHN-VOSSEN

The theme of this book is *insight*. Not merely proofs, but proofs that offer *insight*—intuitive understanding—into *why they are true*. Not merely properties of the hyperboloid or of Pascal's hexagon, but insight into *why they have these properties*. In this wide-ranging survey, one of the world's greatest and most original mathematicians uses insight as both his technique and his aim. Both the beginner and the mature mathematician will learn much from this fascinating treatise.

Translated from the German by P. NEMENYI.

CHAPTER HEADINGS: I. The Simplest Curves and surfaces. II. Regular Systems of Points. III. Projective Configurations. IV. Differential Geometry. V. Kinematics. VI. Topology.

"A mathematical classic . . . The purpose is to make the reader *see* and *feel* the proofs."—*Science.*

"A fascinating tour of the 20th-century mathematical zoo."—*Scientific American.*

"Students . . . will experience the sensation of being taken into the friendly confidence of a great mathematician and being shown the *real significance* of things."—*Science Progress.*

"A glance down the index (*twenty-five columns of it*) reveal the breadth of range:—

"Annulus; Atomic structure; Automorphic functions; Bubble, soap; Caustic Curve; Color problem; Density of packing, of circles; Four-dimensional space; Gears, hyperboloidal; Graphite; Lattices; Mapping; "Monkey Saddle"; Table salt; Zinc.

"*These are but a few of the topics* . . . The title evokes the imagination and the text must surely capture it."—*Math. Gazette.*

—1952. 358 pp. 6x9.   [87]   **$6.00**

SQUARING THE CIRCLE, and other Monographs
By HOBSON, HUDSON, SINGH, and KEMPE

FOUR VOLUMES IN ONE.

SQUARING THE CIRCLE, by *Hobson*. A fascinating account of one of the three famous problems of antiquity, its significance, its history, the mathematical work it inspired in modern times, and its eventual solution in the closing years of the last century.

RULER AND COMPASSES, by *Hudson*. "An analytical and geometrical investigation of how far Euclidean constructions can take us. It is as thoroughgoing as it is constructive."—*Sci. Monthly.*

THE THEORY AND CONSTRUCTION OF NON-DIFFERENTIABLE FUNCTIONS, by *Singh*. I. Functions Defined by Series. II. Functions Defined Geometrically. III. Functions Defined Arithmetically. IV. Properties of Non-Differentiable Functions.

HOW TO DRAW A STRAIGHT LINE, by *Kempe*. An intriguing monograph on linkages. Describes, among other things, a linkage that will trisect any angle.

"Intriguing, meaty."—*Scientific American.*
—388 pp. 4½x7½. [95] Four vols. in one **$3.25**

SPHERICAL AND ELLIPSOIDAL HARMONICS
By E. W. HOBSON

"A comprehensive treatise . . . and the standard reference in its field."—*Bulletin of the A. M. S.*
—1930. 512 pp. 5⅜x8. Orig. pub. at $13.50. [104] **$6.00**

DIE METHODEN ZUR ANGENÄHERTEN LÖSUNG VON EIGENWERTPROBLEMEN IN DER ELASTOKINETIK
By K. HOHENEMSER

—(Ergeb. der Math.) 1932. 89 pp. 5½x8½. Orig. pub. at $4.25. [55] **$2.75**

ERGODENTHEORIE
By E. HOPF

—(Ergeb. der Math.) 1937. 89 pp. 5½x8½. [43] **$2.75**

HUDSON, "Ruler and Compasses," see Hobson

THE CALCULUS OF FINITE DIFFERENCES
By CHARLES JORDAN

". . . destined to remain the classic treatment of the subject . . . for many years to come."—*Harry C. Carver, Founder and formerly Editor of the* ANNALS OF MATHEMATICAL STATISTICS.

—1947. Second edition. xxi + 652 pp. 5½x8¼. [33] **$6.00**

DIOPHANTISCHE GLEICHUNGEN
By T. SKOLEM

"This comprehensive presentation . . . should be warmly welcomed. We recommend the book most heartily."—*Acta Szeged.*

—(Ergeb. der Math.) 1938. ix + 130 pp. 5½x8½. Cloth. Orig. publ. at $6.50. [75] **$3.50**

ALGEBRAISCHE THEORIE DER KOERPER
By E. STEINITZ

"Epoch-making."—*A. Haar, Aca Szeged.*
—177 pp. including two appendices. 5¼x8¼. [77] **$3.25**

INTERPOLATION
By J. F. STEFFENSEN

"A landmark in the history of the subject.

"Starting from scratch, the author deals with formulae of interpolation, construction of tables, inverse interpolation, summation of formulae, the symbolic calculus, interpolation with several variables, in a clear, elegant and rigorous manner . . . The student . . . will be rewarded by a comprehensive view of the whole field. . . . A classic account which no serious student can afford to neglect."—*Mathematical Gazette.*

—1950. 2nd ed. 256 pp. 5¼x8¼. Orig. $8.00. [71] **$4.95**

A HISTORY OF THE MATHEMATICAL THEORY OF PROBABILITY
By I. TODHUNTER

Introduces the reader to *almost every process and every species of problem which the literature of the subject can furnish.* Hundreds of problems are solved in detail.

—640 pp. 5¼x8. Previously publ. at $8.00. [57] **$6.00**

SET TOPOLOGY
By R. VAIDYANATHASWAMY

In this text on Topology, the first edition of which was published in India, the concept of partial order has been made the unifying theme.

Over 500 exercises for the reader enrich the text.

CHAPTER HEADINGS: I. Algebra of Subsets of a Set. II. Rings and Fields of Sets. III. Algebra of Partial Order. IV. The Closure Function. V. Neighborhood Topology. VI. Open and Closed Sets. VII. Topological Maps. VIII. The Derived Set in T_1 Space. IX. The Topological Product. X. Convergence in Metrical Space. XI. Convergence Topology.

—2nd ed. 1960. vi + 305 pp. 6x9. [139] **$6.00**